P9-AQT-697

DATE DUE			

Mechanism

DESIGN-ORIENTED KINEMATICS

Charles E. Wilson, Jr.
Newark College of Engineering

Walter J. Michels
Newark College of Engineering

American Technical Society • Chicago, Illinois 60637

COPYRIGHT © 1969, BY AMERICAN TECHNICAL SOCIETY

Library of Congress Catalog Number: 68-55618

No portion of this book may be reproduced by the mimeograph process or by any other process without permission of the publishers.

PRINTED IN THE UNITED STATES OF AMERICA

Preface

The authors have observed that students have a capacity for storage of abstract theory which often exceeds their understanding of that theory. The application of vaguely-understood formulas can "get students through the course." But it cannot substitute for a working knowledge of the fundamentals. *With this in mind, the theory of kinematics is herein presented through the medium of practical application, with an emphasis on understanding. Putting the application before the theory is a reversal of traditional procedure, but it permits students to think in terms of a mechanism or machine rather than in terms of an equation.*

There is considerable merit in dividing a text of this type into chapters covering basic principles; thus, the first three chapters of this text cover motion in machines, velocity analysis, and acceleration analysis. The first three chapters also serve to introduce cams, gears, and drive trains, but due to their special characteristics these groups of machine elements require more detailed analysis. Hence, the remaining chapters of the book are arranged in terms of these elements.

Methods of attack have been chosen on the basis of effectiveness rather than tradition. Graphical methods, which provide some of the best tools for velocity and acceleration analysis, are emphasized as a means to complete solutions and as a means to formulation of analytical solutions. *An attempt has been made to develop the most efficient and general techniques, whether graphical or analytical, and to select practical rather than purely academic examples to illustrate those techniques. In every case, the goal has been to provide the reader with a sound basis for the design of machines.*

The authors wish to thank their wives for their patient help, and to express their gratitude to the Newark College of Engineering for its support and to their colleagues of the Mechanical Engineering Department for their helpful suggestions. In addition, the authors are indebted to Mr. Leo R. Rakowski, the Technical Editor, and to Mrs. Bernadette Lang for her careful typing.

Charles E. Wilson, Jr.
Walter J. Michels

Table of Contents

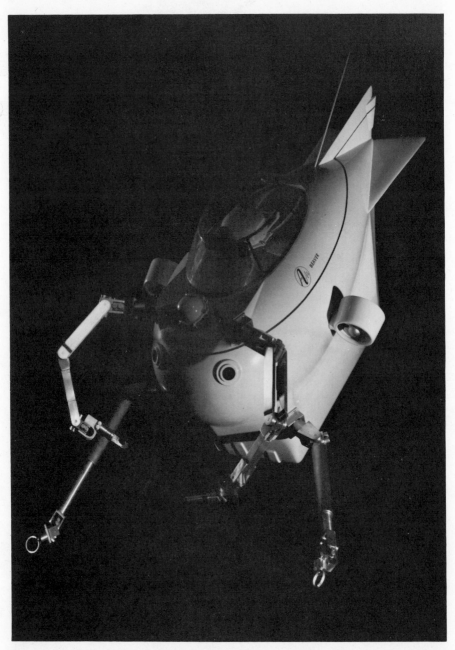

The mechanical arms on this research submarine enable modern man to gather specimens from, and carry out work projects at, the still-unknown bottom of the sea. (Autonetics Div., North American Aviation, Inc.)

Linkages and Motion

Introduction

The study of motion in machines is called *mechanism* or *kinematics*. It includes analysis and design of linkages, cams, gears and other machine components in terms of their motion characteristics. In the design of machines, the first phase of problem solving involves obtaining the desired motion relationships for the machine members. For example, it might be necessary to obtain intermittent linear motion with an input of constant speed rotation. On the other hand, the requirement might be continuous (stepless) variation of output speed (including reversing direction) while input rotation speed remains constant. Problems of this type are included in the scope of mechanism. Also included are detailed analyses of velocities and accelerations in machine members. This part of the design process is followed by the analysis of forces, and then computation of stresses and deflections—studies which are usually considered outside the province of mechanism.

The design process for a particular type of machine may continue long after first models of the machine have been produced and includes redesigns of components which affect velocities and accelerations. In order to successfully compete from year to year, most manufacturers must continuously modify their product and their methods of production. Increases in production rate, upgrading of product performance, redesign for cost and weight reduction, and motion analysis of new product lines are frequently required. All of these situations involve applied kinematics. In each case, success or failure could depend on the kinematic analysis of the problem.

Terminology and Definitions

While some fields of study have a language all their own, this is not generally true of mechanism. But, because we cannot afford ambiguities and other semantic problems, some terms are given restrictive meanings. These and a few other words of particular interest are noted below.

Linkages and Constrained Motion

A device intended to do useful work is generally called a *machine*, but the term may apply to any combination of links grouped together for a specific purpose. The term *linkage* may be used to denote a combination of rigid links joined by pins or other constraints. If one of the links is fixed and the motion of each individual link is related to the motion of every other link, the linkage is called a *mechanism*.

Fig. 1 shows several basic types of link combinations. The symbols shown in the key of this illustration to represent rigid links, pins, bearings and sliders will be used throughout most of this work. Fig. 1A shows a *cam and follower*. Link 0, representing both the cam center of rotation and the follower constraint, is fixed. Link 0 is called the frame. For any position of link 1, the cam, there is a definite location of link 2, the follower, provided the follower is spring loaded or otherwise *constrained* to keep in contact with the cam. The cam and follower form a mechanism.

The *four-bar linkage*, Fig. 1B, is also a mechanism, since for every position of link 1, there is a definite orientation of links 2 and 3. If positions of link 3 are specified, link 1 positions are double-valued; that is, there are two possible positions of link 1 (and also link 2) for a single position of link 3. Ordinarily, the circumstances of the problem indicate which set of positions to consider.

The *five link system* shown in Fig. 1C is not generally considered

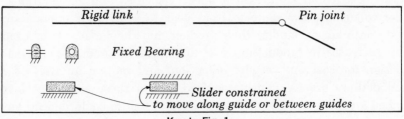

Key to Fig. 1.

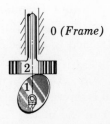

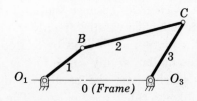

FIG. 1A. The cam is a mechanism since the motion of the follower (2) is a function of the motion of the cam (1).

FIG. 1B. This linkage is also a mechanism. The motion of links 2 and 3 is directly related to the motion of link 1.

FIG. 1C. This linkage does *not* have constrained motion and, therefore, cannot be considered a mechanism. If only the motion of link 1 is specified, the motion of the other links cannot be found.

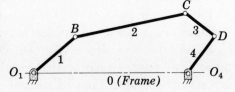

FIG. 1D. The *differential.* It is necessary to specify the motion of *both* input gears (1 and 2) to obtain a specific output.

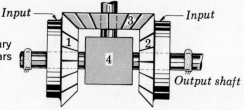

FIG. 1E. A structure is not a mechanism. There is *no* relative motion.

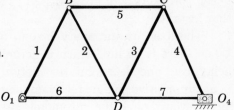

a mechanism because the motion of links 2, 3 and 4 cannot be determined when we specify only the motion of link 1. The requirement that the motion of all links be related to (constrained to a specific path by) the motion of any single link is not met. Such a strict definition would also eliminate the bevel gear differential, Fig. 1D, from the class of linkages called mechanisms. The differential is, however, one of the most useful of mechanisms as will be shown later in the text.

By interpreting our original definition of a mechanism to include those linkages in which the motion of all links is related, linkages such as the differential are conditionally classified as mechanisms. The condition to be met is an additional relationship which prevents the links from just assuming random positions. In the case of the differential, the motion of both bevel gears 1 and 2 may be specified inputs as discussed later in Chapter Seven. Likewise, by specifying the motion of *two* links of the five bar linkage, Fig. 1C, that linkage may be classified as a mechanism instead of an unconstrained collection of links.

The links and pins of Fig. 1E are arranged so that there can be no relative motion (except that resulting from link deformations). It is a *structure* and will not be treated since we are interested in motion.

Links

The term *rigid link* or sometimes simply *link* is an idealization used in the study of mechanisms which does not consider deflections due to strains in machine members. A perfectly rigid or inextensible link can exist only as a textbook-type model of a real machine member. For typical machine parts, maximum dimension changes are of the order of only one one-thousandth of the part length. We are justified in neglecting this small motion when considering the much greater motion which is characteristic of most mechanisms. The word *link* is used in a general sense to include cams, gears and other machine members in addition to straight bars. The part of a belt between pulleys, Fig. 2, or a chain between sprockets at a given instant, may be considered a rigid link for that instant.

The fixed or stationary link in a mechanism is called the *frame*. When there is no link which is actually fixed, we may consider one as being fixed and determine the motion of the other links relative to it. In an automotive engine, for example, the engine block is considered the frame, even though the automobile may be moving.

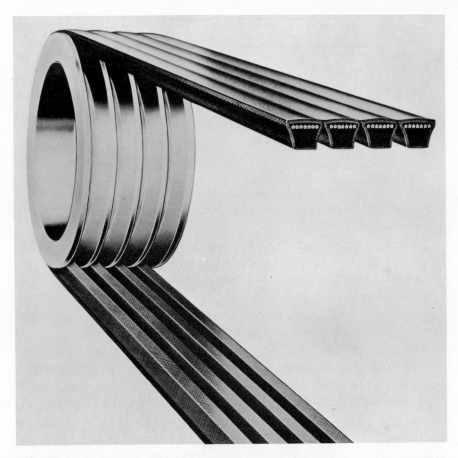

FIG. 2. A set of of V-belts with a common back. The section of belt between the driver and the driven pulleys acts (instantaneously) as a rigid link. (Dodge Mfg. Co.)

Motion

Plane motion refers to motion in a single plane or in a set of parallel planes. Plane motion is best characterized by plane vectors; we will therefore become familiar with the use of vectors before attempting a study of the various aspects of motion. *Plane mechanisms* are those which have plane motion and may be fully described in a single two-dimensional view. While a special case of the more general spatial (three

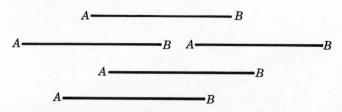

FIG. 3. Link *AB* is shown translated to a number of alternate positions.

dimensional) mechanism, plane mechanisms are of particular interest. They include major components of the piston engine, spur gear trains and most cams.

The plane motion of a rigid link may be pure *translation* (also called rectilinear motion) in which case all points in the link move in the same direction at the same speed. For example, the cam follower in Fig. 1A moves in *rectilinear translation* (i.e., translation along a straight line). Translation of a rigid body in general implies motion in space such that any line connecting two points in the body remains parallel to its original position. Link *AB* shown in Fig. 3 moves in plane *translation*.

In another special case, the plane motion of a body is described by pure *rotation* in which case a point in the link is fixed (e.g., the cam in Fig. 1A). *Oscillation* refers either to a back and forth rotation (e.g., the motion of a pendulum) or a back and forth translation (the motion ·of a piston). In Mechanism, oscillation is commonly used in the first sense, and the motion of a piston is described instead as *reciprocating motion*. In every case, the meaning should be clear in context.

Vectors

Vectors are an important part of the language of mechanism and the other branches of mechanics. They provide us with a graphical means to represent motion or force. *Any quantity possessing both magnitude and direction can be considered a vector and can be graphically represented by an arrow.* The length of the arrow is proportional to the magnitude of the vector quantity and the direction of the arrow is the direction of the vector quantity. See Fig. 4A. As an example of a vector, consider the velocity of point *A* moving to the right at 15 inches per second. We are free to select any convenient scale to represent the

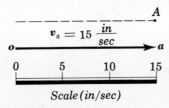

$$v_a = 15 \, \frac{in}{sec}$$

Scale (in/sec)

FIG. 4A. The motion of point A can be represented by a vector of scaled length drawn in the proper direction.

FIG. 4B. A vector of known sense but unknown magnitude is indicated by a double arrowhead.

magnitude of the velocity. If a velocity scale of 1 in $=$ 10 in/sec is chosen, the arrow representing the velocity of A will be

$$15 \text{ in} \times \frac{1 \text{ in}}{10 \text{ in/sec}} = 1.5 \text{ in long.}$$

It will be directed to the right with origin at o and terminus (head) at a as shown in Fig. 4A. Directly alongside the arrow we indicate the magnitude of the actual velocity which the arrow represents rather than the length of the arrow (*i.e.*, we indicate that $v_A = 15$ in/sec rather than $v_A = 1.5$ in).

When we use vectors to describe the motion of a linkage, it is advisable to make a sketch of the linkage adjacent to the vector diagrams so that vector *direction* can be referred to linkage orientation. When solving mechanism problems, we sometimes know the direction of a vector, but not its length. The double-headed arrow of Fig. 4B indicates a vector of unknown magnitude in the horizontal direction (but not necessarily to the right). The vector *sense* tells us whether the actual vector quantity represented by the figure is to the right or left. When a vector is described as having known direction and unknown magnitude, the word *magnitude* may imply *sense* as well as *length*. Thus, we may describe a vehicle on a highway as traveling along a north-south *direction*. The *sense* of the velocity of the vehicle may be either to the north or to the south. If a sign convention is adopted, vector sense is indi-

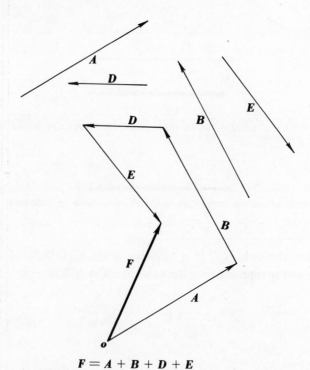

$$F = A + B + D + E$$

FIG. 5A. The graphic addition of several vectors.

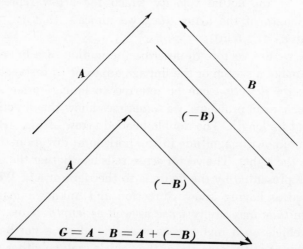

$$G = A - B = A + (-B)$$

Fig. 5B. Vector subtraction. Simply *reverse the sense of* the vector being subtracted and add it like any other vector.

cated by a plus or minus sign before the magnitude. When there is no possibility of ambiguity, direction is sometimes used with the same meaning as sense.

Vector Addition. Vector addition differs from addition of scalar quantities like time or money. Both vector direction and vector magnitude must be considered. We know intuitively that if we travel one mile north and then one mile east we will not be two miles (straight line distance) from the starting point. To illustrate vector addition, let us graphically add vectors *A, B, D,* and *E,* Fig. 5A, and label the sum *F.* (i.e., *A + B + D + E = F*). Note: The addition of vector quantities (represented by *bold face* characters) requires that due regard be given to the direction and sense of the vectors being added. Beginning at an arbitrary point *o,* we draw vector *A,* then successively add vectors *B, D* and *E,* the tail of each added vector beginning at the head of the vector drawn last *and drawn with the correct sense.* The vector sum is given by the vector *F* with tail at *o* and head drawn to the head of the last vector of the series to be added, vector *E.* The reader may verify that the addition of vectors is commutative, *i.e.* the above vectors may be added in any order to obtain the same result: *A + B = B + A,* etc.

Vector Subtraction. Vector subtraction is sometimes required when we consider relative motion. Thus, if the vector *G* is given by vector *A* minus vector *B,* we write

$$G = A - B \text{ or } G = A + (-B)$$

where vector $(-B)$ is identical with vector *B* except that the sense is reversed as shown in Fig. 5B. The second form of the expression for the difference between two vectors is preferred, particularly when many vectors are to be combined.

Vector Components. Vectors can also be expressed in terms of their *vector components* (projections) along a set of coordinate axes. For a vector in three dimensional space, three independent coordinate axes are used, the X, Y and Z axes, which are usually mutually perpendicular. Fig. 6A shows a vector *A* which has been projected onto the three axes to form components A_x, A_y and A_z. Note that vector *A* is equal to the *vector sum* of its components. See Fig. 6B.

An alternate method of adding several vectors, therefore, is to add

9

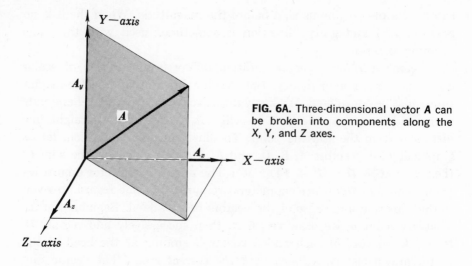

FIG. 6A. Three-dimensional vector **A** can be broken into components along the X, Y, and Z axes.

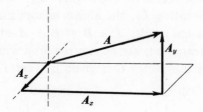

FIG. 6B. Vector **A** is equal to the sum of its projected components.

their respective vector components. Addition of vector components is a method used when the work requires considerable precision. Each of the vectors is broken into its components along the separate axes; all of the components along each axis are then added separately. Addition of two vectors (or vector components) *in the same direction* is carried out as if they were scalars. Also, when a vector is multiplied by a scalar quantity, the result is a vector, with the same direction as the original vector, having a magnitude equal to the product of the vector and scalar magnitudes.

Consider vector *A* at an angle α to the horizontal which we will add to vector *B* at an angle β to the horizontal, Fig. 7A. In Fig. 7B, vector *A* is resolved into its horizontal component *A* cos α (the length

10

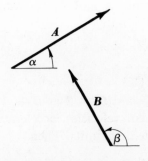

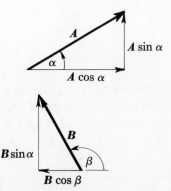

FIG. 7A. Vectors to be added.

FIG. 7B. Vectors resolved into their respective components.

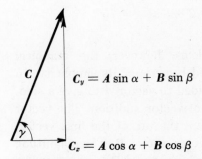

FIG. 7C. The respective components are added together to obtain the horizontal and vertical components of the resultant vector.

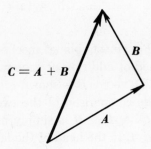

FIG. 7D. The two vectors are shown added graphically.

of vector A times cos α) and its vertical component A sin α. Vector B is similarly resolved into its horizontal and vertical components, retaining the proper signs in each case. The sign is an important consideration. In this case A cos α, the horizontal component of vector A, is positive and points to the right while B cos β, the horizontal component of vector B, is negative and points to the left. In Fig. 7C the horizontal components (A cos α and B cos β) are shown added together to form C_x, the horizontal component of the sum of vectors A and B. Similarly, the vertical components (A sin α and B sin β) are added to form C_y, the vertical component of the sum of vectors A and B. The magnitude of vector

Mechanism

C, which is the sum (or resultant) of vectors A and B, is given by

$$C = \sqrt{C_x^2 + C_y^2} \tag{1}$$

and the direction is given by $\gamma = \tan^{-1}(C_y/C_x)$.

As an example, let $A = 2$ at $\alpha = 30°$ and $B = 2$ at $\beta = 120°$, where the lengths of A and B might represent velocities, accelerations, or any quantity, as long as A and B have identical units. Then

$$C_x = A \cos 30° + B \cos 120° = 1.732 - 1 = 0.732$$

and

$$C_y = A \sin 30° + B \sin 120° = 1 + 1.732 = 2.732$$

from which, according to Formula (1)

$$C = \sqrt{(0.732)^2 + (2.732)^2} = 2.828 \text{ at } \gamma = 75°.$$

For most plane mechanism problems, however, the graphical method of addition of vectors is preferred because of its simplicity. In Fig. 7D, vector B is shown *graphically* added to vector A to give a side-by-side comparison of the two methods of vector addition. The vector sum $C = A + B$ is simply measured from the tail of the first vector, vector A, to the head of the last-added vector, vector B. The magnitude of C is obtained from the vector scale to which A and B are drawn. The angle of vector C can be measured with a protractor.

In addition to velocity, the time rate of position change, vectors may represent *displacement*, the change in position of a point, and *acceleration*, the time rate of change in velocity of a point. Since velocity is a vector, it is important to note that an acceleration arises from velocity direction change as well as from changes in velocity magnitude.

Plane Motion

Displacement and Path. Displacement, as used in kinematics, refers to a change in location. The displacement of a point during some time interval is represented by a vector drawn from the initial to the final position of the point during the interval. The displacement magnitude is simply the straight-line distance between the two positions. *Note: Displacement must not be confused with the path which the*

12

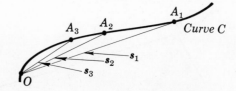

FIG. 8A. For smaller and smaller time intervals, the displacement vectors (s₁, s₂, and s₃) approach the length and direction of the path along curve C.

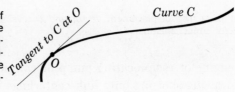

FIG. 8B. The *instantaneous* direction of travel (the path at any instant) and the *instantaneous* direction of the displacement vector are identical. They are represented by a tangent to the path at the point. The tangent is therefore the instantaneous velocity direction.

point travels in going from the initial to the final position. *In general, length of path and displacement are not equal.*

Suppose curve C in Fig. 8A describes the path of a point A traveling with plane motion. Over a certain interval of time, the point travels from O to A_1. The displacement vector s_1 and the path OA_1 along curve C differ appreciably. Starting again at O, but cutting the time interval in half, we obtain a displacement vector s_2 which is a fair approximation of the path OA_2 along curve C, both in length (magnitude) and direction. If we take a very small time interval so that the point moves only from O to A_3, the magnitude of displacement vector s_3 and the curve length from O to A_3 are practically identical. Furthermore, during this small time interval, the direction of displacement vector s_3 is essentially the same as the direction of travel of the point moving along curve C. We can, of course, sketch only finite displacements over finite time intervals. However, it follows that, *as the time interval approaches zero, the infinitesimal displacement vector s and the corresponding path become identical* in direction and length for any smooth curve. Also, the direction of travel (path) along curve C and the displacement vector direction at any instant are defined by a tangent to the curve, Fig. 8B.

As a further example of instantaneous displacement, consider the *slider-crank mechanism*, Fig. 9, the basic mechanism of a reciprocating

Mechanism

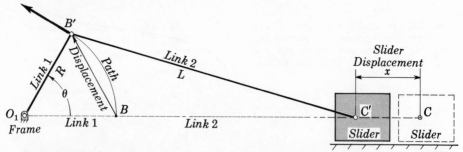

FIG. 9. The displacement vector and the velocity vector as illustrated by the slider-crank mechanism.

engine or reciprocating pump or compressor. For simplicity, a skeleton drawing showing only link centerlines is used when analyzing mechanisms. Link 1 is the *crank* of length R (measured from the crank pin B to crankshaft center O_1). The mechanism is shown rotating from its initial position (light lines) to its final position (solid lines). As the crank turns counterclockwise through an angle θ, point B moves to B' along a circular arc BB' with length of path given by:

$$\text{arc } BB' = R \, \theta \tag{2}$$

where θ is measured in radians ($2\,\pi$ radians $= 360°$ or 1 radian $=$ about $57.3°$). The displacement of B is given by:

$$\text{chord length } BB' = 2\,R \sin \frac{\theta}{2}.$$

For $\theta = \pi/3$ radians ($60°$), path BB' is almost 5% greater in length than displacement BB' but for small values of θ, $\sin \theta/2$ may be approximated by $\theta/2 - \theta^3/48$ and the ratio of path to displacement is given approximately by:

$$\frac{\text{arc}}{\text{chord}} = 1 + \frac{\theta^2}{24}$$

with θ again measured in radians. Length of path (arc) and displacement (chord) approach one another rapidly as θ decreases; for $\theta = 0.49$

14

radians (28°), the path is about 1% greater than the displacement, and for $\theta = 0.155$ radians (8.9°), the difference is only 0.1%. Finally, for infinitesimal time periods, displacement and path coincide; they have the same magnitude and direction.

While the above numerical example applies to the circular path of point B in Fig. 9, the final result is the same for any smooth curve. As noted above, *for an infinitesimal time period, length of path and displacement magnitude are the same,* and the displacement vector direction is given by a tangent to the path. Thus, while chord BB' is the total displacement of point B as link 1 rotates thru the angle θ, to point B', the instantaneous displacement (displacement at any instant) is represented by a line tangent to the path and perpendicular to the link.

Velocity. *Average speed* is given by total distance traveled divided by the time required, and does not usually include information on the direction of travel. In the case of a round trip, for example, direction could not be assigned. *Instantaneous speed,* which is the speed found at a given instant, is defined as *the limiting value of distance traveled divided by the time required as the time interval approaches zero.* This is exactly the infinitesimal displacement vector magnitude divided by the corresponding time interval. By way of experiment, instantaneous speed (usually referred to as instantaneous velocity) may be found approximately by measuring distance traveled over a very short time interval and dividing by the interval. Accuracy is adversely affected when velocity changes significantly during the time interval, but results are usually fairly accurate for "smooth" motion-time relationships.

The direction of the instantaneous *velocity* vector is the same as the direction of the instantaneous *displacement* vector, and is given by the instantaneous tangent to the path of the point, Figs. 8B and 9. Infinitesimal changes in a variable are called *differentials,* and are designated by the symbol d (dt for an infinitesimal time interval, ds for the corresponding displacement change, etc.) Thus, the instantaneous velocity of a point is given by the expression

$$v = \frac{ds}{dt} \tag{3}$$

which represents the limit of the ratio of displacement change to the corresponding time interval *as the time interval approaches zero*. This is precisely the process illustrated by Fig. 8A. *Direction as well as magnitude* is implied by the above expression since the infinitesimal displacement vector *ds* has the direction (at that instant) of a tangent to the path of the point. Note: ***vector quantities*** such as instantaneous velocity and acceleration will be indicated by ***bold face*** notation. Scalar (non-vector quantities) will be indicated by *italic* notation.

Rectilinear (Straight-Line) Motion

We have seen that, to completely describe a motion, both the direction and the magnitude of the motion must be specified. Let us now consider a special category of the more general plane motion—motion in a straight line. This special case of motion may be referred to as rectilinear motion, linear motion, or translation.

Rectilinear Displacement. When the motion of a body is described as rectilinear, its position may be described completely with a scalar quantity rather than by a vector. This is an important consideration. Since the direction of the path remains constant in rectilinear motion, the vector aspect of the motion may be conveniently disregarded when examining the motion.

The slider in Fig. 9 illustrates rectilinear displacement. The path of the wristpin C on the slider is a straight line at all times. Since the direction cannot change, the rectilinear displacement can be considered a scalar. This special case (straight-line motion where path and displacement coincide for any given interval) permits us to make a plot of the displacement against time (x vs. t). See Fig. 10A. Returning to the slider crank mechanism shown in Fig. 9, if the crank is drawn in a series of positions representing successive instants in time, we may complete the linkage sketch and easily find the corresponding slider displacement at each instant. Plotting these displacements against time, we obtain a curve similar to the one shown in Fig. 10A. Note that the coordinates in Fig. 10A are *displacement* and time, whereas curve C in Fig. 8 represents the path of a point.

Rectilinear Velocity. Let us measure the change in displacement, $x_2 - x_1$ inches, which occurs during a finite interval of time, $t_2 - t_1$ seconds. The *average velocity* of the slider during the interval is given by the expression

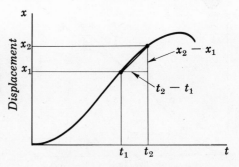

FIG. 10A. The rectilinear displacement of the slider of Fig. 9 is plotted against the time required for the displacement. The average velocity is represented by the *slope* of the hypotenuse of the triangle, or the rise $(x_2 - x_1)$ divided by the run $(t_2 - t_1)$.

$$v_{av} = \frac{x_2 - x_1}{t_2 - t_1} \; \frac{\text{in}}{\text{sec}}. \qquad (4)$$

Since displacement x is considered a scalar, the above expression for average velocity can also be considered a scalar, and is referred to as either average linear speed or average linear velocity.

Instantaneous Velocity. Let us now consider the *instantaneous* velocity of the slider, or the velocity of the slider considered at a point or a single instant in time. The average velocity of the slider was found by dividing the change in linear displacement, $x_2 - x_1$, by the time required for the change, $t_2 - t_1$. The expression

$$\frac{x_2 - x_1}{t_2 - t_1}$$

can be considered as the tangent of a right triangle formed by sides $x_2 - x_1$ and $t_2 - t_1$, or the *slope* of the triangle, Fig. 10A. The slope is defined as the rise (in this case, $x_2 - x_1$) divided by the run (in this case, $t_2 - t_1$). As smaller intervals are considered, the sides of the triangle, $x_2 - x_1$ and $t_2 - t_1$, become correspondingly small. The slope more and more approximates the curve of the displacement-time plot. Finally, at t_0 the slope represents the *instantaneous linear velocity* of the slider at the instant t_0, and is tangent to the curve, Fig. 10B. The magnitude of the instantaneous linear velocity is given by the numerical

17

Mechanism

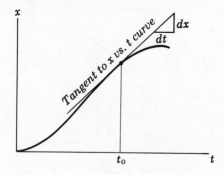

FIG. 10B. The instantaneous velocity (at some instant t_0) is given by the tangent to the curve at the point being considered. The magnitude of the instantaneous velocity is given by the slope (dx/dt) of the tangent.

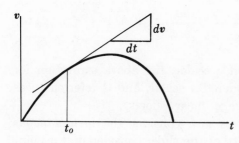

FIG. 10C. Acceleration is given by the slope of the tangent to the velocity vs. time curve.

value of the slope of the tangent. You will recognize this procedure as simply a restatement of Equation (3),

$$v = \frac{dx}{dt}. \tag{3}$$

The values dx and dt in Fig. 10B can be measured by taking any convenient time interval dt and measuring the corresponding change dx required to complete the triangle to obtain the tangent line.

The process described above is the basis of differential calculus. If motion x can be described algebraically as a function of time t (say, $x = 3t^2 + 1$), then the notation $v = dx/dt$ represents the process of differentiation with respect to time, and can usually be performed analytically, eliminating the need to plot x vs. t. We will make use of this procedure in Chapter Two.

If we do not have an analytical expression for displacement as a function of time, the accuracy of our velocity determination hinges on the accuracy of our displacement-time curve, and on the accurate construction of a tangent. There are many instances, however, where it is not practical to make a sufficiently accurate plot. For this reason, other methods to determine velocities have been developed. Those most suitable to our purposes are discussed in Chapter Two, where velocity is examined in detail.

Rectilinear Acceleration. Acceleration is defined as the time rate of change of velocity. We can measure a change in velocity during a finite time interval and divide by the time interval to obtain an *average acceleration:*

$$a_{av} = \frac{v_2 - v_1}{t_2 - t_1}. \tag{5}$$

This is precisely the method used to determine average velocity.

EXAMPLE—PROBLEM 1: The velocity of a piston is 100 in/sec to the right at the midpoint of its stroke. Velocity is 90 in/sec to the right 0.01 seconds later. Find the *average piston acceleration* during the 0.01 second interval.

Solution: The time rate of change in velocity is given by the formula

$$a_{av} = \frac{\text{final velocity—initial velocity}}{\text{time interval}}$$

$$= \frac{90 - 100 \text{ in/sec}}{0.01 \text{ sec}} = -1000 \ \frac{\text{in}}{\text{sec}^2}.$$

The minus sign indicates that the acceleration sense is opposite the velocity sense, i.e., the acceleration is 1000 in/sec² to the left.

Generally, however, the word *acceleration* without modification refers to an *instantaneous* time rate of velocity change which, in general,

19

takes into account changes in velocity *direction* as well as changes in velocity magnitude. For the moment, however, let us continue to consider only the rectilinear motion of the slider in Fig. 9. In this special case of motion, we have only velocity magnitude changes to consider, since velocity direction is restricted to straight line motion. Thus we can continue to consider the motion — in this case the acceleration — as a scalar quantity. Fig. 10C is a plot of slider velocity as a function of time. Instantaneous slider acceleration at any time t_0 is found by drawing a tangent to the velocity-time curve at t_0 just as instantaneous velocity was found by drawing a tangent to the displacement-time curve. The slope of the tangent represents the value of the slider acceleration at time t_0:

$$a = \frac{dv}{dt}. \tag{6}$$

As before, any convenient time interval dt is used and the corresponding velocity magnitude change dv is measured to obtain the slope of the tangent line.

When an analytical expression is given for velocity as a function of time, the velocity can be differentiated with respect to time to obtain acceleration. (This method is used for the slider crank linkage in Chapter Three.) Since acceleration is the derivative of velocity, and since velocity itself is the derivative of displacement with respect to time, acceleration represents the second derivative of displacement with respect to time, written:

$$a = \frac{dv}{dt} = \frac{d}{dt}\frac{dx}{dt} = \frac{d^2x}{dt^2}.$$

This expression for acceleration is perfectly valid when we have an analytical expression for displacement x as a function of time t, say $x = 4t^2 + 7t$.

If displacement is plotted as a function of time, we could construct a plot of velocity vs. time. This is done by finding the slope of tangents to the displacement curve at a series of points and plotting the values of the slopes. It is theoretically possible to repeat this process with the velocity curve, obtaining an acceleration vs. time curve. Graphical errors, however, make the accuracy of successive graphical differentiation doubtful. Thus we do not recommend graphical differentiation of a velocity curve which was itself obtained by graphical differentiation.

Rotation

We have examined the special case of rectilinear motion, or motion in a straight line. Another special category of motion is rotation. In this section we will take up rotational (or angular) displacement, velocity, and acceleration—which are analagous to rectilinear displacement, velocity and acceleration. In the following section we will go on to examine the relationship between the rotational motion of a body and the instantaneous linear motion of a point on the rotating body. Still later, we will see that all plane motion can be treated as a combination of pure rectilinear motion and pure rotational motion.

Angular Displacement. The motion of a body about a fixed point is called rotation (or pure rotation). In the case of a plane mechanism, rotation represents motion in the plane of the mechanism about a fixed point. *Angular displacement* is the change in angular position (or the amount of rotation) during some time interval. Angular displacement is measured in *radians*, where 2π radians represent one complete rotation, or one radian equals approximately $57.3°$.

An angle measured in radians is *defined* as equivalent to the arc length subtending the angle divided by the radius of the arc. Fig. 11A is the crank of the linkage shown in Fig. 9. The angle θ, in radians, is equal to arc length BB' (in inches) divided by radius R (also in inches)

$$\theta = \frac{BB'}{R} \tag{2}$$

thus, radians are dimensionless. You will note that this definition is merely a restatement of Equation (2).

An infinitesimal angular displacement is a vector quantity. In the case of plane mechanisms, though, angular motions are treated as scalar quantities. Although angular motions have magnitude and direction and therefore are vector quantities, *the vector directions are always perpendicular to the plane of the mechanism and directed along the axis of rotation.* Thus, the vector nature of rotational motion can be conven-

21

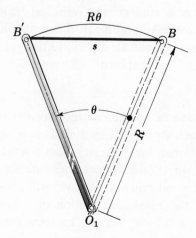

$R\theta$

B' B

s

θ

R

O_1

FIG. 11A. An angle θ, measured in radians, is defined as equal to the subtended arc length BB' divided by the radius, R, of the arc.

iently disregarded. The student need only concern himself with whether the rotation is clockwise or counterclockwise.

EXAMPLE—PROBLEM 2: In Fig. 11A, let the length of link O_1B equal 5 inches. Find the *length of the path of point B* as the link rotates 3° clockwise.

Solution: First, converting 3° to radians, we obtain

$$\theta = \frac{3 \text{ degrees}}{57.3 \text{ degrees/radian}} = 0.0524 \text{ radians}$$

The path of point B is therefore an arc of length

$$R\,\theta = OB\,\theta = 5 \text{ in} \times 0.0524 \text{ rad} = 0.262 \text{ in.}$$

The answer is given in inches because the angle θ radians is a pure (dimensionless) number. Note that the displacement of point B, or the straight-line distance from the initial to the final position of point B, is almost identical to the path of point B since the angular displacement of the link (angle θ) is very small.

    Angular Velocity. Referring again to the crank shown in Fig. 11A, we see that the link rotates about fixed point O_1. During some time interval the crank rotates through some angle θ (in radians), where $\theta = BB'/R$. If we divide the total angular displacement θ by the time interval in seconds, we obtain the *average angular velocity* of the crank in radians/second:

$$\omega_{av} = \frac{\theta}{t} \; \frac{\text{rad}}{\text{sec}}. \tag{7}$$

The term, angular velocity, usually refers to the *instantaneous angular velocity*, ω, which is the limit of the ratio of angular displacement to the time interval as the interval approaches zero:

$$\omega = \frac{d\theta}{dt} \frac{\text{rad}}{\text{sec}}. \tag{8}$$

By analogy to the x vs. t curve of Fig. 10, we may plot a curve of angular displacement θ vs. time t. The slope of a tangent to this curve at any time gives us the instantaneous angular velocity.

Angular Acceleration. Angular acceleration is the time rate of change in angular velocity. *Average angular acceleration* is obtained when we consider the angular velocity change over a finite time interval. *Instantaneous angular acceleration*, α, refers to the limit of the ratio of angular velocity change to the time interval as the time interval approaches zero

$$\alpha = \frac{d\omega}{dt} \; \frac{\text{rad}}{\text{sec}^2}. \tag{9}$$

Thus angular velocity ω is analogous to linear velocity v, and angular acceleration α to linear acceleration a. We may therefore plot a curve of ω vs. t (similar to Fig. 10C, the v vs. t curve) and find instantaneous angular acceleration, α, from the slope of the curve. Of course, the warning regarding successive graphical differentiation applies to angular motion as well as linear motion. When we have an analytical expression for angular displacement θ as a function of t, we may differentiate with respect to time to obtain

$$\omega = \frac{d\theta}{dt}$$

and differentiate again to obtain

Mechanism

$$\alpha = \frac{d\omega}{dt} = \frac{d^2\theta}{dt^2}.$$

The terms *constant angular velocity* and *uniform angular velocity* imply zero angular acceleration.

In many cases, the motion of a link is neither pure translation nor rotation, but is described by a combination of both. Consider, for example, the connecting rod (link 2) in Fig. 9. The rate of change in angular position is considered separately from the translational motion so that angular velocity ω and angular acceleration α may be obtained for any link having general motion. This procedure will be discussed in detail in the chapters to follow.

Relationships between Linear and Angular Motion

In the case of pure rotation, the angular velocity of a rotating body and the linear velocity of any point on that body are related simply. Consider point B which lies at a distance R from the fixed center of rotation O_1 of a link, Fig. 11A. If the link is given an angular displacement θ radians, we know from the definition of the radian that point B on the link moves through an arc distance (path) $R\theta$. The average angular velocity of the link is given by θ/t. The average speed of point B is found by dividing the arc distance $R\theta$ by the time required for the motion:

$$v_{av} = \frac{R\theta}{t}.$$

Let us now consider what happens when the time interval becomes smaller and smaller. Let the link in Fig. 11B rotate through an infinitesimal angle $d\theta$ during the infinitesimal time dt. As the time interval approaches zero, the displacement ds more and more approximates the length of the path, $R\,d\theta$. Finally, at any given instant, the instantaneous displacement and the corresponding path of point B are identical in magnitude and direction:

$$ds = Rd\theta. \tag{10}$$

Dividing both sides of the equation by the time interval required for the displacement, dt, we obtain

$$\frac{ds}{dt} = R \ \frac{d\theta}{dt} \cdot$$

Noting that, from Formula (8),

$$\omega = \frac{d\theta}{dt}$$

and that, from Formula (3),

$$v = \frac{ds}{dt}$$

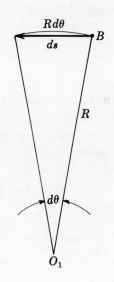

FIG. 11B. As the angle of rotation becomes infinitesimally small, the arc distance $Rd\theta$ approaches the value of the displacement *ds*. Thus, as the time approaches zero, $ds = Rd\theta$.

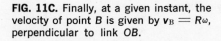
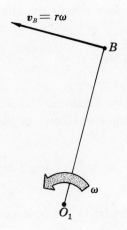

FIG. 11C. Finally, at a given instant, the velocity of point *B* is given by $v_B = R\omega$, perpendicular to link *OB*.

25

we have the instantaneous velocity of point B in terms of the instantaneous angular velocity of the link and the distance of point B from the axis of rotation, given by the formula

$$v = R\omega \, \frac{\text{in}}{\text{sec}} \qquad (10)$$

where R is expressed in inches and ω in radians/second. See Fig. 11C. If the velocity v of any point is known and we wish to obtain the angular velocity of the link, ω, we simply rewrite the expression to obtain

$$\omega = \frac{v}{R} \, \frac{\text{rad}}{\text{sec}} \, .$$

EXAMPLE—PROBLEM 3: In Fig. 11C let the length of link O_1B equal 5 inches. Find the *instantaneous velocity of point B* on link O_1B as the link rotates with an angular velocity of 1800 revolutions/minute counterclockwise.

Solution: To begin, the angular velocity in rev/min must be converted to radians/sec

$$1 \, \frac{\text{rev}}{\text{min}} = \frac{2\pi}{60} \, \frac{\text{rad}}{\text{sec}} \text{ or } 1 \, \frac{\text{rev}}{\text{min}} = 0.1047 \, \frac{\text{rad}}{\text{sec}} \text{ (approx.)}$$

We therefore obtain the angular velocity ω of the link in rad/sec

$$\omega = 1800 \, \frac{\text{rev}}{\text{min}} \times \frac{0.1047 \text{ rad/sec}}{1 \text{ rev/min}} = 188.5 \, \frac{\text{rad}}{\text{sec}} \, .$$

Then, using Equation (10), which relates the velocity of a point on a link to the angular velocity of the link, we obtain

$$v_B = OB \, \omega = 5 \text{ in} \times 188.5 \, \frac{\text{rad}}{\text{sec}} = 942 \, \frac{\text{in}}{\text{sec}}$$

perpendicular to the link as shown in Fig. 11C.

EXAMPLE—PROBLEM 4: Surface speeds of from 800 to 2000 ft/min are recommended for milling aluminum. Find the *corresponding speeds (angular velocities) in rev/min* for a 4 in diameter milling cutter.

Solution: We will let the radius of the cutter be represented by $R = 2$ in. The lowest surface speed is

$$v_B = 800 \,\frac{\text{ft}}{\text{min}} \times 12 \,\frac{\text{in}}{\text{ft}} \times \frac{1 \text{ min}}{60 \text{ sec}} = 160 \,\frac{\text{in}}{\text{sec}}.$$

Using Equation (10),

$$\omega = \frac{v_B}{R} = \frac{160 \text{ in/sec}}{2 \text{ in}} = 80 \,\frac{\text{rad}}{\text{sec}}.$$

We divide by $0.1047 \,\dfrac{\text{rad/sec}}{1 \text{ rev/min}}$ to obtain the $765 \,\dfrac{\text{rev}}{\text{min}}$,

which is the minimum value. Similarly, 2000 ft/min gives us a maximum value of 1920 rev/min.

EXAMPLE—PROBLEM 5: An automobile accelerates from zero to 60 mi/hr in 15 seconds. Find the *average angular acceleration of the rear axle*. The tires have a 13 inch outer radius.

Solution: This problem is equivalent to a dynamometer test, where the 60 mi/hr speed is the linear velocity of a point on the tread of the tire. Let us convert this speed to more manageable dimensions:

$$60 \,\frac{\text{mi}}{\text{hr}} \times \frac{5280 \text{ ft}}{1 \text{ mi}} \times \frac{1 \text{ hr}}{3600 \text{ sec}} \times \frac{12 \text{ in}}{1 \text{ ft}} = 1056 \,\frac{\text{in}}{\text{sec}}.$$

Since we know that the point rotates about a circle of radius $R = 13$ in, we can use the formula equating the angular velocity of a rotating body ω to the linear velocity v of a point on the body at a distance R from the axis of rotation: $v = R\omega$. Dividing by wheel radius, then, we find

$$\omega = \frac{1056 \text{ in/sec}}{13 \text{ in}} = 81.2 \,\frac{\text{rad}}{\text{sec}}.$$

Average angular acceleration was defined as the time rate of change in the angular velocity. Therefore

$$\alpha_{av} = \frac{\omega \text{ (final)} - \omega \text{ (initial)}}{\text{time interval}}$$

$$= \frac{81.2 - 0 \text{ rad/sec}}{15 \text{ sec}} = 5.41 \frac{\text{rad}}{\text{sec}^2}.$$

Let us now consider the instantaneous acceleration of point B on the link as the link rotates. In Fig. 12A, the link is rotating at constant angular velocity ω. The link is shown in its initial position and at a

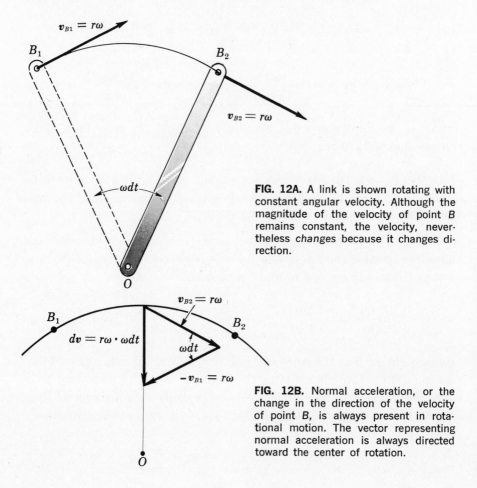

FIG. 12A. A link is shown rotating with constant angular velocity. Although the magnitude of the velocity of point B remains constant, the velocity, nevertheless *changes* because it changes direction.

FIG. 12B. Normal acceleration, or the change in the direction of the velocity of point B, is always present in rotational motion. The vector representing normal acceleration is always directed toward the center of rotation.

rotated position ωdt. In both positions, the *magnitude* of the velocity of point B on the link is constant: $|v_{B1}| = |v_{B2}| = r\omega$, where r is the distance from the center of rotation O to point B. However, since the vector representing the velocity of point B at the rotated position lies in a *different direction*, the two vectors are not identical.

Let us consider this difference between the two vectors, or the change in direction of the velocity of point B. The average acceleration of point B has already been defined as the difference in velocity divided by the corresponding time interval. We can obtain the vector difference between v_{B2} and v_{B1} by graphically adding v_{B2} and $(-v_{B1})$. Since we are considering the vector difference as the average acceleration of point B between B_1 and B_2, let us add v_{B2} and $-v_{B1}$ at a point midway between B_1 and B_2. In Fig. 12B, v_{B2} is redrawn starting at the midpoint of arc B_1B_2 retaining its correct sense. Vector $-v_{B1}$ is drawn starting at the head of v_{B2} but in a sense opposite to v_{B1}. The vector difference dv is shown as a vector normal to the path of point B and pointing to the center of rotation. As the arc interval B_1B_2 becomes smaller, the angle of rotation, ωdt, becomes correspondingly small. At the same time the magnitude of the vector difference approaches the magnitude of an arc subtending angle ωdt. Thus, as dt approaches zero, the acceleration, or velocity difference, is given by

$$dv = r\omega\,\omega dt$$

$$= r\omega^2\,dt$$

$$\frac{dv}{dt} = r\omega^2$$

$$a^n = r\omega^2 \tag{11}$$

or, using Eq. (10): $\omega = v/r$, we obtain

$$a^n = \frac{v^2}{r}.$$

Because the velocity change (or acceleration) vector is always along the radius of rotation (along the link) and points to the center of rotation, the acceleration is always *normal* to the path of the point. This acceleration is therefore referred to as the normal component of acceleration, a^n.

We can now state that wherever rotation occurs a normal acceleration is present. Since we have just seen that it occurs even in the case

29

of a constant angular velocity, ω, (an absence of angular acceleration) we can also conclude that normal acceleration is independent of angular acceleration. In Fig. 12B, the normal acceleration of point B at any instant depends *not* on the angular acceleration (which in this case is zero), but solely on the angular velocity at that instant.

EXAMPLE—PROBLEM 6: In Fig. 12, let us assume that point B is 2 in. from point O. The link rotates at 9549 rev/min clockwise. Find the acceleration of point B.

Solution: It is best to begin by converting the angular velocity of the link from rev/min to rad/sec.

$$1 \frac{\text{rev}}{\text{min}} = 2\pi \frac{\text{rad}}{\text{rev}} \times \frac{1 \text{ min}}{60 \text{ sec}} = \frac{2\pi}{60} \frac{\text{rad}}{\text{sec}} = 0.1047 \frac{\text{rad}}{\text{sec}} \text{ (approx.)}$$

$$\omega = 9549 \frac{\text{rev}}{\text{min}} \times 0.1047 \frac{\text{rad/sec}}{\text{rev/min}} = 1000 \frac{\text{rad}}{\text{sec}}.$$

The velocity of point B is found by multiplying the angular velocity of the link by the distance of B from the axis of rotation.

$$v_B = \omega\, OB = (1000 \frac{\text{rad}}{\text{sec}})(2 \text{ in}) = 2000 \frac{\text{in}}{\text{sec}} \text{ to the right.}$$

To find the normal acceleration of point B, we can use either

$$a^n{}_B = \omega^2\, OB = (1000\ \frac{\text{rad}}{\text{sec}})^2\,(2 \text{ in})$$

or

$$a^n{}_B = \frac{v^2{}_B}{OB} = \frac{(2000 \text{ in/sec})^2}{2 \text{ in}}$$

from which $a^n{}_B = 2{,}000{,}000\ \dfrac{\text{in}}{\text{sec}^2}$.

Now let us consider the case where the rotating link of Fig. 12 is given an angular acceleration, α. The angular acceleration of the link results in a change in the velocity magnitude during time interval dt. This change is in the tangential direction, along the path of point B, and will be labeled dv^t. In Fig. 13A, the initial velocity of point B is

$$v_{B1} = r\,\omega$$

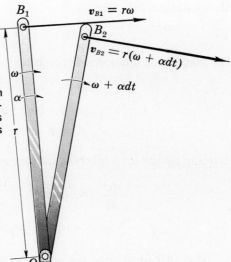

FIG. 13A. The link is shown rotating with angular acceleration. In the rotated position, the velocity of point *B* has changed (increased) in *magnitude* as well as direction.

$v_{B1} = r\omega$

$v_{B2} = r(\omega + \alpha dt)$

$\omega + \alpha dt$

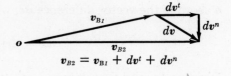

FIG. 13B. The tangential component of the velocity change responsible for the increased velocity magnitude is referred to as tangential acceleration.

$v_{B2} = v_{B1} + dv^t + dv^n$

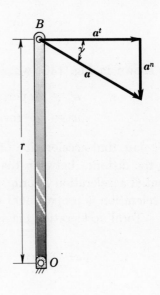

FIG. 13C. The acceleration of point *B* is shown separated into its normal and tangential components.

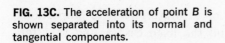

Mechanism

After rotation, the velocity is

$$v_{B2} = r\,(\omega + \alpha\,dt).$$

The magnitude difference is given by

$$dv^t = |\,v_{B2}\,| - |\,v_{B1}\,|$$
$$= r\,(\omega + \alpha\,dt) - r\,\omega$$
$$= r\,\alpha\,dt.$$

Dividing by the time interval, dt, we have

$$\frac{dv^t}{dt} = r\,\alpha,\text{ or}$$

$$a^t = r\,\alpha,\text{ the tangential acceleration.} \qquad (12)$$

Fig. 13B illustrates the changes in velocity in the normal and tangential directions. Velocities v_{B1} and v_{B2} are drawn from a common origin o showing the vector difference dv, where

$$dv = dv^t + dv^n.$$

Dividing by the time interval dt, we have the total acceleration of a point on a rotating link.

$$\frac{dv}{dt} = \frac{dv^t}{dt} + \frac{dv^n}{dt},\text{ or } a = a^t + a^n$$

as shown in Fig. 13C, where

$$a^t = r\,\alpha \text{ perpendicular to the link, and}$$
$$a^n = r\,\omega^2 \text{ toward } O, \text{ the center of rotation.}$$

We note that acceleration of a point on a rotating body is proportional to the distance between the point and the fixed center, and that tangential acceleration is proportional to angular acceleration and normal acceleration is proportional to the square of the angular velocity.

Total acceleration magnitude and direction are given by

$$a = \sqrt{(a^n)^2 + (a^t)^2} \quad \text{and} \quad \gamma = \tan^{-1}\frac{a^n}{a^t} \qquad (13)$$

as shown in Fig. 13C. In acceleration analyses of linkages in Chapter Three, we will utilize the normal and tangential acceleration components to graphically solve linkage problems.

EXAMPLE—PROBLEM 7: The link of Example Problem 6 rotates with an angular velocity of 1000 rad/sec clockwise. It is given an angular acceleration $\alpha = 750,000$ rad/sec^2 counterclockwise (causing the link to slow down). Find the acceleration of point B.

Solution: The normal acceleration of point B is independent of the angular acceleration; thus

$$a^n_B = OB\,\omega^2$$
$$= 2,000,000 \ \frac{in}{sec^2} \ \text{along } BO \text{ toward } O.$$

The tangential acceleration is given by

$$a^t_B = \alpha\,OB$$
$$= -(750,000 \ \frac{rad}{sec^2})\ (2\ in)$$
$$= -1,500,000 \ \frac{in}{sec^2}$$

perpendicular to OB to the left (since α is counterclockwise). Adding the vectors, we obtain the total acceleration of point B

$$a_B = a^t_B + a^n_B = \sqrt{(a^t_B)^2 + (a^n_B)^2}$$
$$= \sqrt{(-1,500,000)^2 + (2,000,000)^2}$$
$$= 2,500,000 \ \frac{in}{sec^2}, \text{ to the left and downward}$$

at an angle

$$\gamma = \tan^{-1} \ \frac{a^n_B}{a^t_B}$$
$$= \tan^{-1} \ \frac{2,000,000}{-1,500,000}$$
$$= 126.87°.$$

A careful graphical addition of the two components of acceleration gives the same result.

Dimensions

Any consistent set of units may be used, but to be sure of accurate results it is advisable to work with a single set of units throughout. Since we are principally concerned with machines, it is appropriate to measure distances in inches. Velocities will be given in inches per second and accelerations in inches per second square. Acceleration of an automobile given in miles per hour per second would ordinarily be converted to inch and second units before proceeding to investigate the mechanisms involved.

Angular displacement will be measured in radians (a pure number equivalent to inches of arc per inch of radius where, as noted above, 1 radian $= 360°/2\pi =$ approximately $57.3°$). Then, angular velocity ω will be measured in radians per second (sec^{-1}) and angular acceleration α in radians per second square (sec^{-2}). The symbols ω and α are to be reserved for angular velocity and angular acceleration in radian and second units only; measurements in other sets of units such as revolutions per minute and revolutions per minute per second will be converted to the above units to ensure consistency.

Ratios (including velocity ratios and angular velocity ratios) are, of course, dimensionless and the ratio of two angular velocities in RPM, for example, is identical to the ratio in radians per second. When solving equations, the units should be included with the numerical value of each term as partial insurance against errors. Each calculation should be checked to see that the solution has the correct units. Frequently, a missing term or wrong term will be detected because the units do not check.

Mechanisms for Specific Applications

Before we begin detailed kinematic analysis of the mechanisms, it is worthwhile to consider the basic motion characteristics of some of the commonly available linkages. In the design of a machine it may be practical to combine simple linkages and other components to obtain the required output-to-input motion relationship. The designer may wish to become familiar with many of the linkage configurations which are in the public domain and should become aware of the proprietary packaged drive trains and other machine components which are available. He may then use his skill and ingenuity to combine these components for optimum results without having to "reinvent the wheel."

Some familiarity with various classes of available mechanisms will be obtained by leafing through this and other design-oriented books and by using manufacturers' catalogs and engineering periodicals.

Of course, the probable cost advantages of using commercially available components should not prevent the designer from exploring entirely new solutions, even though they may represent significant departures from traditional designs.

Drafting Instruments

The *drafting instrument* using rigid links and pins shown in Figs. 14A and B is proportioned so that distances $AB=CD$ and $AD=BC$

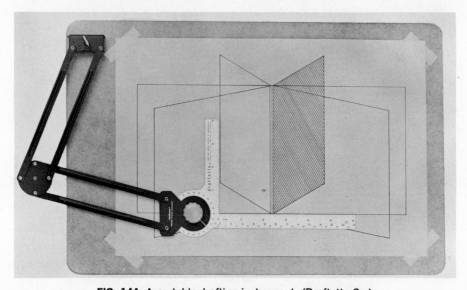

FIG. 14A. A portable drafting instrument. (Draftette Co.)

FIG. 14B. The linkage of the portable drafting instrument shown above consists of two parallelograms, which permits translation of the straight-edge in any direction without rotating.

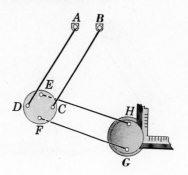

form a parallelogram. If the line between fixed centers A and B is horizontal, then DC is also horizontal at all times. Since a straightedge attached at DC would not allow sufficient freedom of movement, another parallelogram linkage is added. A parallelogram linkage can also be used to restrain independently suspended automobile wheels to a vertical plane, reducing "tucking under" during turns.

Another drafting instrument, Figs. 15A and B, uses tight steel bands (belts) on pairs of disks with equal diameters. Disk 1 is not permitted to rotate and, as the arm between disks 1 and 2 is moved, disks 2 and 3 translate without rotating. The bands between disks 3 and 4 prevent rotation of disk 4 and the attached straightedges.

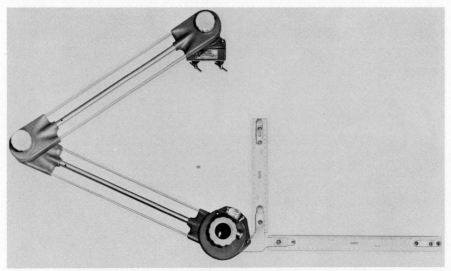

FIG. 15A. A band-type drafting machine. (Charles Bruning Co.)

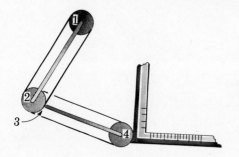

FIG. 15B. The belts arranged as shown permit translation of the straight-edge, but prevent rotation.

Pantograph Linkages

The parallelogram also forms the basis for *pantograph linkages* which may be used to reproduce and *change* the scale of drawings and patterns. Both pantographs of Fig. 16 are made up of rigid links *AC*, *CD*, *DE* and *EB* with pin connections. Lengths *BC=DE* and *BE=CD* form a parallelogram. Link *BE* is parallel to *CD* at all times for both linkages and *F* is located on a line between *A* and *D* making triangles *ABF* and *ACD* similar. Thus, in Fig. 16A the ratio *DA/DF* is a constant for all positions of the linkage and if a tracing point located at *F* is used to trace a pattern, a drawing tool at *A* will reproduce the pattern enlarged by the factor *DA/DF*. If the actual part is to be smaller than the pattern, then the tracing point can be located at *A* and the drawing tool at *F*. The result will be a size reduction of the ratio of *DF/DA*. The pantograph may be made adjustable to produce various enlargement or reduction ratios provided the key features are maintained: the linkage must form a parallelogram and points *A*, *F* and *D* must lie on a straight line.

If the pattern is to be reproduced full size or nearly full size, point

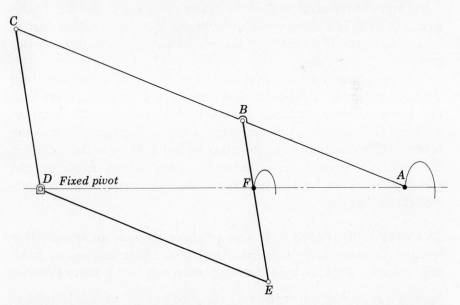

FIG. 16A. A pantograph with fixed point *D*. The pattern can be traced enlarged by the ratio of *DA/DF* if the tracing point is located at point *F*. Reversing the tracing point and drawing tool produces a reduced tracing.

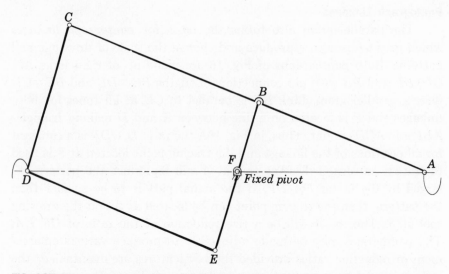

FIG. 16B. The pantograph with point *F* used as the fixed point will produce a tracing approximately the same size as the pattern.

F will serve as the pivot with *D* the tracer point and *A* the tool holder as in Fig. 16B. The pattern will be faithfully reproduced with a part to pattern size ratio of *AF/DF* but the orientation will be changed in this case.

The operation may be automated by using a sensing device to drive the tracing point over the pattern. A number of other linkages are used for similar purposes, including the *engine indicator*, Fig. 17, which reproduces and enlarges a pressure signal. Engine or compressor pressure is measured by a small piston operating against a spring in the indicator. The indicator linkage, which resembles a pantograph, magnifies and records the motion of the indicator piston producing approximately straight-line motion.

EXAMPLE—PROBLEM 8: Design a linkage to guide an oxyacetylene torch in rough-cutting parts from steel plate. Part dimensions to be approximately 6 inches by 6 inches; pattern will be 1.5 times full size.

Solution: A pantograph of the type sketched in Fig. 16B will be used so that the pattern will not be too near the cutting torch. The pattern dimensions will be approximately 9 inches by 9 inches and the linkage must be designed so that tracing point D moves freely over at least that area. It can be seen that by dimensioning the links so that $CB=DE=12$ inches and $CD=BE=10$ inches, the tracing point will cover the required area without nearing its limiting (extreme) positions. To obtain the size reduction factor of 1/1.5, $AB/CB = 1/1.5$ or $AB = 8$ inches. Points A, F and D must form a straight line, from which $BF/CD = AB/AC$ or $BF = 4$ inches, locating the fixed pivot.

For a practical design, it might be necessary to allow the tracing point position A to be adjusted to various positions along the link so that several ratios of pattern to part size could be accommodated. For each position of A, a new point F; the fixed point on link BE, would have to be established to maintain the straight line relationship between D, F and A.

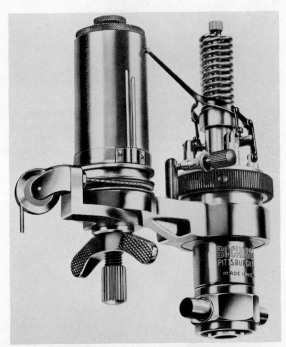

FIG. 17. This pantograph-like mechanism is used to plot a pressure vs. volume diagram (on a paper card wrapped around the drum on the left) for a reciprocating engine or compressor. The drum at the left is rotated in proportion to the piston location, while the pointer height is proportional to the pressure in the engine or compressor cylinder. (Bacharach Industrial Instrument Co.)

FIG. 18A. This gasoline powered engine develops one horsepower at 6300 RPM but weighs less than four pounds and can fit into a six inch cube (approx.). Considerable kinematic analysis was required to design an engine compact enough to compete with small electric motors used in portable power tools and other consumer products. (O & R Engines, Inc.)

FIG. 18B. The piston and connecting rod for the above engine. The rod was made as short as possible to reduce engine size. (O & R Engines, Inc.)

In-Line Slider Crank Mechanism

The *in-line slider crank mechanism* is probably the most common of all mechanisms because of its simplicity and versatility. We are familiar with it in the reciprocating pump and compressor in which the input rotation is changed to reciprocating motion of the piston. In the piston engine the situation is reversed and the piston is the driver. Of course, if there are several cylinders, the several pistons alternate as driver and if the engine is a single cylinder engine, the energy stored in the flywheel and other components actually drives the piston between power strokes. Fig. 18 shows one application of the slider-crank linkage, a compact, one horsepower gasoline-powered motor, and some associated

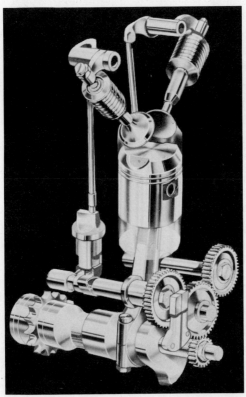

FIG. 19. One cylinder of a reciprocating engine is illustrated, showing the basic slider-crank mechanism, cam shaft, and valve train. (Curtiss-Wright Corp.)

mechanical components. A single slider crank mechanism and the associated cam and valve train typical of a multi-cylinder internal combustion engine are shown in Fig. 19.

Rotating Combustion Engine

The *rotating combustion engine*, Fig. 20A, is another solution to
the same problem with little kinematic resemblance to the conventional piston-type engine. The three-sided rotor moves eccentrically
within a two-lobed engine block. These two parts (the rotor and the
shaped block) are equivalent to the pistons, cylinders, combustion
chambers, and valve train of an ordinary reciprocating engine. An internal gear, part of the three-lobed rotor, actually acts as a planet gear
as it meshes with a smaller fixed sun gear. The tooth ratio of the two
gears is 3:2, so that the eccentric (crankshaft) which carries the rotor
and internal planet gear makes three rotations as the rotor makes one
rotation. Many other possible configurations of the rotating combustion
engine with various numbers of rotor sides and engine block lobes were
examined before the design shown in Fig. 20A was chosen.

The combustion cycle of a rotating combustion engine is illustrated
in Fig. 20B. At intake, an intake port is uncovered by the rotor. A mixture of air and fuel is drawn into the increasing space between the rotor
and block. The eccentric rotor then seals the intake port and compresses
the mixture in the now-decreasing space between rotor and block. The
mixture is ignited when the space is very small, increasing the pressure
and driving the rotor around (the expansion phase). Finally, an exhaust
port is uncovered and the products of combustion are discharged. The
cycle is then repeated.

In the above discussion, we traced only one charge of air and fuel
through a complete cycle. The three-sided eccentric rotor and two-lobed
engine block, however, correspond to three sets of pistons and cylinders.
At the time of ignition of the first charge of air and fuel, the intake
process is occurring in another chamber. When the first chamber is in
the exhaust position, a third chamber is in the intake position. Fig. 20B
shows the combustion cycle for only one chamber, but at any time a
different phase of the process is occurring in each of the other chambers.

The fixed sun gear and the larger ring gear are shown as circles in
Fig. 20B. Rotation of the crankshaft and eccentric rotor carrier is seen
by observing the point of contact between the fixed sun gear and the

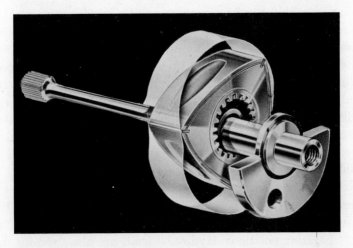

FIG. 20A. The rotating combustion engine, showing the three-sided eccentric rotor and internal gear. A major advantage of this engine is its basic simplicity. The rotor and eccentric shaft are the only rotating parts; cams and valves are not required. (Curtiss-Wright Corp.)

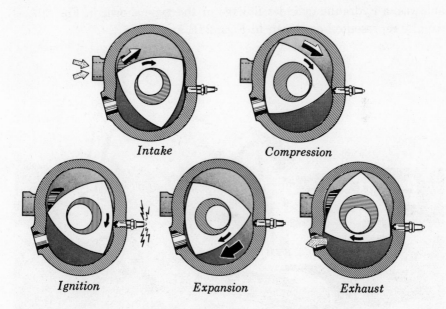

Fig. 20B. A complete combustion cycle of the rotating combustion engine. The rotor speed is one third of the eccentric crankshaft speed, maintaining one power impulse for each crankshaft revolution. (Curtiss-Wright Corp.)

planet-like internal gear. In observing one thermodynamic cycle of this engine represented by one rotor rotation, Fig. 20B, we see that the "crankshaft" (represented by the eccentric carrying the rotor) is given more than one rotation. Actually, the "crankshaft" is given three rotations where the ratio of internal gear teeth on the rotor to teeth on the fixed gear meshing with it is 1.5 to 1. This result may be determined (with difficulty) by making successive sketches or may be calculated using principles to be discussed in Chapter Seven: Drive Trains.

Fluid Links

Mechanical systems frequently include *fluid links* utilizing hydraulic or pneumatic cylinders or fluid drive transmissions. The backhoe shown in Fig. 21 uses hydraulic cylinders arranged to give it a wide range of operating positions. Hydraulic feeds are also used for machine tools. By using a variable delivery pump or a relief valve for control, speed and thrust may be regulated precisely by the operator. In the case of machine tools, the fluid system may be programmed to go through a complete cycle of operations automatically. For kinematic analysis, a hydraulic cylinder linkage of the type shown in Fig. 22A is usually represented as shown in Figs. 22B and C.

FIG. 21. The motion of this hydraulic backhoe is determined by several independently-controlled mechanisms. (Insley Mfg. Corp.)

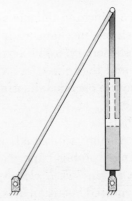

FIG. 22A. A linkage which includes a hydraulic cylinder.

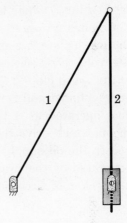

FIG. 22B. A kinematic representation of the linkage shown in A: Link 2 slides within a sleeve pinned to the frame.

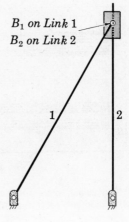

FIG. 22C. Alternate representation of same linkage: Link 2 slides within a sleeve pinned to link 1 at point B_1. Point B_2 is taken as the identical point on link 2 at this instant. Then, the absolute motion of point B_1 and the motion of B_2 relative to B_1 are considered.

Mechanism

A complicated linkage arrangement can sometimes be divided into several simple mechanisms for analysis. If none of the links in a mechanism is stationary, a link having known motion may be considered fixed at first, and then the effect of its motion added later. The linkages that comprise the backhoe illustrated in Fig. 21 can be handled this way.

Swash Plate

Converting rotational motion to reciprocating rectilinear motion is a common problem and many mechanisms have been devised for this purpose. In the *swash plate* type mechanism, (Fig. 23) a cam-like swash plate is rotated about an axis which is not perpendicular to its face. The plate drives plungers in a cylinder block, the stroke of the plungers being equal to $d \tan \phi$ where the several parallel cylinders are arranged in a circle of diameter d as shown in Fig. 23. The angle ϕ is measured between the swash plate face and a plane perpendicular to the cylinder axes. For 100% volumetric efficiency, the volume of liquid pumped per revolution of the swash plate is $Q = ANd\tan \phi$ where A is the cross sectional area of one cylinder and N the number of cylinders.

When operated as a hydraulic motor, oil pressure is applied to the plungers which drive the swash plate. Each cylinder is alternately connected to the oil supply and then to the exhaust by a distribution system operated by the swash plate shaft.

An *inversion* of a mechanism exhibits the same relative motion but

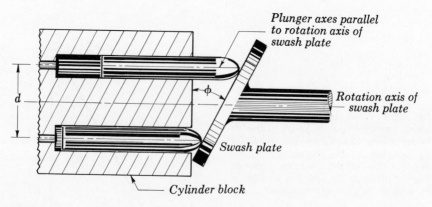

FIG. 23. The swash plate mechanism is but one of a large number of mechanisms designed to convert rotational motion to rectilinear motion.

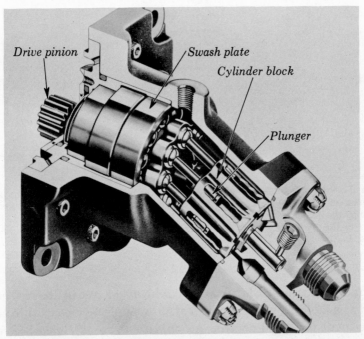

Drive pinion

Swash plate

Cylinder block

Plunger

FIG. 24. This *inversion* of a swash plate mechanism has been designed as a *fixed-displacement, piston-type hydraulic pump*. The cylinder block, drive shaft, and the nine pistons all rotate as a unit. The pump is available with the cylinder block axis offset relative to the drive shaft by 15° to 30°. This offset determines the stroke of the pistons and, therefore, the flow rate. (Vickers, Inc.)

the links do not have the same absolute motion. The link which is fixed in the original mechanism is not fixed in the inversion. The cylinder block is fixed in the swash plate mechanism of Fig. 23. If, instead, the cylinder block is rotated and the swash plate fixed, the motion of the plungers relative to the cylinders will not change. Hydraulic oil will be pumped at the same rate. Fig. 24 shows an inversion of the basic swash plate mechanism. In this case the link which acts as swash plate actually rotates, but its rotation is in a plane and of no significance to the relative motion. This arrangement is kinematically equivalent to the plunger ends riding on a fixed disk.

A *volume control* is effected by designing the pump so that the angle between the cylinder axes and the plane of the swash plate may be varied. The volume control may be actuated manually or automati-

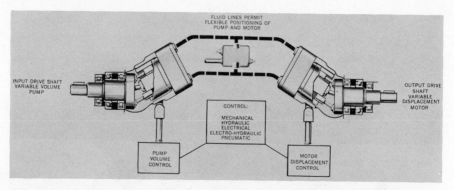

FIG. 25. Two *variable-offset* swash plate mechanisms—one used as a pump and the other used as a motor—are combined to create an adjustable speed transmission. In the pump, the piston stroke can be varied by changing the angle of offset. Fluid is pumped to the hydraulic motor, operating the pistons which drive the output shaft. (Vickers, Inc.)

cally by a mechanical, electrical or fluid control. When the mechanism is used as a motor, a similar control of offset angle may be used to change displacement for speed control. An *adjustable speed transmission* may be assembled from two identical variable swash plates, one used as a variable-offset *pump*, Fig. 25, and the other used as a variable-offset *hydraulic motor*. Speed is continuously variable over a wide range with fine control and high torque capabilities. The fluid link between the two components allows considerable flexibility in positioning input and output.

Gear Trains

Gear trains are particularly suitable for use at high speeds and in drives with high power ratings. Since gears offer precise speed ratios, they are also used in mechanical computers, machine tools and in other applications where precision is required. Differential gears are used to distribute power in automobiles, but may also be used to add or subtract inputs for control of certain processes. If two machines are to perform a production line function in a certain sequence, one machine may drive the other through a differential so that phase adjustment is possible between the operations. Fig. 26 shows a differential transmission. The differential itself is made up of four bevel gears; the other gears in the transmission are helical gears.

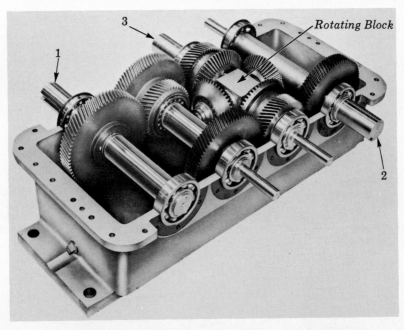

FIG. 26. A differential transmission. Differential gears are most commonly used to distribute power to the rear wheels of an automobile. Other uses of differentials and differential transmissions include phase shifting, cycling, ratio changing, and computation. (Fairchild-Hiller)

Gearing is often combined with other mechanical components. A worm and worm wheel drive a power screw in the *linear actuator* of Fig. 27. To reduce friction, a ball screw is used. Because the translational motion of the screw is proportional to rotation of the worm, the actuator may be used as a precision jack or locating device. Gears will be discussed in much greater detail beginning with Chapter Five.

Analyzing Linkages by Studying Their Limiting Positions

The extreme positions of a linkage are of particular importance. Let us arbitrarily designate an input and an output link in a mechanism where the input link rotates continuously in one direction. Let the output link rotate in a clockwise direction through some angle, then return

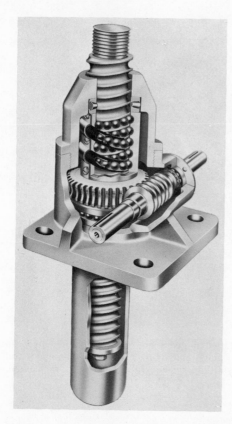

FIG. 27. A ball-screw actuator. Rotating motion is efficiently transformed into translation through the use of a worm and worm wheel directly driving the nut of the ball screw. (Duff-Norton Co.)

counterclockwise to the starting position to repeat the cycle of motion over and over. The configuration of the linkage at the instant the follower changes direction is called a *limiting position*. In the linkage just described, there are two limiting positions.

The speed ratio, output angular velocity to input angular velocity, is zero when the mechanism is in a limiting position. If the output link translates instead of rotating, the discussion of the velocity ratio at the limiting positions still holds, and the ratio of output linear velocity to input angular velocity is zero at the limiting positions.

The input link (having constant velocity) can drive the output link *through* its limiting (zero velocity) position. Suppose, however, that the oscillating or reciprocating link serves as the driver. We must then use a flywheel or similar device as a reservoir of energy to insure that the oscillating link is carried through its limiting positions. The oscillating link, by itself, cannot drive the mechanism through the limiting positions in the mechanism's cycle of motion, since at these points its velocity is zero.

Some linkages have no limiting positions. A pair of spur gears for example, has a continuous input and output. On the other hand, some linkages exhibit more than two limiting positions for each cycle of motion.

Slider Crank Mechanisms

A slider crank mechanism with the usual proportions (connecting rod longer than crank) has two limiting positions, both occurring when the crank and connecting rod are colinear. See Figs. 28A and B. When reciprocating steam engines were in common use, these positions were called *dead center positions, crank dead center* referring to the position with the piston nearest the crankshaft (Fig. 28A, *left*), and *head dead center* referring to the position with the piston farthest from the crankshaft (Fig. 28A, *right).* Piston direction reverses at these two points; piston velocity at these points is therefore zero. Piston acceleration, however, is not zero. In fact, at the extreme positions of the mechanism, piston acceleration will be maximum or nearly maximum (depending on the linkage dimensions). Acceleration of linkages will be covered in a later chapter.

When the extended path of the wristpin C goes through the center of the crankshaft O_1 (as in Fig. 28A) the linkage is then called an *in-line* slider crank mechanism. The stroke, referred to as *piston travel*, equals $2R$, twice the crank length. The crank turns through 180° as the piston moves from left to right, and 180° as it returns to the left. If the crank turns at constant angular velocity ω, the piston takes the same time to move from left to right as it takes to return to the left.

Offset Slider Crank Mechanisms. The wristpin path of the *offset* slider crank mechanism, Fig. 28B, does not extend through the crankshaft center. The limiting positions shown represent positions of zero piston velocity, but the angles through which the crank turns between the limiting positions are not equal. If the crank turns counterclockwise, it turns through an angle greater than 180° as the piston moves from left to right, and through less than 180° as the piston moves back to the left. If the crank turns counterclockwise at constant angular ve-

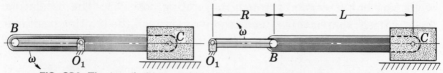

FIG. 28A. The two limiting positions of an *in-line* slider crank mechanism.

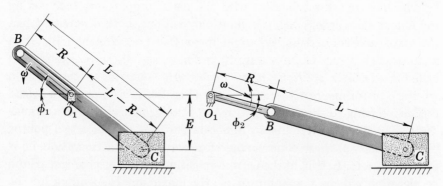

FIG. 28B. The two limiting positions of the *offset* slider crank mechanism.

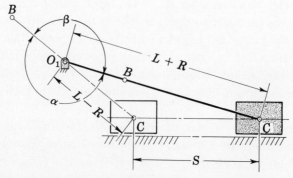

FIG. 28C. The limiting positions of the offset slider crank mechanism imposed to find the time ratio of forward to return strokes.

locity, the piston takes longer in its stroke to the right than it takes to return to the left. From its limiting position in Fig. 28B, *left*, to its limiting position in Fig. 28B, *right*, the crank turns through the angle

$$\alpha = 180° + \phi_1 - \phi_2$$

as shown in Fig. 28C. During the return stroke the crank turns through the angle

$$\beta = 180° - \phi_1 + \phi_2$$

where
$$\phi_1 = \sin^{-1} \frac{E}{L-R}$$

$$\phi_2 = \sin^{-1} \frac{E}{L+R}$$

for crank length R, connecting rod length L, and offset distance E less than $L-R$.

When the crank turns at constant angular velocity ω, the time ratio of forward to return stroke is given by α/β. The length of the stroke is

$$S = \sqrt{(L+R)^2-E^2} - \sqrt{(L-R)^2-E^2} \ . \tag{14}$$

The limiting positions of the linkage may be superimposed to form a triangle, Fig. 28C. Using the triangle inequality (the sum of the lengths of any two sides exceeds the length of the remaining side) we obtain

$$L - R + S \quad \text{greater than} \quad L + R$$

from which we see that the stroke length will always exceed 2R when the wristpin path is offset from the crankshaft. The above relationships are valid when both of the following conditions are met: offset E less than $L-R$, and R less than L. Of course angles α and β and stroke S can be found simply by superimposing the limiting positions of the linkage as in Fig. 28C. This graphical solution is used to check the analytical solution or, as is often the case, the accuracy of the graphical solution alone is adequate.

53

Four Bar Linkages

The *four bar linkage* is an important basic mechanism and one of the simplest. We will consider the following four classes of four bar linkages:

(I)   The crank rocker mechanism,

(II)   The drag link mechanism,

(III) The double rocker mechanism, and

(IV) The class of four bar linkages for which the driver-to-follower relationship is indefinite on the basis of linkage dimensions.

The class to which we assign a linkage is based on (1) the absolute motion of the links (which, in turn, depends on which one of the links is fixed), and (2) on link proportions. For a linkage of given proportions, *relative motion*, the motion of one link relative to another, depends on instantaneous link orientation, but does not depend on which of the links is fixed.

To begin with, the linkage under consideration must be an actual mechanism. This will be ascertained by making a scale drawing or by checking the link lengths to see that each link is shorter than the sum of the other three. The reader can verify by graphical construction that if a given link were as long as the sum of the lengths of the other three links, that the linkage could not operate. If the length of any link exceeded the sum of the other three lengths, no four bar mechanism could be assembled from the links.

Class I—Crank Rocker Mechanisms. Fig. 29A represents Class I of the four bar linkage. It is called a *crank rocker mechanism*. In a crank rocker mechanism, one link will oscillate through a fixed angle as the crank is rotated continuously in one direction. The symbol L will be used to represent link *length*. The links will be subscripted as follows: 0 for the fixed link (the line of centers), 1 for the smaller crank (which will be called the driver), 2 for the connecting rod or coupler, and 3 for the large (follower) crank. In each case, the length of a link will be measured between bearing or pin joint centers and will not be the same as the overall length of the actual link. We observe in Figs. 29B and C that limiting positions occur when two links are colinear and the linkage arranges itself in the form of a triangle. The length of one side of the "triangle" is less than the sum of the lengths of the other two sides;

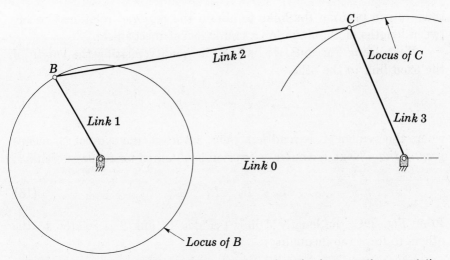

FIG. 29A. A crank rocker mechanism. For this class of mechanisms, continuous rotation of the driver results in oscillation of the follower.

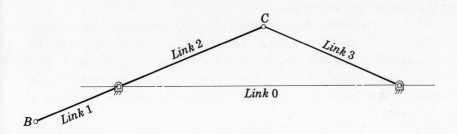

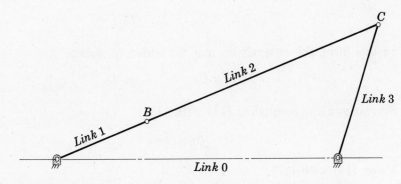

FIGS. 29B and C. The limiting positions of the crank rocker mechanism.

thus we can position the links to obtain the *required* relationships between lengths of the links for a crank rocker mechanism.

First, using Fig. 29B, we have an inequality relating the length of the fixed link to the others:

$$L_0 < L_2 - L_1 + L_3 \tag{15}$$

where the symbol $<$ is read *less than;* reversed, the symbol $>$ means *greater than.* Next, a similar expression is obtained for follower crank 3:

$$L_3 < L_2 - L_1 + L_0. \tag{16}$$

From Fig. 29C, the length of link 1 added to link 2 is related to the others to form the inequality:

$$L_1 + L_2 < L_0 + L_3. \tag{17}$$

Actually, there are three possible inequalities based on the triangle formed in Fig. 29B and three more from Fig. 29C, but the three remaining inequalities are redundant.

Many of the rules which apply to algebraic equations also apply to inequalities. We may, for example, add the same quantity to both sides of an inequality and the inequality so formed will also be valid. This rule includes subtraction of the same quantity from both sides. Using this rule, inequalities (15) and (16) respectively may be rewritten in the following form:

$$L_1 < -L_0 + L_2 + L_3 \tag{15}$$

$$L_1 < L_0 + L_2 - L_3. \tag{16}$$

In this form, the inequalities may be added to obtain

$$2L_1 < 2L_2 \quad \text{or} \quad L_1 < L_2. \tag{18}$$

Similarly, using inequality (15) with (17),

$$L_1 < L_3. \tag{19}$$

Using (16) with (17),

$$L_1 < L_0. \tag{20}$$

Thus, if the driver crank (which we label link 1) is the shortest link in a four bar mechanism, we *may* have a crank rocker mechanism. If inequalities (15), (16), and (17) are satisfied for the given mechanism, the identification of the mechanism as a crank rocker mechanism is then positive; link 3 will oscillate as link 1 rotates continuously.

Class II—Drag Link Mechanisms. When both cranks of a four bar linkage turn through 360°, the linkage is called a *drag link mechanism* (class II). Fig. 30A shows driving crank 1 dragging the coupler (link 2) and follower (link 3) through a complete circle. Limiting positions of the follower crank do not exist as they do for the oscillating follower in the crank rocker mechanism. Instead, *critical positions* of the linkage occur twice each cycle when the follower is colinear with the fixed link O_1O_3 as in Fig. 30B. In order for the linkage to actually assume these positions, the links must form triangles resembling those in the figure. Taking advantage of the rule that the length of one side of a triangle must be less than the sum of the lengths of the other sides, we obtain the following set of inequalities for the drag link:

$$L_0 + L_3 < L_1 + L_2 \tag{21}$$

$$L_1 < L_2 + L_3 - L_0 \tag{22}$$

$$L_2 < L_1 + L_3 - L_0. \tag{23}$$

Adding the above inequalities in pairs, it is seen that the fixed link L_0 (O_1O_3) is the shortest link in a drag link mechanism. Thus, if we have a four bar linkage in which the fixed link is shortest, we can try to establish inequalities (21), (22) and (23). If these conditions are met the linkage under examination is a drag link mechanism, and both cranks, L_1 (the driver) and L_3 (the follower), rotate through 360° without reversal. Contrast this motion with that of the crank rocker in which one crank will oscillate as the other rotates continuously. It is thus seen that link lengths can affect linkage motion.

Class IV—Indefinite Motion Mechanisms. The above criteria for crank rocker and drag link mechanisms, inequalities (15) through (23), contain the inequality sign < (less than), rather than the sign ≤ (equal or less than). The distinction can be important. Suppose for example

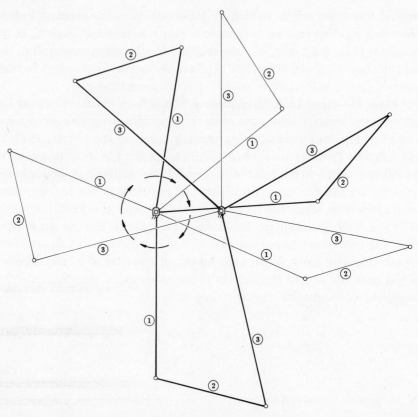

FIG. 30A. A drag link mechanism. For this class of mechanisms, continuous rotation of the driver results in continuous rotation of the follower.

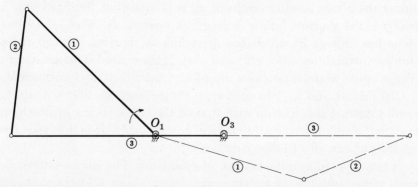

FIG. 30B. The critical positions for determining the dimensional relationships of a drag link mechanism. Critical positions occur when the follower and fixed axis (O_1 O_3) are colinear.

that the first criterion for the crank rocker mechanism, inequality (15), was changed to read.

$$L_0 = L_2 - L_1 + L_3. \tag{24}$$

The linkage which satisfies equation (24) may reach a limiting position with links 1, 2, 3, and the fixed link all colinear. Consider Fig. 31 with the linkage in the position subscripted with the letter a. As link 1 rotates counterclockwise from position 1_a to 1_b, link 3 rotates counterclockwise until all the links are colinear with fixed link $O_1 \ O_3$. If the motion occurred slowly and if there is a clockwise torque applied to link 3 (e.g. torque due to a spring), then position b is a limiting position. Under these conditions, link 3 will rotate clockwise back to position 3_a under the influence of the clockwise torque as link 1 continues counterclockwise from position 1_b thru 1_c to 1_a.

We obtain an entirely different motion relationship, however, if the inertia effects on link 3 *exceed* any opposing torque applied directly to link 3. Then, beginning at position a, the links continue *through* limiting position b until all links reach limiting position c. If inertia effects continue to govern, link 1 will rotate counterclockwise from position 1_c through 1_a through 1_b, through 1_c to 1_a, while link 3 rotates clockwise from position 3_c to 3_a. Thus, one cycle of motion represents two complete rotations of link 1 while link 3 makes one complete oscillation. The student may find it helpful to sketch the linkage in several positions for each of the two possibilities.

Based on link dimensions alone, the linkage of Fig. 31 has an *indefinite motion relationship* which we will call class IV. When the operating conditions of the linkage are specified, then we may describe the output motion and identify the mechanism with one of the other classes. Furthermore, if other inequality signs in the above relationships for class I and II mechanisms are changed to equal signs, the input to output motion relationships may also be indefinite.

A similar situation occurs when the rocker link of a crank rocker mechanism is nominally designated as driver. In some doubtful cases gravity forces, inertia forces (the effect of a flywheel or other large mass), spring forces, and friction may determine the actual mode of operation of a linkage.

Class III—Double Rocker Mechanisms. Four bar linkages which

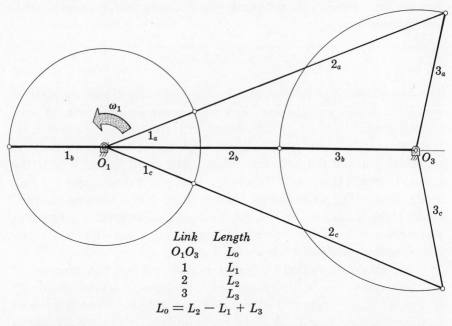

$$L_0 = L_2 - L_1 + L_3$$

FIG. 31. This four bar linkage has an indefinite driver-to-follower relationship.

do not fall into classes I, II, or IV (including all linkages for which the coupler is the shortest link) are *double rocker mechanisms* (class III). In this class of mechanisms, both input crank and output crank oscillate; neither can turn through 360°. An example of the double rocker mechanism is given in Fig. 32.

By combining inequalities we may summarize the above criteria of motion for each class of four bar linkage where lengths are defined as follows:

$$L_0: \text{fixed link}$$
$$L_1: \text{driver crank}$$
$$L_2: \text{coupler}$$
$$L_3: \text{follower crank}.$$

Class I: If the drive crank (1) is the shortest link and

$$L_1 + | L_2 - L_3 | < L_0 < L_2 - L_1 + L_3 \tag{25}$$

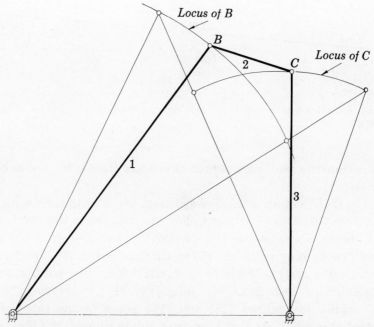

FIG. 32. A double rocker mechanism. Both driver and follower oscillate; neither can rotate. Note the limiting positions of each link.

the linkage is a *crank rocker mechanism*. (The quantity $|L_2 - L_3|$ represents the absolute value of $L_2 - L_3$, i.e., $L_2 - L_3$ or $L_3 - L_2$, whichever is positive.)

Class II: If the fixed link (0) is the shortest link and

$$|L_1 - L_2| + L_0 < L_3 < L_1 + L_2 - L_0 \tag{26}$$

the linkage is a *drag link mechanism*.

Class III: If the coupler (2) is the shortest link or if the double inequality (25) is not satisfied for class I, or if the double inequality (26) is not satisfied for class II, the linkage operates as a *double rocker mechanism* except as noted under class IV.

Class IV: If an equal sign appears in place of an inequality sign in inequalities (25) or (26), there may be an *indefinite motion relationship* based on link dimensions alone. Further information such as ap-

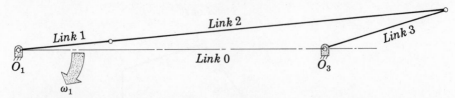

FIG. 33. A Class I mechanism which may not operate properly because of improper link length.

plied and inertia loads may permit us to place the mechanism in class I, II or III.

The motion of an actual linkage may, under certain circumstances, differ from that described above. For example, while the crank of the crank rocker mechanism of Fig. 29 should be able to drive the rocker through its limiting positions, the mechanism of Fig. 33 is probably an unsatisfactory design. The latter is shown in a limiting position and the triangle formed insures us that inequality (17) is satisfied, *but just barely* (while inequalities (15) and (16) are obviously satisfied by a substantial margin). As link 1 tends to rotate through the limiting position in Fig. 33, the direction of force transmitted along link 2 to link 3 results in very little torque on link 3, but a high bearing force at O_3. The probable result is that friction torque would exceed driving torque and the mechanism would jam. Dimensional tolerances including looseness at pins and bearings often tends to worsen the situation. In most cases, then, it is advisable to provide a reasonable "margin of safety" in satisfying the inequalities which determine linkage motion.

Quick Return Mechanisms

Quick return mechanisms include an oscillating link or reciprocating slider which moves forward slowly and returns quickly (with constant speed input). The forward and return directions are arbitrarily assigned as above to correspond with machine tool usage where a working stroke would have high force capability at low speed and the return stroke could be rapid with no load.

The designation *quick return* has as much to do with the function of a mechanism as with its mode of operation. If there is an intentional difference between the time required for the forward and return strokes, the linkage may be called a *quick return mechanism*. Most crank rocker mechanisms exhibit unequal forward and return times for the rocker. If we take advantage of the unequal strokes in designing a piece of machinery, we call the linkage a quick return mechanism.

Forward and return strokes for the in-line slider crank mechanism take equal time, but the offset slider crank acts as a quick return mechanism. The time ratio of the strokes is the same as the ratio of angles given by equations $\alpha = 180° + \phi_1 - \phi_2$ and $\beta = 180° - \phi_1 + \phi_2$. Binford and Sampson used a digital computer to examine several thousand slider crank mechanisms with various dimensions and offsets, and plotted the effect of offset on stroke time ratios, stroke length, peak velocities and accelerations.[1]

Other linkage combinations offer considerably more flexibility for quick return design than the offset slider crank. The *drag link*, for example, may form part of a mechanism designed for large forward-to-return time ratios. Fig. 34A shows four bar linkage O_1BCO_3 which appears to satisfy the criteria for a drag link mechanism. Slider D will represent a machine element which is to have different average velocities for its forward and return strokes while driving crank 1 turns at constant angular velocity. The two extreme positions of the slider occur when follower link 3 lies along the line of centers O_1O_3. Since link 4 is also colinear with the line of centers at both of the extreme positions, we see that the slider *stroke* is twice the length of link 3:

$$S = 2\,L_3 . \tag{27}$$

The time for the slider to travel between limiting positions is propor-

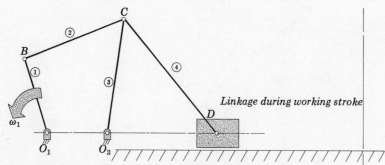

FIG. 34A. A drag link mechanism is combined with a slider to form a quick return mechanism.

1. R. C. Binford and R. J. Sampson, "Slider-Crank Charts for Offset Crankshafts," A.S.M.E. paper No. 66-*Mech*-39, 1966.

tional to the angle between corresponding positions of driving crank as long as the driving crank angular velocity is constant.

EXAMPLE—PROBLEM 9: Design a *quick return mechanism* with a 7 inch stroke; the working stroke to take .3 seconds and the return stroke .1 seconds.

Solution: Step 1. There are many linkage configurations which will satisfy the above requirements. Due to the large ratio of working stroke to return stroke, we will try a mechanism based on the drag link. Using a mechanism suggested by Fig. 34A, a 7 inch stroke will be obtained if the length of the follower link

$$L_3 = 3.5 \text{ in}$$

from equation (27). The remaining links must be selected using only the drag link criteria and the stroke time ratio. As is the case for most practical problems we are forced to make an educated guess and then check our results, repeating the process until a reasonable design is obtained. Let us select the following lengths:

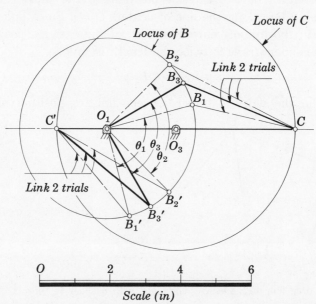

FIG. 34B. A sketch of a drag link quick return mechanism to determine the length of link 2 needed for a 3 to 1 time ratio. The mechanism is drawn with link 3 in its critical positions.

Fixed link: $L_0 = 2$ inches (shortest link)
Driving crank: $L_1 = 2.5$ inches
Then, using the double inequality (26) we have:

$$| \, 2.5 - L_2 \, | + 2 < 3.5 < 2.5 + L_2 - 2$$

from which

$$3 < L_2 < 4.$$

Step 2. The design is completed graphically in Fig. 34B. Link 3 is shown in its critical positions, O_3C and O_3C', and a circle of 2.5 inch radius about O_1 represents the locus of B. For our first approximation, we will try a coupler length $L_2 = 3.1$ inches. In its critical positions, the linkage is described by $O_1B_1CO_3$ and $O_1B'_1C'O_3$. The slider moves from the extreme right to extreme left, as link 3 moves counterclockwise from position O_3C to O_3C'. For this stroke, the working stroke, the driver rotates counterclockwise from position O_1B_1 to $O_1B'_1$ (through an angle $360° - \theta_1$). Then, the slider returns to the right as the driver turns through angle θ_1. The working stroke to return stroke time ratio given by $(360° - \theta_1)/\theta_1$ is less than the required value.

The value of θ for a working stroke to return stroke time ratio of 3 is found by setting

$$\frac{360 - \theta}{\theta} = 3 \quad \text{or} \quad \theta = 90°.$$

Angle θ_1 obtained in our first approximation is, by observation, too large.

Step 3. As a second approximation, we try a larger coupler length, $L_2 = 3.7$. Redrawing the linkage, the critical positions of the linkage are now $O_1B_2CO_3$ and $O_1B'_2C'O_3$. This time θ_2 is too small and the resulting time ratio too large.

Step 4. The third approximation, $L_2 = 3.5$, results in critical positions $O_1B_3CO_3$ and $O_1B'_3C'O_3$ with θ_3 near $90°$. The required working stroke to return stroke time ratio of 3 is obtained (approximately) with this linkage having dimensions:

$$L_0 = 2 \text{ inches,}$$
$$L_1 = 2.5 \text{ inches,}$$
$$L_2 = 3.5 \text{ inches,}$$
$$L_3 = 3.5 \text{ inches.}$$

L_4 may be any reasonable length greater than L_3. For this problem, we will let $L_4 = 4.5$ inches.

Mechanism

The total time for a working stroke and a return stroke is to be .4 seconds; accordingly, crank 1 will be given one rotation in .4 seconds or 60/.4 = 150 RPM. The final design is sketched in Figs. 34C, D and E,

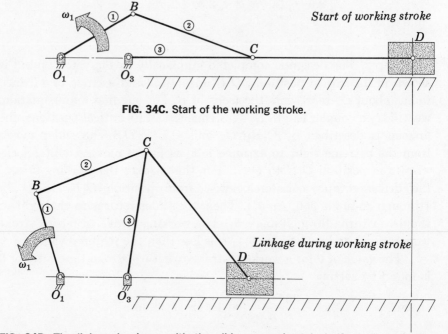

FIG. 34C. Start of the working stroke.

FIG. 34D. The linkage is shown with the slider approximately half-way through the working stroke.

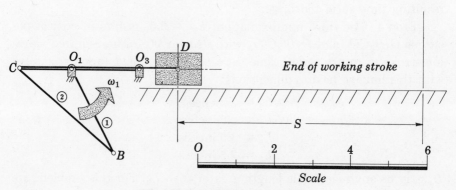

FIG. 34E. End of the working stroke.

showing the linkage at the beginning and the end of the working stroke and at one intermediate position.

Sliding contact linkages also form a basis for quick return mechanisms. Fig. 35 shows one type which has been used to drive the cutting tool in a mechanical shaper. We use the term *sliding contact linkage* when the slider moves along a rotating link. (Note that the path of the slider is fixed in a slider crank mechanism.) Crank 1 is the driver turning at essentially constant angular velocity and slider D represents the tool holder. Limiting positions occur when links 1 and 2 are perpendicular. The time ratio of working stroke to return stroke is equal to the ratio of angles between corresponding positions of link 1.

EXAMPLE—PROBLEM 10: Design a mechanism with a stroke which may be varied from 3 to 8 inches, having a working stroke to return stroke time ratio of 2 to 1 at maximum stroke length.

Solution: The 2 to 1 ratio is obtained if the angle θ between limiting positions is given by

$$\frac{360 - \theta}{\theta} = 2, \quad \text{or} \quad \theta = 120°$$

as in Fig. 35B. Often, the key to determining link lengths is to *assign* a reasonable value to *one* or more of the unknown links. The geometric relationships in the linkage are next observed when the linkage is drawn in its limiting positions. The lengths of the remaining unknown links are then obtained. A satisfactory design may be obtained in the first trial. If not, this trial is used as a basis for improving the design.

If distance O_1O_2 is taken as 4 inches, then the maximum length of the drive crank

$$L_{1(max)} = 4 \sin (90° - \frac{\theta}{2}) = 2 \text{ inches.}$$

Since link 3 lies at the same angle at both limiting positions (the path of D is perpendicular to O_2O_1), the maximum stroke length

$$S_{(max)} = D'D = C'C = 8 \text{ inches,}$$

from which we obtain the length of link 2.

Mechanism

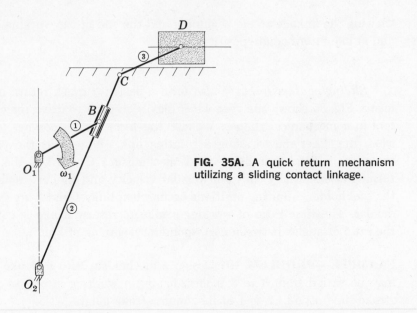

FIG. 35A. A quick return mechanism utilizing a sliding contact linkage.

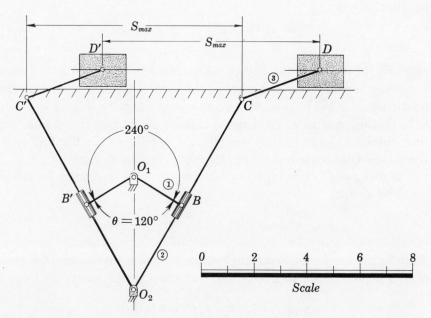

FIG. 35B. The linkage is shown in its limiting positions (link 1 perpendicular to link 2). The stroke, S, of the slider is adjusted by changing the length of link 1.

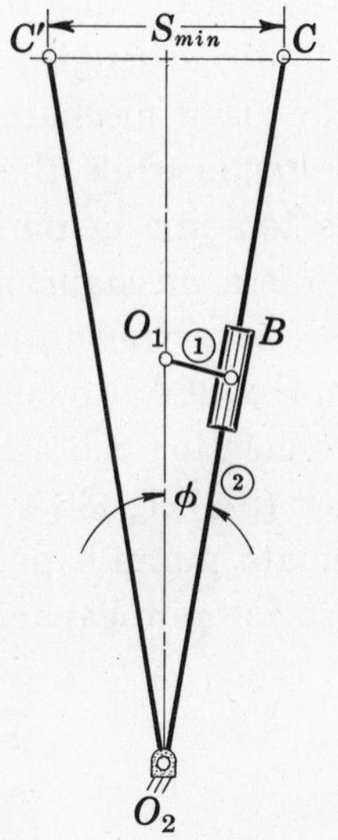

FIG. 35C. Link 1 is shown adjusted to provide minimum slider stroke.

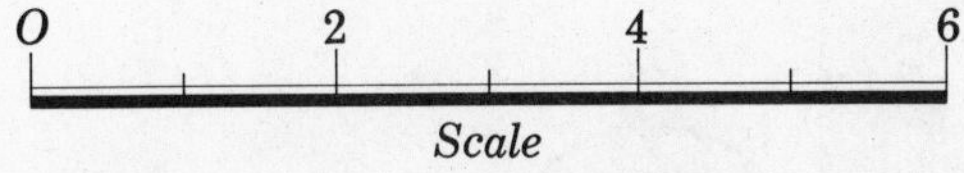

$$O_2C = \frac{S_{(max)}/2}{\sin(90° - \theta/2)} = 8 \text{ inches}.$$

The length of link 3 is arbitrarily taken as 3 inches and the distance from O_1 to the path of D as 3.5 inches. For the minimum stroke $S_{min} = 3$ inches, the crank must be adjusted to a length

$$L_{1(min)} = O_1O_2 \sin\phi = O_1O_2 \frac{S_{(min)}/2}{O_2C} = .75 \text{ inches}$$

as shown in Fig. 35C. The actual mechanism may differ considerably from the schematic of Fig. 35 as long as the motion characteristics are unchanged. Link 1 may be part of a large gear driven by a pinion in which case the crank pin (B on link 1) will be moved in or out along an adjusting screw. Link 2 may be slotted so that the crankpin rides within it.

Mechanism

There are many other methods of adjusting output characteristics (speed, stroke length, stroke time ratios, etc.). Some linkages are designed so that mechanical adjustments within the driving linkage itself can be made while the system is operating, often automatically in response to some demand on the system. The variable stroke pump of Fig. 36 is a mechanism of this type. Pump stroke length is controlled by a "stroke transformer" driven by a pressure actuated adjustment piston. Fig. 36A is a cutaway drawing of the pump, identifying the crank (1), connecting rod (2), coupler link (3), stroke transformer (4), and plunger (5). Fig. 36A shows the stroke transformer positioned for intermediate pump capacity. Fig. 36B shows the stroke transformer positioned for zero capacity. In Fig. 36C the stroke transformer has been

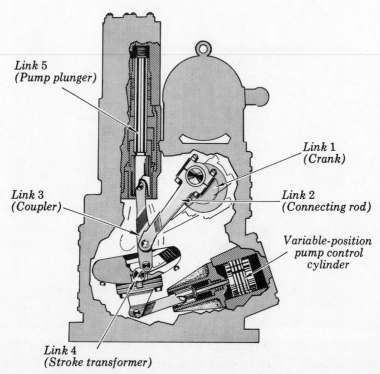

*Link 5
(Pump plunger)*

*Link 1
(Crank)*

*Link 3
(Coupler)*

*Link 2
(Connecting rod)*

*Variable-position
pump control
cylinder*

*Link 4
(Stroke transformer)*

FIG. 36A. A variable stroke pump. A curved-track *stroke transformer* allows a plunger stroke variation of 0-2 inches on some models and of 0-6 inches on other models. The stroke transformer is shown set (by the adjustment cylinder) for an intermediate stroke. (Ingersoll-Rand Co.)

70

replaced by an equivalent link, where the center of rotation of the equivalent link corresponds with the center of curvature of the curved track of the stroke transformer.

Link 1, the driver rotates at constant angular velocity. It drives connecting rod 2 which, in turn, drives links 3 and 4, moving the plunger E up and down in its cylinder. The position of O_4, the center of curvature of the stroke transformer, is adjustable. When O_4 is farthest from the wristpin E we have maximum plunger stroke (maximum pump capacity). Moving O_4 closer to E reduces plunger stroke until, when O_4 and E coincide, the plunger does not move and there is no pump discharge. Velocities in the variable stroke pump are analyzed in Chapter Two.

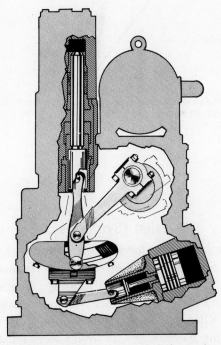

FIG. 36B. The adjustment cylinder piston is set so that the center of curvature of the stroke transformer coincides with the wrist pin. Thus, the plunger remains stationary. (Ingersoll-Rand Co.)

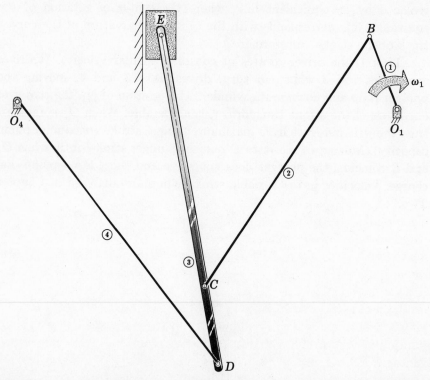

FIG. 36C. In this linkage diagram, link 4 replaces the curved track of the stroke transformer. As O_4 is brought closer to E, the movement of the plunger decreases. When O_4 coincides with E, the plunger will become stationary.

Design (Synthesis)

Analysis, as applied to mechanisms, implies that we are given the dimensions of a linkage and required to find its motion characteristics. Synthesis is exactly the opposite; the motion characteristics are specified and we are to find the linkage which will reproduce that specified motion. Since our ultimate goal is more often design of linkages than analysis of existing mechanisms, it would seem natural to expend most of our efforts in the study of synthesis. With a few important exceptions, however, this is not the case. It is not possible, with the present state of the art, to produce a given arbitrary input-output relationship over an unlimited range of values.

Certain special classes of motion, harmonic motion for example, can be synthesized. For any input angle θ, an eccentric cam or Scotch yoke mechanism will produce the output displacement $x = R \sin \theta$ or $x = R (1 - \cos \theta)$ or a similar harmonic function depending on the initial values of θ and x (where R is any constant). The Scotch yoke and eccentric cam are discussed in Chapter Two. Cams are the most flexible function generators. Any input-output relationship which is sufficiently "smooth" may be represented over a limited range by some type of cam. Furthermore, the desired follower motion must be repetitive if the cam is to rotate continuously. Design of a cam to produce a given follower motion is covered in Chapter Four.

Four bar linkages may also be used as function generators. Their low friction and higher load capacity make them preferable to cams for certain applications. An important disadvantage of the four bar linkage function generator, however, is its inability to represent an arbitrary function exactly except at a few points, called *precision points*. The range of input and output motion is further limited by the limiting positions of the linkage itself and problems of mechanical advantage. A brief introduction to analytical linkage synthesis follows. *Since an understanding of synthesis is not a prerequisite for study of velocity and acceleration, the reader may postpone this rather difficult section until later.*

Consider the problem of designing a four bar linkage so that output angle ϕ is a specified function of input angle θ, where links and angles are identified as in Fig. 37. Each of the four links of the mechanism is considered a vector. Each link has a magnitude (length) and a direction (at any instant) as shown in Fig. 37 (*bottom*). The coupler link vector is equated to the vector sum of the other three link vectors, and both sides of the equation are squared (forming the square of the coupler link length and the scalar product of the vector sum with itself. Thus, we have the **vector** relationship:

$$-2 = 1 + 0 + 3 \text{ and}$$
$$2^2 = (1 + 0 + 3) \cdot (1 + 0 + 3)$$

where the right side of the latter equation represents the *dot product*

Mechanism

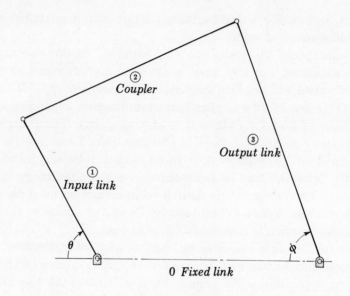

$$2 = 1 + 0 + 3$$

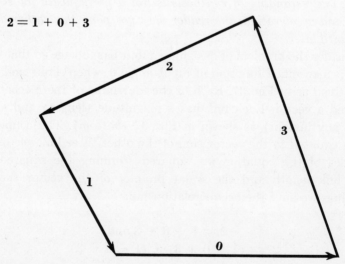

FIG. 37. Synthesis of a four bar linkage. Since each link has magnitude (length) and direction (at any instant), the links can be considered *vectors* (as shown at bottom).

defined in texts on vector analysis. Freudenstein developed this method to obtain linkage dimensions of a function generator by using three, four or five precision points.[2] Freudenstein's three point approximation is obtained as follows:

1) Select three input angles θ_1, θ_2, and θ_3 and the corresponding output angles ϕ_1, ϕ_2, and ϕ_3. Compute ϕ_2 so that the required relationship between θ and ϕ is satisfactory at each of the three precision points for the function $\phi = f(\theta)$.

Fig. 38 shows the input link 1 and output link 3 at the three precision points. The desired relationship between θ and ϕ is achieved exactly at (θ_1, ϕ_1), (θ_2, ϕ_2), and (θ_3, ϕ_3) and satisfied approximately at other values of θ and ϕ.

2) In order to simplify the expressions for the lengths of links 1 and 3, compute the following angle relationships which will be used in equations (28) below:

$$A = \cos \theta_1 - \cos \theta_2$$
$$B = \cos \theta_1 - \cos \theta_3$$
$$C = \cos \phi_1 - \cos \phi_2$$
$$D = \cos \phi_1 - \cos \phi_3$$
$$E = \cos (\theta_1 - \phi_1) - \cos (\theta_2 - \phi_2)$$
$$F = \cos (\theta_1 - \phi_1) - \cos (\theta_3 - \phi_3).$$

3) If the fixed link is arbitrarily given a length L_0, the lengths of the input and output cranks are respectively:

$$L_1 = \frac{BC - AD}{AF - BE} L_0 \quad \text{and} \quad L_3 = \frac{BC - AD}{CF - DE} L_0. \tag{28}$$

If L_1 is found to be negative, link 1 is drawn in a direction opposite that originally intended (i.e., each θ is increased or decreased by 180°). Similarly, if L_3 is negative, each ϕ is increased or decreased by 180°.

4) The linkage is drawn to scale for several pairs of θ and ϕ values. Although the computed lengths satisfy the required input-output relationship, the mechanism may not be practical because of disproportionate link sizes or mechanical advantage problems. In some cases, the links would not be able to assume all positions in the required range due to limiting positions. When one of these difficulties occurs, it is

---

2. F. Freudenstein, "Approximate Synthesis of Four Bar Linkages," *Trans. A.S.M.E.*, Vol. 77, pp. 853-61, Aug. 1955.

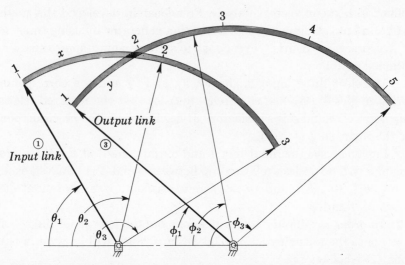

FIG. 38. Function generator of Example Problem 11. The input and output links of this four bar linkage generate the function y (output) $= x^{1.5}$ for values of x (input) between 1 and 3. The link dimensions are to be determined. The coupler (link 2) is not shown.

necessary to try another combination of input and output angles which represent the desired function, a change in the initial value of ϕ, for example. When a satisfactory linkage is finally obtained, a velocity and acceleration analysis is required unless operating speed is very low. Then the designer may specify actual mechanism components and consider stresses, deflections, weight and other characteristics.

EXAMPLE—PROBLEM 11: Design a four bar linkage to generate the function $y = x^{1.5}$ for values of x between 1 and 3.

Solution: Step 1. Angular displacement θ of the input crank will be proportional to x and angular displacement ϕ of the output crank proportional to y. At our disposal, we have the initial values of θ and ϕ which will be taken as $\theta_1 = 60$ and $\phi_1 = 40°$. We are also free to select the ranges of θ and ϕ which will both be $90°$ for this example. See Fig. 38. Measured from the initial values, the change in θ is proportional to the change in x, or, when $x_1 = 1$

$$\theta = \theta_1 + \frac{\text{range of } \theta}{\text{range of } x} (x - x_1) = 15 + 45\, x. \qquad (29)$$

Similarly,

$$\phi = \phi_1 + \frac{\text{range of } \phi}{\text{range of } y} (y - y_1) \ .$$

As x varies from 1 to 3, y varies from $(1)^{1.5} = 1$ to $(3)^{1.5} = 5.196$ from which we obtain output crank angle:

$$\phi = 18.55 + 21.45\, y \quad \text{(both } \theta \text{ and } \phi \text{ measured in degrees)} . \quad (30)$$

Step 2. For convenience, the precision points will be selected as

$$x_1 = 1, x_2 = 2 \text{ and } x_3 = 3 \ .$$

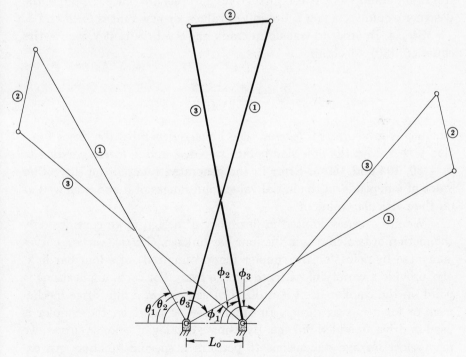

FIG. 39. The function generator of Fig. 38 is shown at three precision points.

Mechanism

The above equations give the corresponding values of y, θ and ϕ:

point	x	y	θ	ϕ
1	1.000	1.000	60°	40°
2	2.000	2.828	105	79.21
3	3.000	5.196	150	130

Step 3. Using these values in equation (28), and arbitrarily letting $L_0 = 2$ inches, we calculate the lengths of the input and output cranks:

$$L_1 = 10.40 \text{ in} \quad \text{and} \quad L_3 = 10.06 \text{ in} .$$

The coupler length, L_2 may be found analytically, or simply by drawing the input and output cranks in positions θ_1 and ϕ_1 respectively. The positions for the other precision points are also sketched to check for limiting positions, as in Fig. 39. It can be seen that the limiting positions do not fall within the range of the links, making the design satisfactory from that standpoint. If the linkage proportions are not acceptable, the designer would try a new set of initial values, or new ranges for θ and ϕ.

Step 4. In order to transform crank angle ϕ to output y, we rewrite equation (30) to obtain

$$y = \frac{\phi - 18.55}{21.45}$$

where ϕ is measured in degrees. The linkage generates the exact function $y = x^{1.5}$ for the precision points $x = 1$, 2 and 3 (corresponding to $\theta = 60$, 105 and 150°). Error in the generated function for any other value of x depends on the initial values and ranges of θ and ϕ as well as on the particular value of x.

We are severely limited in flexibility of design if we consider only the motion of two cranks in the four bar linkage. *Coupler curves*, curves generated by points on the coupler (connecting rod) of a four bar linkage, provide a variety of paths to choose from. For some applications, a point on the coupler itself is utilized directly as in a film drive mechanism or for a mixing device. In other cases, a point on the coupler is used to drive an added linkage. By using a catalog of coupler curves, we may select linkage dimensions to perform a specific function. An exhaustive catalog of coupler curves for the crank rocker mechanism (over

7000 curves made up of about half a million plotted locations and velocities) is given by Hrones and Nelson.[3] A work of this type might be used to solve a problem such as the following:

EXAMPLE—PROBLEM 12: A link is to oscillate through an angle of 20° at a rate of one cycle per second with a dwell of 1/6 second between oscillations.

Solution: Problems of this type are common in the design of machinery. The solution almost always involves a cam, but we will attempt to use a four bar linkage for purposes of illustrating linkage design procedures. Examining a catalog of coupler curves, we see several possibilities, one of which is sketched in Fig. 40. During about 1/6 of each cycle, the coupler curve described by point *P* in that figure approximates a straight line. By combining the four bar linkage with a sliding contact linkage, Fig. 41, we may take advantage of the straight line portion of the coupler curve to provide the required dwell.

Link 4, the output link is located by using the coupler curve. The straight line portion of the coupler curve defines one limiting position of link 4. The other limiting position is defined by a tangent to the coupler curve which intersects the first (limiting position) line at an angle of 20°. Link 4 is pivoted at that intersection and its length must be sufficient to allow the slider to assume all positions on the coupler curve. Since a complete cycle of motion corresponds with one rotation of link 1, that link will be driven at 60 RPM. When link 1 turns with constant angular velocity, the time required for output link 4 to rotate from one position to another is proportional to the angle between corresponding positions of link 1. On this basis, the approximate motion of link 4 is as follows: dwell 17%, clockwise rotation 30%, counterclockwise rotation 53% (expressed in terms of the time required for one complete cycle, i.e., one clockwise rotation of link 1).

Since the publication of the extensive catalog of coupler curves by Hrones and Nelson (1951), computers have increased considerably in number and in capacity. Once a mechanism problem has been sufficiently defined graphically, it may be expressed analytically. If many trials are necessary to establish optimum mechanism dimensions, a digital computer program can save the designer hours of repetitive numerical calculations or graphical work.

---

3. Hrones and Nelson, *Analysis of the Four Bar Linkage* (New York: Wiley & Sons, Inc., 1951).

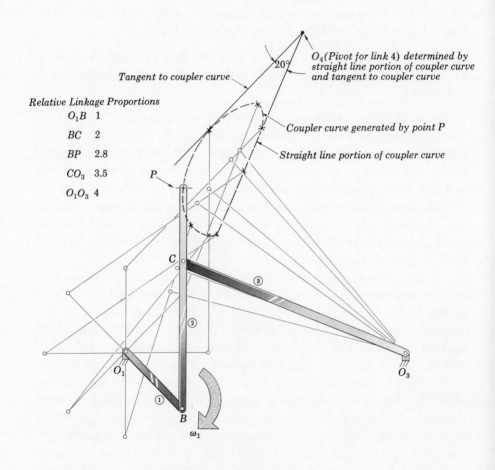

FIG. 40. Coupler curve of a four bar linkage.

Further advances in computer analysis permit the designer to sketch trial mechanism designs into the computer without the intermediate step of programming. The tentative design is displayed graphically and analyzed while allowing for immediate modifications. Mann (1964) describes "Sketchpad," a graphical language which is interpreted directly by the computer and used to design and analyze two and three

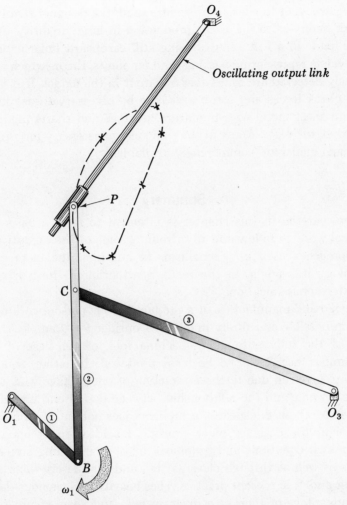

FIG. 41. Link 4 and a slider are added to the four bar linkage of Fig. 40. The mechanism is an oscillating linkage with a dwell period.

dimensional linkages.[4] Direct two-way communication between designer and computer is efficient in that many classes of linkages may be tried and link dimensions may be adjusted without the delay inherent in most computer programs. In addition, results are recorded for use in stress and weight analyses and for the selection of bearings and other components.

4. R. W. Mann, "Computer-Aided Mechanism Design," A.S.M.E. paper No. 64-*Mech*-36, 1964.

Regardless of the design procedure used, the designer should verify his work before releasing it for production in large quantity. A model may be made in a few minutes using stiff cardboard links joined with metal eyelets representing bearings and pin joints. Errors which were not previously detected are sometimes apparent in the model. If it is necessary to check forces and torques, it may be necessary to use iinks cut from thin sheet metal with miniature bearings and shafts mounted on a "breadboard" plate. Many of the components necessary for a precision mechanism model are commercially available.

Summary

The material in this chapter is intended to form a basis for the analytical work to follow and to introduce some of the analytical tools and approaches used in Mechanism. In addition, the more common terminology is brought to the reader's attention to form a common ground for communication.

Design and manufacture of a product by one person working alone is seldom possible and rarely practical. Consider for example, the complexity of the fully automated machine tool, or the case of a relatively simple mechanism to be mass produced. In either case, many people are involved due to the interaction of one linkage with the machine as a whole and the relationship between design and manufacture. Thus, the Mechanism aspect of a problem does not end with a satisfactory design; the designer must transmit his ideas to others through mathematical equations and graphical analyses including step-by-step sketches as well as through clear written and oral descriptions.

Past and even present practice relies heavily on ingenious designers taking advantage of their own inventiveness and years of practical experience. But, the trend is toward more kinematic analysis and synthesis including computer-aided optimization. One automobile manufacturer investigated about 8000 linkage combinations in a computer-aided study of four bar window regulator mechanisms described by Gustavson.[5] From those satisfying all design requirements (less than 500 did), the computer proceeded to select the one "best" linkage based on a set of predetermined criteria.

---

5. R. E. Gustavson, "Computer-Aided Design of Window Regulator Mechanisms," A.S.M.E. paper No. 66-*Mech*-41, 1966.

Velocity:

Methods of Analysis

Relative Motion

Relative motion is the difference in motion between two points. Let B and C be two arbitrary points. Then, v_{CB}, the velocity of C relative to B, is the vector velocity of C minus the vector velocity of B. In symbolic form,

$$v_{CB} = v_C - v_B. \tag{1}$$

Note: The student must bear in mind that an equation which calls for the addition or subtraction of vector quantities (vectors are indicated by bold face notation) requires that the direction as well as the magnitude of vectors be considered. Thus, in general, vectors can not be added or subtracted like scalars. In Equation (1) then, the *vector* difference is required between v_C, the velocity of C, and v_B, the velocity of B.

The "velocity of B" without any further qualification implies the absolute velocity of B, i.e., the velocity of B with respect to a stationary frame of reference. In the study of mechanism, the earth is most often selected as a "stationary reference frame." However, problems of space flight and even problems of long range ballistics on the earth require that the earth's motion be considered.

Equation 1 may be written in the equivalent form

$$v_C = v_B + v_{CB} \tag{2}$$

where the addition sign indicates the *vector* sum. For a simple example of relative velocity, let an aircraft carrier B move northward with a velocity $v_B = 15$ knots. Suppose an aircraft, C, on the flight deck has a velocity relative to the carrier $v_{CB} = 25$ knots *in the same direction.*

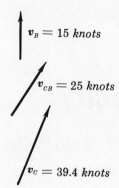

$v_B = 15$ *knots*
$v_{CB} = 25$ *knots*
$v_C = 39.4$ *knots*

FIG. 1A. The three vectors represent the velocity of the carrier, v_B, the velocity of the aircraft relative to the carrier, v_{CB}, and finally the absolute velocity of the aircraft, v_C.

25
v_{CB}
20°
39.4
v_C
v_C *found graphically*
15
v_B
θ
o

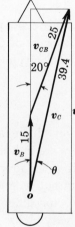

FIG. 1B. The velocity of the aircraft relative to the carrier, v_{CB}, is graphically added to the velocity of the carrier, v_B, to find the absolute velocity of the aircraft v_C.

B: Aircraft carrier
C: Aircraft

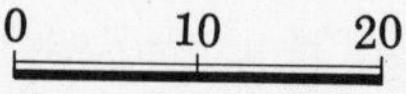

0
10
20
Velocity Scale (knots)

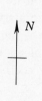

N

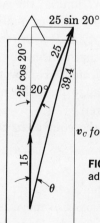

25 sin 20°
25 cos 20°
25
39.4
20°
v_C *found analytically*
15
θ

FIG. 1C. The same result is obtained by adding the *components* of the vectors.

Then, the true aircraft velocity is, in this special case, simply the scalar sum $v_C = v_B + v_{CB} = 15 + 25 = 40$ knots to the north.

The above example is a special case. A more common situation involves velocities which are not in the same direction and which cannot be added as scalars. Suppose, for example, that the direction of the path of the aircraft across the flight deck differs from aircraft carrier velocity direction by 20° as shown in Fig. 1A. The vector v_B which represents the carrier velocity is drawn to a convenient scale starting at an arbitrary point o in Fig. 1B. Then the vector v_{CB} which represents the velocity of the plane *relative to the carrier* is drawn, beginning at the head of vector v_B. The vector sum

$$v_B + v_{CB} = v_C$$

is the vector beginning at o with its head at the head of v_{CB}. Measuring it against the scale, we find the absolute aircraft velocity to be 39.4 knots at 12.5°.

Analytical Vector Solutions

If greater accuracy is required, the components of v_C may be found using angle functions as shown in Fig. 1C. The components of C to the north and east are, respectively

$$v_n = 15 + 25 \cos 20° \quad \text{and} \quad v_e = 25 \sin 20°.$$

Then,

$$v_C = \sqrt{v^2_n + v^2_e}$$

at an angle $\theta = \arctan (v_e/v_n)$ which may be calculated to the desired degree of accuracy using a slide rule or function tables and a desk calculator or a digital computer.

A graphical solution, whether to scale or free hand, should always precede the analytical solution. Errors in analysis which might remain unnoticed in mathematical calculations are frequently discovered by using graphics. The component method of vector analysis is discussed in more detail later in this chapter.

Analysis of Linkage Motion by the Methods of Relative Velocity

We are seldom called on to solve problems as straightforward as the one above. Given data is ofter sparse and it becomes necessary to

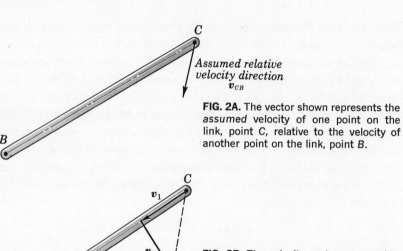

FIG. 2A. The vector shown represents the *assumed* velocity of one point on the link, point *C*, relative to the velocity of another point on the link, point *B*.

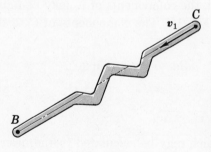

FIG. 2B. The velocity vector *assumed* to represent the velocity of point *C* relative to point *B* can be broken into two components—along and perpendicular to the link.

FIG. 2C. If a component of v_{CB} exists which lies along the link, this would mean that the length of the link is changing as point *C* moves toward or away from point *B*. Since this is clearly impossible, we must conclude that *no component of velocity can lie along the link.*

FIG. 2D. The only possible orientation of the vector representing the velocity of point *C* relative to point *B* is perpendicular to the link, as shown.

study certain physical relationships in the analysis and design of mechanisms.

Most linkage problems involve the relative velocity between points on a rigid body. Let v_{CB} represent the *assumed* velocity of point C relative to point B on rigid link BC in Fig. 2A. In order to examine whether the actual relative velocity could be so oriented, v_{CB} is replaced by its components v_1 and v_2 respectively along and perpendicular to line BC in Fig. 2B. It is seen from Fig. 2C that component v_1 along line BC can not exist since it would cause the length of the link to change as point C moves toward point B. Thus, the true direction of the relative velocity v_{CB} is perpendicular to BC for any two points B and C on a rigid link, Fig. 2D.

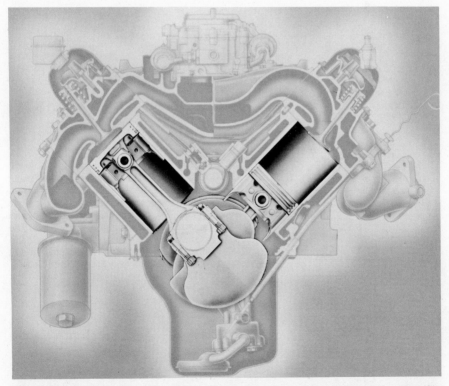

FIG. 3. This section view of a modern V-8 engine shows two pistons and connecting rods (slider crank mechanisms) at their extreme positions. The crankshaft represents the crank of the mechanisms. (General Motors Engineering Journal)

Mechanism

Analyzing Motion of the In-Line Slider Crank Mechanism

The slider crank mechanism is a basic part of reciprocating engines, pumps, compressors, and other machines. See Figs. 3 and 4. Fig. 5A is a representation of an in-line slider crank. The sketch is further simplified in Fig. 5B by showing only the centerlines, sizes, and angular positions of the links. Link O represents the frame, link 1 the crank, link 2 the connecting rod, and link 3 the piston. The crankshaft center is point O_1, the crankpin point B and the wristpin point C.

Applying what was learned above about the direction of relative velocity, the direction and magnitude of any other point on a mechanism can be found if we are given or assume the magnitude and direction of an initial point. Suppose that point B has a velocity of 20 in/sec

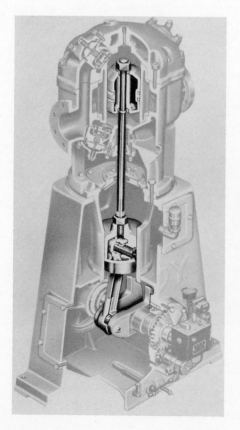

FIG. 4. A vertical compressor. The crank (at bottom) drives the connecting rod, which moves the crosshead within a guide. The compressor is designed with a crosshead and piston rod so that the piston may be double-acting; air is compressed as the piston moves upward and as it moves downward. (Joy Mfg. Co.)

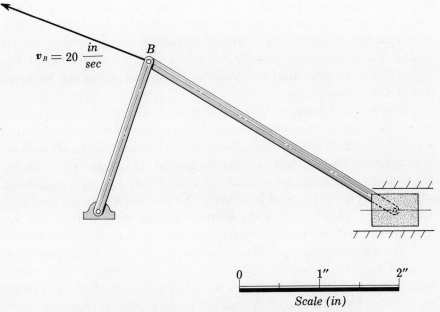

$v_B = 20 \dfrac{in}{sec}$

B

0   1″   2″

Scale (in)

FIG. 5A. Simplified sketch of an in-line slider crank mechanism.

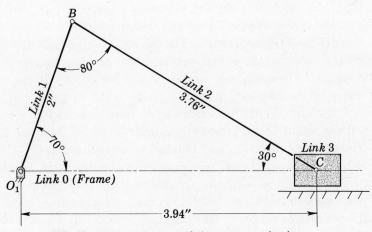

B

80°

Link 1
2″

Link 2
3.76″

70°

30°

Link 3

C

O_1

Link 0 (Frame)

3.94″

FIG. 5B. Linkage diagram of the same mechanism.

as link 1 turns counterclockwise. A velocity scale is selected which will result in vectors large enough for accurate results. Velocities v_B and v_{CB} are drawn perpendicular to lines O_1B and BC respectively as shown in Fig. 5C, an exploded view of the mechanism. The direction of the velocity of C is horizontal because the piston is constrained to move within the cylinder.

The single arrowhead of v_B in Fig. 5C indicates that it has been drawn to scale to represent a known magnitude and direction. Vectors v_{CB} and v_C are given *double arrowheads* indicating that, while their directions are known, their magnitudes are not. When we draw a vector of unknown magnitude, we will call it a *trial vector*. The term *magnitude* will be interpreted to mean both vector length and vector sense. Thus, trial vector v_C may be to the left as shown in Fig. 5C or to the right. v_{CB} may be oriented as shown or it may be in exactly the opposite direction.

The solution to the problem of finding v_C, the velocity of the piston, is again based on the vector equation $v_C = v_B + v_{CB}$. Beginning at an arbitrary point o in Fig. 5D, the vector v_B is drawn to scale. Then, trial vector v_{CB} is added to it starting at the head of v_B. Next, trial vector v_C is drawn beginning at the point o. Since $v_C = v_B + v_{CB}$, we have the equivalent of two simultaneous equations, one representing the line v_C and the other the line v_{CB} added to v_B. The solution is represented by the intersection. In Fig. 5E, the double arrowheads have been replaced by single arrowheads since the magnitudes of the relative velocity v_{CB} and piston velocity v_C are determined by the construction. The vector lengths are measured, and, using the velocity scale, the velocities represented are written directly on the figure. We note that the piston velocity is 22.8 in/sec.

Fig. 5D has been redrawn in Fig. 5E only to illustrate the steps in obtaining a solution; in actual practice, the construction in Fig. 5D would simply be "cleaned up" and darkened for clarity. It can be seen that the solution does not depend on our ability to guess the correct sense of v_{CB} and v_C. If, for example, v_C were assumed to be to the right, there would be no intersection, and we would then try drawing it in the opposite direction and obtain the correct solution.

Sometimes the required accuracy is greater than can be obtained by a simple graphical solution. Or, we may wish to make a velocity analysis based on freehand sketches without using drafting tools. Using the above example problem, let crank angle BO_1C in Fig. 5B be given as 70°.

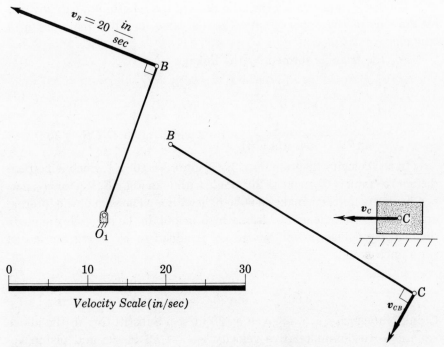

FIG. 5C. The relative velocity vectors are drawn perpendicular to the respective links: v_B is perpendicular to link O_1B, v_{CB} is perpendicular to link BC, and v_C is constrained to a straight line motion as shown.

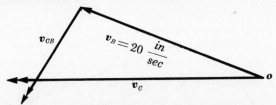

FIG. 5D. The vectors can be added together to form a *velocity diagram*. Absolute velocity vectors (velocities relative to the fixed frame) are drawn from a common reference, point **o.** The vectors are drawn to a convenient scale, each in the correct direction. The relative velocity vector is drawn starting at the head of the known absolute velocity vector, and with the correct direction ($\perp$ *BC*). The points of intersection determine the magnitude of the unknown vectors and whether the assumed sense of the vector is correct.

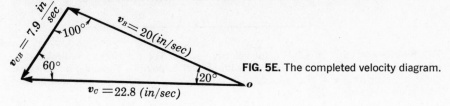

FIG. 5E. The completed velocity diagram.

Mechanism

The law of sines states that the ratio of the length of a side divided by the sine of the opposite angle is the same for all three sides in a triangle.

For the triangle formed by the linkage:

$$\frac{BC}{\sin(BO_1C)} = \frac{O_1B}{\sin(O_1CB)} \tag{3}$$

or $\dfrac{3.76}{\sin 70} = \dfrac{2}{\sin(O_1CB)}$, from which, angle $O_1CB = 30°$.

In the velocity diagram, v_C is horizontal. Vector v_B, which is perpendicular to crank O_1B, makes a 20° angle with v_C in Fig. 5E. Vector v_{CB}, perpendicular to link BC, makes a 60° angle with v_C. The sum of the internal angles in any triangle is 180° from which we obtain the remaining angle in the velocity polygon: 100° where v_{CB} is added to v_B Using the law of sines once more:

$$\frac{v_B}{\sin 60°} = \frac{v_{CB}}{\sin 20°} = \frac{v_C}{\sin 100°}$$

Crank pin velocity v_B was given as 20 in/sec. Substituting in the above equation, we obtain relative velocity $v_{CB} = 7.9$ in/sec and piston velocity $v_C = 22.8$ in/sec.

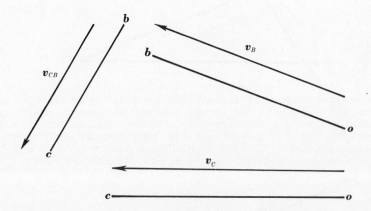

FIG. 6. Alternate form of notation for velocity vectors. The notation v_B is replaced by **ob;** both indicate the velocity of point B with respect to point O. Thus, **v**$_C$, becomes **oc**. Note, however, that **v**$_{CB}$, the velocity of point C relative to point B, becomes **bc** (the letters are reversed).

The Velocity Polygon Method of Analyzing Mechanisms

If the relative velocity vector v_{CB} is replaced by the vector **bc** with **c** at the head of v_{CB}, we have the basis for an alternate form of notation for the method of relative velocity, the *velocity polygon*. See Fig. 6. Absolute velocity v_B might as well have been called v_{BO}, the velocity of point B with respect to the frame O. Thus, v_B is replaced by **ob** and, likewise, v_C (or v_{CO}) by **oc**. The velocity equation $v_C = v_B + v_{CB}$ now becomes:

$$oc = ob + bc. \tag{2}$$

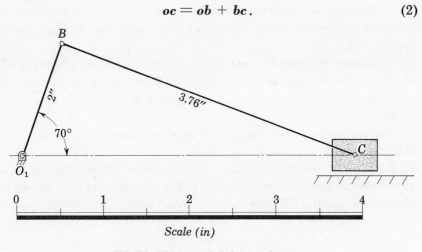

Scale (in)

FIG. 7A. Slider crank linkage redrawn.

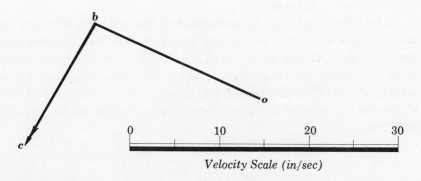

Velocity Scale (in/sec)

FIG. 7B. Velocity of point B (given) is drawn to scale as vector **ob** perpendicular to crank O_1B. From the head of **ob**, vector **bc**, the velocity of point C relative to point B, is drawn perpendicular to link BC. We do not know the magnitude of vector **bc**.

We identify **ob** with the actual velocity in inches per second rather than letting **ob** mean a length in inches on a sketch.

Using this alternate notation, let us now review the entire procedure for the slider crank mechanism step by step. The mechanism is redrawn in Fig. 7A and the velocity of point B is again given as 20 in/sec as crank O_1B turns counterclockwise.

1.) Select a velocity scale. $1'' = K$ in/sec

2.) Draw **ob** perpendicular to O_1B so that **b** falls above and to the left of **o** (since link O_1B turns counterclockwise). The length of **ob** on the sketch is the velocity of B (20 in/sec) divided by the velocity scale K. See Fig. 7B.

3.) Beginning at point **b**, draw trial vector **bc** of arbitrary length perpendicular to link BC as shown in Fig. 7B. A double arrowhead at **c** indicates that **c** lies on that line, but its exact location has not yet been found.

4.) Beginning at **o**, draw trial vector **oc** of arbitrary length in the direction of the path of C as in Fig. 7C.

5.) Locate **c** at the intersection of the lines just drawn. The construction lines are then removed as in Fig. 7D or lightened so they do not obscure the results. We have now solved the velocity equation:

$$oc = ob + bc.$$

6.) Determine piston velocity **oc** and relative velocity **bc** using the velocity scale $1'' = $ K in/sec. Write the values for the velocities directly on these vectors as shown.

The velocity polygon just constructed has considerable utility. In addition to **oc**, the piston velocity, we have determined **bc**, the velocity of the wrist pin C relative to the crank pin B. If **bc** is not zero, the motion of the connecting rod BC includes rotation. The value of ω_2, the angular velocity of rod BC, is determined just as with links having a fixed center of rotation. It is equal to the relative velocity divided by the distance BC. Thus,

$$\omega_2 = \frac{bc}{BC} \qquad (4)$$

where **bc** is the actual velocity of C relative to B and BC is the distance

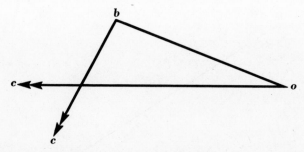

FIG. 7C. Point *C* is constrained to move horizontally. Thus, vector **oc** is drawn horizontally to intersect vector **bc**. The intersection determines the lengths (magnitudes) of the unknown vectors.

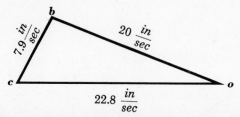

FIG. 7D. The completed velocity polygon is shown here for purposes of clarity. In actual problem-solving, however, the student need only remove the extraneous lengths and clean up his construction to obtain the completed polygon.

between pins *B* and *C* on the actual linkage, not a distance on the sketch. Substituting in Eq. (4), we find

$$\omega_2 = \frac{7.9 \text{ in/sec}}{3.76 \text{ in}} = 2.1 \frac{\text{rad}}{\text{sec}}.$$

Angular velocity direction of rod *BC* is found by locating the ve-

Mechanism

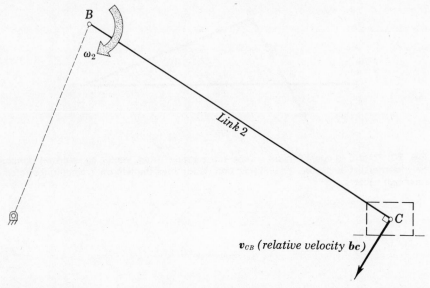

FIG. 8A. Determining the angular velocity of link *BC* from *bc,* the velocity of point *C* relative to point *B*.

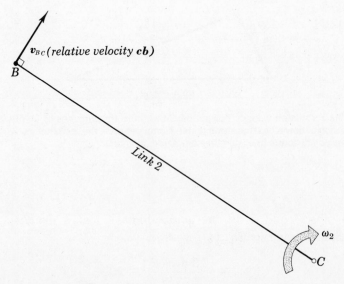

FIG. 8B. The angular velocity of link *BC* can also be obtained by determining *cb,* the velocity of point *B* relative to point *C*.

locity of C relative to B at point C on the linkage sketch. The direction of the relative velocity given by the order of the letters **bc** is downward and to the left as shown by the velocity diagram in Fig. 7D. Therefore, ω_2 is clockwise as shown in Fig. 8A. Note that while the piston velocity **bc** must be horizontal, there is a different restriction on the relative velocity **bc;** it must be perpendicular to BC.

Alternately, the velocity of B relative to C may be located at point B to find the direction of ω_2. Since **cb** $= -$**bc,** Fig. 8B, the magnitude of ω_2 has the same value as found above.

Noting the letter order **cb** and inspecting Fig. 7D, we see that **cb** is upward and to the right and therefore, ω is clockwise. The result is the same whether we consider **bc** at C or **cb** at B.

Layout Techniques

A few words about layout may be helpful at this point. In most linkage problems, the velocity polygon can be drawn with sufficient accuracy that measurements may be taken directly from it. In only a few instances is it necessary to determine angle relationships analytically and use trigonometric tables or a slide rule when computing velocities. But the care used in drawing the velocity polygon bears heavily on the results.

The mechanism to be analyzed should be sketched in skeleton form. Only link centerlines, pins, fixed centers, and sliders are shown, as in Fig. 5B. If a sketch must be copied, the use of tracing paper or dividers is preferred. The scale of the drawing is indicated and the length of each link (from pin to pin) is shown directly on the link.

When working at a desk and using letter size paper ($8\frac{1}{2}''\times 11''$), lines can be drawn parallel and perpendicular to one another by using two triangles as shown in Fig. 9. The paper should be taped in place to keep it from slipping since accuracy in both vector direction and vector length is critical. Velocity scales like

$$1\text{ in} = \quad 20\text{ in/sec}$$
$$1\text{ in} = \quad 50\text{ in/sec}$$
$$1\text{ in} = 100\text{ in/sec}$$

are easier to work with than scales which do not involve round numbers. Select a scale so that the expected length of the largest velocity

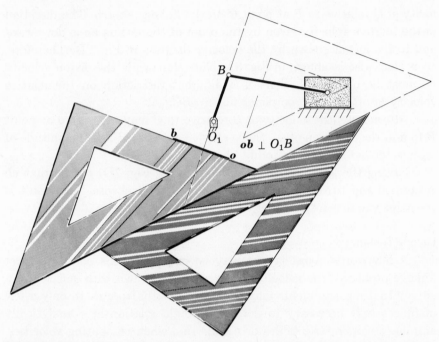

FIG. 9. Vectors are drawn perpendicular to the respective links of the linkage diagram by using two triangles.

vectors will be a few inches. If the entire velocity polygon is only "postage stamp size" accuracy will be poor. On the other hand, since it is not possible to guess the exact size of the polygon in advance, it may run off the paper. When this happens, it is usually best to tape on another sheet of paper and continue the construction. *All graphical work (the velocity polygon and, later on, the acceleration polygon) belongs on the same sheet with the sketch of the mechanism.* If these are separated, errors in vector orientation may occur. All linkage dimensions will be shown in inches and *decimal* parts of an inch; all velocities will be shown in inches per second for ease of calculation. Vectors will be laid out and measured using an engineer's scale graduated in tenths or fiftieths of an inch. A ruler which is graduated in sixteenths or thirty-seconds of an inch is inefficient and may occasionally cause mistakes when the results are converted to decimals.

To summarize, the tools necessary for accurate linkage analysis are:

> two triangles,
> a few sharp pencils,
> a scale graduated in tenths,
> a slide rule,
> a protractor,
> tape
> and occasionally, dividers.

Velocity Image

The utility of the velocity polygon notation is illustrated by problems where several points lie on the same link. Consider a rigid link in plane motion such as *BCD* of Fig. 10. On any rigid link, each relative velocity is perpendicular to the line between the points considered. Thus,

$$bc \perp BC,$$
$$bd \perp BD \text{ and}$$
$$cd \perp CD \text{ satisfy the conditions for similar triangles.}$$

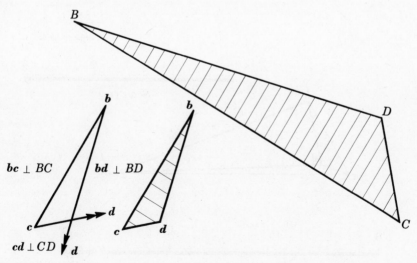

FIG. 10. The velocity image of a link. The vectors are drawn perpendicular to the lines connecting the points on the link. The result is a similar triangle.

Mechanism

Triangle **bcd** of the velocity polygon is similar to triangle *BCD*, the rigid link, and **bcd** is said to be the *velocity image* of rigid link *BCD*. As a result,

$$\frac{bc}{BC} = \frac{bd}{BD} = \frac{cd}{CD} \tag{5}$$

since corresponding sides of similar triangles are proportional. In order to draw **bcd** to the correct scale, however, we must know one of the relative velocities, for example, relative velocity **bc**. For any configuration of points on a rigid link, the velocity polygon contains the exact image except for size and orientation.

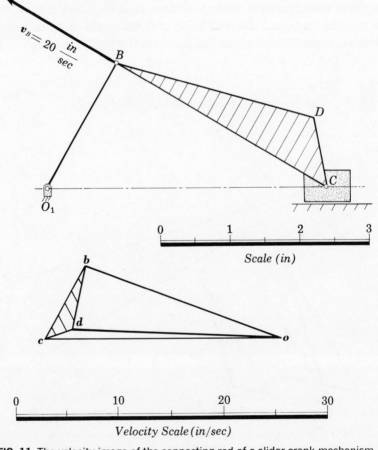

FIG. 11. The velocity image of the connecting rod of a slider crank mechanism.

100

Fig. 11 shows a mechanism containing link *BCD*. Let distances O_1B, BC, and O_1C and the velocity of B be the same as in the example illustrated in Fig. 7. Then we can take the velocity polygon **obc** directly from that figure. Drawing **bd** perpendicular to *BD* and **cd** perpendicular to *CD* as in Fig. 10, we obtain **bcd,** the image of *BCD* directly on the velocity polygon. The absolute velocity of D is found by measuring **od,** a vector of about 20 in/sec magnitude to the left and slightly upward. The reader is again reminded that the velocity image principle applies only to points which lie on the same rigid link.

The path of point D is neither circular (like B) nor a straight line (like C) as can be shown by drawing the mechanism at several different crank positions. A point such as D on a mechanism may provide just the right motion required to perform a given task. In designing machinery, it is often necessary to investigate a large number of mechanisms before the desired input-output relationship is obtained.

Let us now consider the velocity image of three points, B, C and E lying on a straight line, all on the same rigid link as in Fig. 12. Let the link have plane motion, which includes in general both rotation at

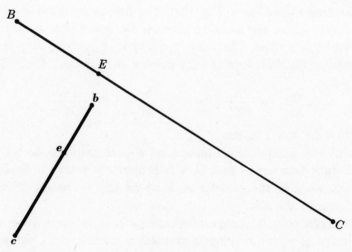

FIG. 12. The velocity image of three points lying on a line in a rigid link is itself a line.

an angular velocity ω and translation. Translation imparts no relative velocity; the rotation gives us the following relative velocities:

$$be = BC\,\omega \text{ which is } \perp BC$$
$$be = BE\,\omega \text{ which is } \perp BE \qquad\qquad (6)$$
$$ec = EC\,\omega \text{ which is } \perp EC.$$

Dividing the second of Equations (6) by the first and the third by the first, we obtain

$$\frac{be}{bc} = \frac{BE}{BC} \quad \text{and} \quad \frac{ec}{bc} = \frac{EC}{BC}. \qquad\qquad (7\ \&\ 8)$$

In practice, the velocity image of points B, E and C on one rigid link is obtained by using either Eq. (7) or (8) and the fact that the order of b, e and c in the velocity polygon is the same as for B, E and C on the link. Since B, E, and C lie on the same line, Equations (6) tell us that b, e and c lie on a line and that line bec is perpendicular to line BEC. One will recall the preceding discussion where the velocity image and link were similar triangles. If the points considered lie on a straight line, this becomes a special case, the triangles having angles $0°$, $0°$ and $180°$. In any event, the proportionality, Eqs. (7) and (8), still holds.

A force analysis of a piston engine may depend on the motion of the connecting rod center of gravity, a point between the crank pin and wrist pin. In this section, let us examine the velocity of a point E lying on connecting rod BC as in Fig. 13A. The linkage is identical with that of Fig. 7 (except for the addition of point E), and B will again be given a velocity of 20 in/sec. The velocity polygon, Fig. 13B, may be taken directly from Fig. 7D, leaving only point e to be found. From Eq. (7),

$$\frac{be}{bc} = \frac{BE}{BC} \quad \text{or} \quad \frac{be}{7.9 \text{ in/sec}} = \frac{1 \text{ in}}{3.76 \text{ in}},$$

from which $be = 2.1$ in/sec.

Point e is located a distance from b corresponding to 2.1 in/sec. Since E falls between B and C, e falls between b and c. Scaling the vector oe, we find the velocity of E to be approximately 20.6 in/sec upward and to the left.

While the velocity image relationships hold in every case, the velocity image of a link moving in translation shrinks to a single point. This is true in the case of a slider which always translates and in the

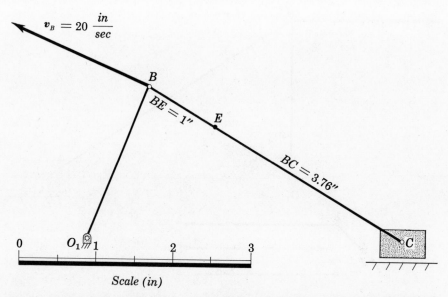

$v_B = 20 \dfrac{in}{sec}$

B

$BE = 1''$

E

$BC = 3.76''$

0 O_1 1 2 3

C

Scale (in)

FIG. 13A. The problem is to find the velocity of point *E* (which could be the center of gravity) at the instant when the linkage is in the position shown.

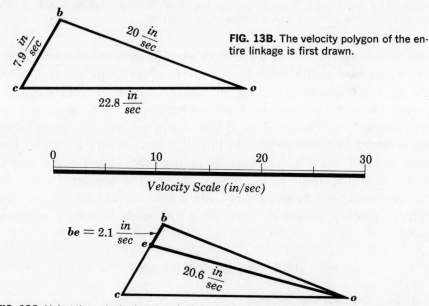

b

$7.9 \dfrac{in}{sec}$

$20 \dfrac{in}{sec}$

c

$22.8 \dfrac{in}{sec}$

o

FIG. 13B. The velocity polygon of the entire linkage is first drawn.

0 10 20 30

Velocity Scale (in/sec)

$be = 2.1 \dfrac{in}{sec}$

b

e

$20.6 \dfrac{in}{sec}$

c

o

FIG. 13C. Using the velocity image principle, point **e** is located on vector **bc**, the velocity image of link *BC*. The velocity of point *E* is found by drawing **oe** on the velocity polygon and measuring its length.

Mechanism

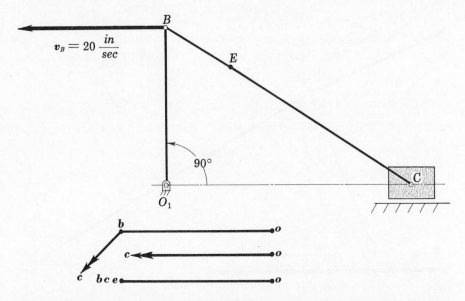

FIG. 14. The connecting rod is shown at the instant where its angular velocity is zero. At this instant there is no relative velocity (*bc* = 0) since all points on the connecting rod translate at the same velocity. The velocity image of the connecting rod, therefore, shrinks to a single point. While *ob* and *oc* are shown parallel, they must actually be colinear since *obc* cannot possibly form a closed polygon.

case of a connecting rod at the instant when its angular velocity is zero. The latter case is illustrated by the in-line slider crank mechanism of Fig. 14. When the crank angle is 90°, *ob,* the velocity of point B is horizontal. The slider velocity, *oc,* is always horizontal and thus, *ob* and *oc* are colinear for an instant. Now, if there was a non-zero relative velocity *bc,* it would be perpendicular to link BC. But *ob* and *oc* lie on the same line and such a relative velocity cannot exist. Therefore the vector *bc* has zero magnitude at the instant shown. The angular velocity of the connecting rod becomes zero instantaneously and all the velocity polygon points representing connecting rod points become a common point.

Analyzing Basic Linkages

Analyzing the Four Bar Linkage

Although the slider-crank mechanism discussed in the preceding sections is a four-bar linkage, this term is ordinarily used to denote a

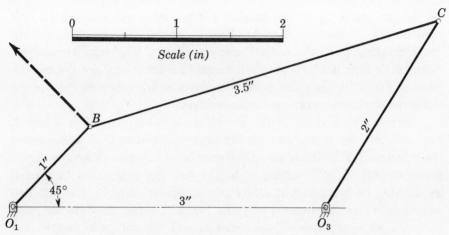

FIG. 15A. A four bar linkage is shown. The velocity of point *B* is given.

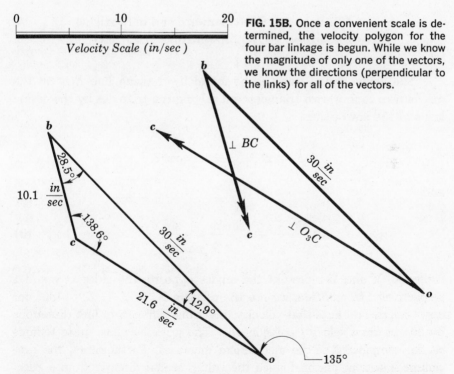

FIG. 15B. Once a convenient scale is determined, the velocity polygon for the four bar linkage is begun. While we know the magnitude of only one of the vectors, we know the directions (perpendicular to the links) for all of the vectors.

FIG. 15C. The completed velocity polygon. The points of intersection determine the unknown vector quantities. Velocity magnitudes are finally obtained by measuring the vector lengths against the velocity scale.

105

mechanism made up of two cranks, a connecting rod and a fixed link (the frame). A common four bar linkage of this type has the driving crank rotating while the output crank oscillates. The velocity analysis differs little from analysis of the slider crank mechanism. For the mechanism of Fig. 15A, the velocity of B is given as 30 in/sec at the instant shown as the crank rotates counterclockwise.

In order to find all of the velocities, a velocity scale is selected, Fig. 15B, and the vector *ob* is drawn perpendicular to O_1B to represent the velocity of B. Relative velocity vector *bc* of unknown length is drawn perpendicular to BC, starting at *b*. The velocity polygon is completed by drawing *oc* beginning at *o* and perpendicular to O_3C. The last two steps locate *c* on the velocity polygon. Fig. 15C shows the velocity polygon with all construction lines removed and the values of the vectors shown directly on the polygon. We see that

$$v_{CB} = 10.1 \text{ in/sec} \perp BC \text{ (downward and to the right)}$$
$$v_C = 21.6 \text{ in/sec} \perp O_3C \text{ (upward and to the left)}.$$

The above values can also be found by drawing line BO_3 on the mechanism to form two triangles and solving the triangles by the cosine law and the law of sines

$$z^2 = x^2 + y^2 - 2xy \cos Z$$

and

$$\frac{\sin X}{x} = \frac{\sin Y}{y} = \frac{\sin Z}{z} \tag{9}$$

where X, Y and Z represent the angles opposite the sides x, y and z respectively. In addition, we use the relation $X + Y + Z = 180°$ for any triangle and note that velocity directions differ from link directions by $90°$ to draw velocity polygon *obc*. The work becomes quite tedious as the complexity of the mechanism increases. Furthermore, the procedure is seldom justified since the values scaled directly from a carefully drawn velocity polygon are sufficiently accurate for most practical purposes.

Analyzing Sliding Contact Linkages

Sliding contact exists between slider and frame in the slider-crank mechanism. In cams, gears, and certain other mechanisms, moving links slide on one another.

The Slider Mechanism. The mechanism of Fig. 16 has a slider pinned to link 1. The slider is constrained to slide along link 2. This mechanism is basic to the mechanically driven shaper and is utilized in combination with other linkages, like the jack knife boom shown in Fig. 17. The key to solving problems of this type is the designation of a double point B. See Fig. 16A. B_1 is a point on the slider and on link 1 and B_2 is a common point on link 2. While, at this instant, B_1 and B_2 are the same point, B_1 moves relative to B_2 by sliding along link 2. Thus, relative velocity b_2b_1 (the velocity of B_1 with respect to B_2) is along link 2. Relative velocity b_1b_2 (equal and opposite b_2b_1) is therefore, also along link 2.

Suppose link 1 of Fig. 16A rotates counterclockwise at 15 rad/sec, making the velocity of B_1 equal to 36 in/sec perpendicular to O_1B_1, upward and to the left. To solve the mechanism, we use the relationship:

$$\boldsymbol{v}_{B2} = \boldsymbol{v}_{B1} + \boldsymbol{v}_{B2B1} \quad \text{or} \quad \boldsymbol{ob}_2 = \boldsymbol{ob}_1 + \boldsymbol{b}_1\boldsymbol{b}_2. \tag{10}$$

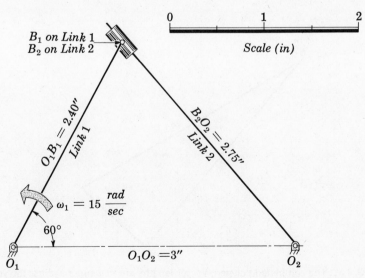

FIG. 16A. A sliding contact linkage. The slider is pinned to link 1 and slides along link 2.

107

Mechanism

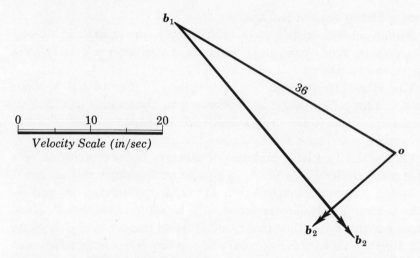

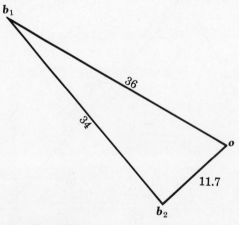

FIG. 16B. The velocity polygon for a sliding contact linkage. Note that the relative velocity vector b_2b_1 is drawn parallel to link 2, since the motion of B_1 relative to B_2 must be along link 2 at any given instant.

FIG. 16C. The completed polygon. Vector lengths are measured against the velocity scale and written directly on the polygon.

Vector ob_1 (representing the velocity of B_1) is drawn to scale in Fig. 16B, beginning at an arbitrary pole point o. Sliding velocity vector b_2b_1 is added to ob_1 beginning at b_1. The vector direction of b_1b_2 is parallel to link 2 but its length and sense are unknown. Thus, we draw trial vector b_1b_2 with a double arrowhead at b_2 (not caring about vector sense because, if our original guess of vector sense is wrong, we later reverse the vector to obtain the velocity polygon). Trial vector ob_2 (also of unknown sense and magnitude) is drawn starting at pole point o and perpendicular to O_2B_2. The length (and, if necessary, the sense) of both vectors b_1b_2 and ob_2 is corrected, completing the velocity polygon ob_1b_2 in Fig. 16C.

Scaling vector b_1b_2, we find the sliding velocity to be 34 in/sec; at this instant, link 2 moves downward and to the right relative to the slider at 34 in/sec (or the slider moves upward and to the left relative to link 2 at that rate). The velocity of B_2 on link 2 scales to 11.7 in/sec downward and to the left, from which we obtain

$$\omega_2 = \frac{ob_2}{O_2B_2} = \frac{11.7 \text{ in/sec}}{2.75 \text{ in}} = 4.25 \frac{\text{rad}}{\text{sec}}$$

counterclockwise. Note that ob_2 and O_2B_2 refer, respectively, to actual velocity of B_2 and length O_2B_2 on the actual link 2. The method for determining the velocities of the sliding contact linkage is essentially the same, even if links 1 and 2 are curved. Velocity vector ob_1 is perpendicular to O_1B_1 and ob_2 perpendicular to O_2B_2. Sliding velocity b_1b_2 is in the direction of the relative path, i.e. b_1b_2 is *tangent* to the instantaneous path of B_1 on link 2 (at B_1).

Sliding velocity is of particular interest because of friction and wear considerations. (Some references state the coefficient of friction in terms of sliding velocity.) In addition, we must find the sliding velocity in order to compute the Coriolis acceleration. This phase of the problem is treated in Chapter Three.

The reader should be alert for mechanisms which are kinematically equivalent to the sliding contact linkage of Fig. 16. Examples include a variable-displacement pump, in which the plungers move within a rotating cylinder block, and the Geneva mechanism. In the Geneva mechanism, a pin on a rotating wheel (the driver) enters radial slots in the driven member, giving it intermittent rotation as the driver

FIG. 17. A jack-knife boom. The boom may be represented by a combination of four bar and sliding contact linkages. (Holan Div. Ohio Brass Co.)

rotates at constant velocity.

Cams and Cam Followers. Almost any motion-time relationship may be generated by using one or more cams. Usually, the cam rotates at constant angular velocity, giving the follower reciprocating or oscillating motion having some predetermined sequence. *When sliding occurs between cam and follower, the key to solving for velocities is again a double point where the two make contact and the solution proceeds as with other sliding contact mechanisms.* The velocity of the point of

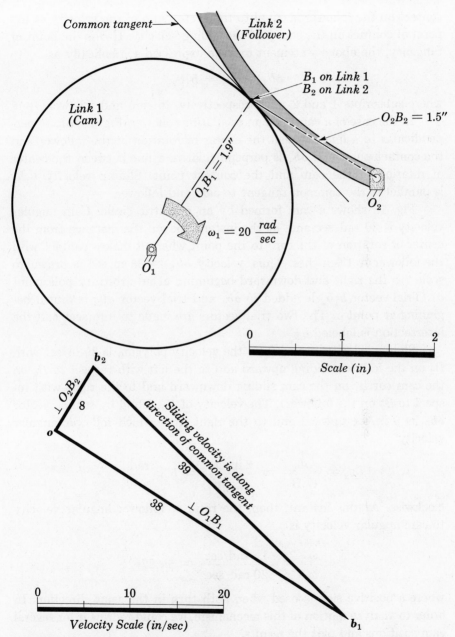

FIG. 18. A cam with an oscillating follower. To obtain the velocity polygon, ob_2 is drawn perpendicular to O_2B_2 and ob_1 is drawn perpendicular to O_1B_1. Sliding velocity b_1b_2 is drawn parallel to the common tangent at B_1B_2.

contact on the follower is equal to the vector sum of the velocity of the point of contact on the cam plus the sliding velocity. If B is the point of tangency, the above statement may be expressed symbolically as

$$ob_2 = ob_1 + b_1b_2$$

where subscripts 1 and 2 refer, respectively, to cam and follower.

In the case of a cam with an oscillating follower, Fig. 18, ob_2 is perpendicular to a line between the center of rotation of the follower and the contact point and ob_1 is perpendicular to a line between the center of rotation of the cam and the contact point. Sliding velocity b_1b_2 is parallel to the common tangent to cam and follower.

Fig. 18 shows a cam formed by an eccentric circle. Cam angular velocity is 20 rad/sec and, at the instant shown, the distance from the center of rotation of the cam to the point where it makes contact with the follower is 1.9 inches. Thus, velocity $ob_1 = 38$ in/sec is drawn to scale (to the right and downward beginning at an arbitrary pole point o). Trial vector b_1b_2 is added to ob_1 and trial vector ob_2 is drawn beginning at point o. The two trial vectors are made to intersect and the intersection is labeled b_2.

Sliding velocity, scaled from the velocity polygon, is 39 in/sec with B_2 on the follower sliding upward and to the left with respect to B_1 on the cam (or B_1 on the cam sliding downward and to the right with respect to B_2 on the follower). The velocity of B_2, found by scaling vector ob_2, is 8 in/sec upward and to the right from which follower angular velocity

$$\omega_2 = \frac{ob_2}{O_2B_2} = \frac{8 \text{ in/sec}}{1.5 \text{ in}} = 5.3 \frac{\text{rad}}{\text{sec}}$$

clockwise. At this instant, then, the ratio of follower angular velocity to cam angular velocity is

$$\frac{\omega_2}{\omega_1} = \frac{5.3 \text{ rad/sec}}{20 \text{ rad/sec}} = +.27$$

where a positive sign is used when both turn in the same direction. In order to analyze motion of this mechanism, we could redraw it for several cam positions and plot the results.

Gears. Motion may be transmitted between two shafts by discs which roll on one another. Consider the friction drive of Fig. 19 where

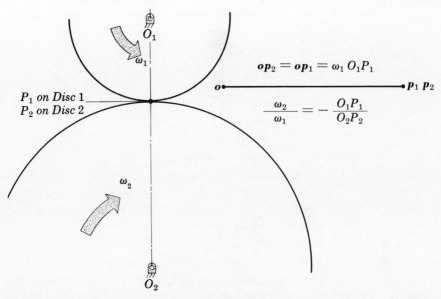

FIG. 19. A friction drive. There is no relative velocity ($\boldsymbol{p_1 p_2} = 0$) if the discs roll without slipping.

P is a point common to both discs. *If they roll together without slipping, the relative velocity $\boldsymbol{p_1 p_2}$ is zero, and Eq. (10) becomes*

$$\boldsymbol{op_2} = \boldsymbol{op_1} = \omega_1 O_1 P_1 \tag{11}$$

where ω is in radians per second and $\boldsymbol{op_1}$ and $\boldsymbol{op_2}$ are true velocities. Since $\omega_2 = \boldsymbol{op_2}/O_2 P_2$, but in a direction opposite ω_1, we have the angular velocity ratio

$$\frac{\omega_2}{\omega_1} = -\frac{O_1 P_1}{O_2 P_2} \tag{12}$$

A drive of this type is quite satisfactory for a small motion picture projector or other low-power applications. However, when large torques are involved the designer might turn to a gear drive, sacrificing the simplicity of a disc drive to insure that power will be transmitted under all conditions.

Spur gear velocities may be found by examining a pair of teeth *at their point of contact.* The velocity of that point on the driven gear

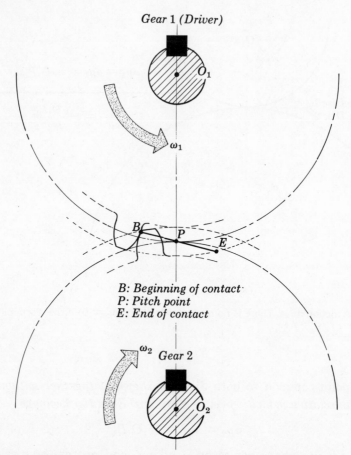

FIG. 20A. A pair of spur gears is shown. For clarity, only two teeth are shown. Point *B* is the point of initial contact (B_1 on gear 1, B_2 on gear 2). As the gears rotate, the point of contact will follow line *BPE*.

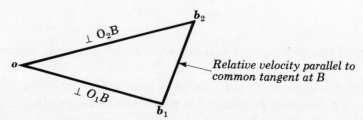

FIG. 20B. The velocity polygon. Vectors ob_1 and ob_2 are drawn perpendicular, respectively, to O_1B_1 and O_2B_2. Relative velocity vector b_1b_2 is drawn from b_1, parallel to the common tangent to the teeth at the point of contact *B*.

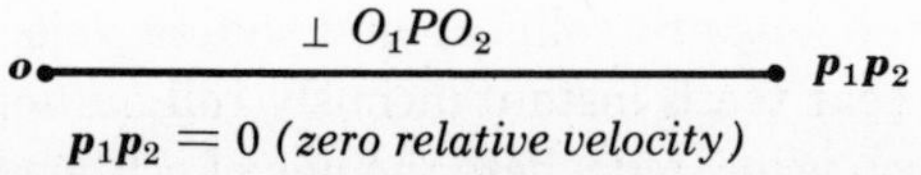

$$o \bullet \xrightarrow{\hspace{1cm} \perp O_1PO_2 \hspace{1cm}} \bullet \, p_1p_2$$

$$p_1p_2 = 0 \; (\textit{zero relative velocity})$$

FIG. 20C. The velocity polygon when contact occurs at the pitch point, P. At the pitch point, vectors op_1 and op_2 of the velocity polygon become colinear and there is *no relative velocity* ($p_1p_2 = 0$).

is the vector sum of the velocity of the same point on the driver and the relative velocity. The equation used earlier for cams and mechanisms which include sliding also applies to gears: $ob_2 = ob_1 + b_1b_2$. In this case, the common point or point of contact is B with subscripts 1 and 2 referring to driver and driven gears respectively.

Fig. 20A shows a pair of involute spur gears with contact occurring at point B. Velocity vector $ob_1 = \omega_1 O_1 B_1$ is drawn perpendicular to O_1B_1 in the velocity polygon, Fig. 20B. Then, trial vector ob_2 is drawn, beginning at o and perpendicular to O_2B_2. Trial vector b_1b_2 is drawn from b_1 (parallel to the common tangent to the teeth where they contact) until it intersects trial vector ob_2. The true location of b_2 is thus found and the angular velocity of gear 2 is given by $\omega_2 = ob_2/O_2B_2$.

The above construction would not be used to find angular velocities however, since the angular velocity ratio of any pair of gears is simply

$$\left| \frac{\omega_2}{\omega_1} \right| = \frac{N_1}{N_2}$$

where N refers to the number of teeth on the gear.

Relative velocity b_1b_2, the sliding velocity, is of importance in the design of gears because gear tooth wear is apparently related to sliding velocities. For the pair of teeth sketched in Fig. 20A, an extreme value of sliding velocity occurs at the instant shown, at the first point of contact. The velocity polygon of Fig. 20B is correct only for the first point of contact (instantaneously), but the method does not change as the gears rotate and contact progresses along the line BPE. But, as the point of contact moves from B to P, sliding velocity diminishes until, at P, vectors op_1 and op_2 are colinear and sliding velocity $p_1p_2 = 0$. See Fig. 20C. The gear teeth instantaneously roll on one another at P, the *pitch point*, which is located where the line of centers O_1O_2 intersects the locus of contact points BE.

Suppose, for a moment, that gear 1 is fixed and gear 2 rolls about it at an angular velocity $\omega_2 - \omega_1$ (the angular velocity of 2 relative to 1). The relative motion is the same, only absolute motion has changed. Rolling contact occurs at P, but at all other points, there is sliding at a velocity proportional to the distance from P to the instantaneous point of contact. Instead of using the vector polygon, we may find sliding velocity magnitude by the expression

$$c_1c_2 = \mid \omega_2 - \omega_1 \mid PC \tag{13}$$

where C is *any point of contact* on line BPE and $\mid \omega_2 - \omega_1 \mid$ is the absolute value of the difference between the two angular velocities. For two external gears, angular velocities ω_1 and ω_2 have different signs and $\mid \omega_2 - \omega_1 \mid$ is the sum of the magnitudes of the two angular velocities. It is seen that sliding velocity again reaches an extreme value when contact occurs at E, the last point of contact.

Crossed Helical Gears. In the case of *crossed helical gears* (gears on non-parallel shafts) sliding velocity and the velocity ratio depend on the helix angles. Let a pair of helical gears (Fig. 21A and B) make contact at a common point B, the point of tangency of the two pitch circles (B_1 on gear 1, B_2 on gear 2). The velocity of B_1, represented to some scale K_v by ob_1 in Fig. 21C is $\omega_1 \, d_1/2$ perpendicular to shaft 1. The velocity of B_2, unknown at this time, is represented by ob_2 perpendicular to shaft 2 using a double arrowhead. Velocity $ob_2 = ob_1 + b_1b_2$, where the relative velocity b_1b_2 must be the sliding velocity *parallel to the gear tooth* in the plane tangent to both pitch cylinders. See Fig. 21B. Any component of relative velocity perpendicular to the tooth in that plane would indicate that the two teeth separated. The point b_2 is therefore located by drawing b_1b_2 *parallel to the gear tooth* until it meets the line ob_2, Fig. 21C. The pitch line velocity of gear 2, ob_2, may then be scaled to find angular velocity

$$\omega_2 = \frac{ob_2}{d_2/2}.$$

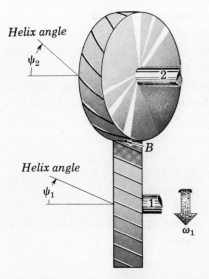

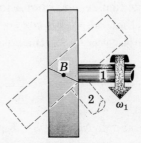

FIG. 21A. *Crossed* helical gears. Point *B* is the point of tangency of the two pitch surfaces. Pitch diameters of gears 1 and 2 are d_1 and d_2 respectively.

FIG. 21B. Section view of the crossed helical gears. Gear 2 is shown in dashed lines. The duration of contact between two teeth is represented by the line through point *B*.

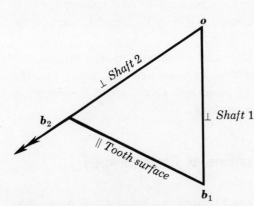

FIG. 21C. Velocity polygon showing pitch line velocities ob_1 and ob_2. Sliding velocity b_1b_2 must be parallel to the gear teeth; if the sliding velocity would be at all perpendicular to the gear teeth, the teeth would be separating (clearly impossible).

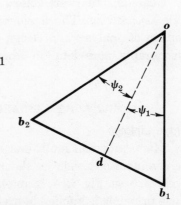

FIG. 21D. A perpendicular from *o* to the sliding velocity b_1b_2 determines the helix angles of the two gears.

Scaled values of velocity in inches per second are written directly on ob_1 and ob_2. When these values are called for, they will be expressed as velocities, not distances. We see from the direction of ob_2 that gear 2 turns clockwise when viewed from the right.

Greater accuracy may be obtained analytically. In Fig. 21D, a perpendicular, *od,* from *o* to line $b_1 b_2$ forms angles ψ_1 and ψ_2. It can be seen that $od = ob_1 \cos \psi_1 = ob_2 \cos \psi_2$. Substituting $ob_1 = \omega_1 d_1 / 2$ and $ob_2 = \omega_2 d_2 / 2$, the velocity ratio

$$\frac{n_2}{n_1} = \frac{\omega_2}{\omega_1} = \frac{d_1 \cos \psi_1}{d_2 \cos \psi_2}. \tag{14}$$

is obtained. Alternately, for any type of gearing, the tooth numbers, if known, may be used to find the velocity ratio

$$\frac{n_2}{n_1} = \frac{N_1}{N_2} \quad .$$

A section view through the point of contact will aid in establishing the direction of rotation.

When we consider contact at a point other than the pitch point there are additional sliding velocity components to be considered. Angular velocity ratio, however, is constant and may be found by one of the methods described above.

Gears and cams are among the most commonly used and most versatile mechanisms. The above material on velocities only touches on the problem of analysis and design of gears and cams, which is covered in considerably more detail in other sections.

Analyzing Combinations of Basic Linkage

Toggle Linkage

Many practical multi-link mechanisms are made up of basic linkage combinations such as slider crank and four-bar mechanisms. The *toggle linkage,* Fig. 22A, is an example of a mechanism of this type; the toggle principle is applied in ore crushers, and in essentially static linkages which act as clamps. The linkage analysis is made by considering the basic linkages separately. To solve for the velocities of the mecha-

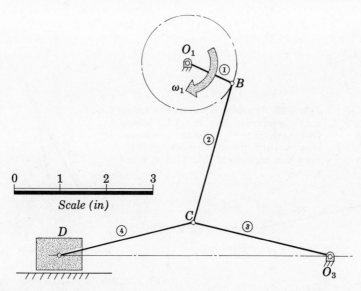

FIG. 22A. This toggle mechanism is a combination of two basic linkages, the four bar mechanism and slider crank mechanism.

nism, we may begin by ignoring the slider and its connecting rod while solving the four-bar linkage separately, Fig. 22B. Then, the velocity polygon may be completed by finding slider velocity.

In this example, link 1 will be 1 inch long and ω_1 will be 100 radians/second clockwise. Examining links 1, 2 and 3 alone (Fig. 22B), the following vectors are drawn to some convenient scale:

vector $ob = \omega_1 O_1 B = 100$ in/sec $\perp O_1 B$ (downward and to the left)
trial vector $oc \perp O_3 C$ and
trial vector $bc \perp BC$. (See Fig. 22C).

Velocity point c is located at the intersection of trial vectors oc and bc, completing the velocity polygon for links 1, 2 and 3.

In order to illustrate the mental process involved in solving multi-link mechanisms, links 3 and 4 and the slider will now be considered separately, Fig. 22D. Beginning at a new pole point (o in Fig. 22E) vector oc is redrawn, its direction and magnitude taken from the four-bar polygon, Fig. 22C. Then, trial vectors are drawn, $cd \perp CD$ and od

119

Mechanism

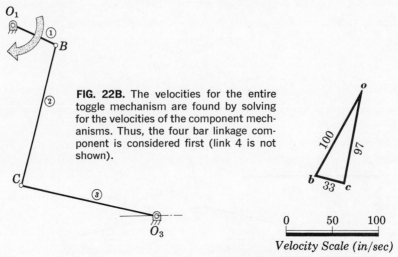

FIG. 22B. The velocities for the entire toggle mechanism are found by solving for the velocities of the component mechanisms. Thus, the four bar linkage component is considered first (link 4 is not shown).

o
100 97
b 33 c

```
0        50        100
```

Velocity Scale (in/sec)

FIG. 22C. After a suitable velocity scale is selected, the velocity polygon for the four bar mechanism is drawn.

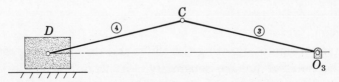

FIG. 22D. The remainder of the toggle mechanism, the slider crank, is next considered.

d 40 o
99 97
c

FIG. 22E. The velocity polygon for the slider crank is drawn. Note that link O_3C is common to both mechanisms. The velocity of point C, **oc**, was already determined in the four bar polygon and serves as a convenient starting point for the construction of the slider crank polygon.

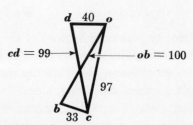

FIG. 22F. The velocity polygon for the entire mechanism.

120

in the direction of the path of the slider from which velocity point *d* is located. Slider velocity at this instant is given by *od*, 40 in/sec to the left.

The above solution in two parts is given for demonstration purposes only. After completing velocity polygon **obc**, *it is faster and slightly more accurate to continue by finding point* **d** *on the same polygon.* Fig. 22F shows velocity polygon *obcd* found in this manner, a compact velocity representation for the entire mechanism. An additional advantage of the complete polygon is that it is only necessary to join points *b* and *d* to find the velocity of *D* with respect to *B* if this velocity is of importance in a particular machine.

An important feature of the toggle mechanism is its ability to produce high values of force at the slider with relatively low torque input. While the study of mechanisms is primarily concerned with motion, forces are of great importance to the designer and intimately related to motion analysis. If a rigid mechanism has a single input and single output with negligible losses, the rate of energy input equals the rate of output, from which force ratios are the inverse of velocity ratios. Specifically, in the toggle linkage at the instant shown, the horizontal force at *D* divided by the tangential force at *B* equals *ob/od* or 100/40 (the mechanical advantage of the mechanism at this instant). In this special case with a crank length $O_1B = 1$ inch, the ratio *ob/od* also represents the ratio of output force at the slider divided by input torque on link 1 (neglecting losses). Clockwise rotation of link 1 from the position shown toward the limiting position of the mechanism produces very high ratios of output force to input torque.

If we sketch the mechanism at the instant that links 3 and 4 are colinear, we see that slider velocity *od* = 0. Thus, the ratio *od/oc*, the theoretical mechanical advantage of the toggle mechanism, becomes infinite. Clamps and ore crushers using the toggle linkage principle are designed to operate near this limiting position. Actual forces at the slider are, of course, finite due to bearing clearances and elasticity of the linkage. In this exceptional case, the small amount of motion due to elastic deformation of the linkage and deformation of the workpiece is of the same order of magnitude as the slider motion. Therefore, any analysis of this problem (which assumes perfectly rigid links) must serve only as a "first approximation."

Mechanism

Shaper Mechanisms

The *mechanical shaper mechanism*, Fig. 23, is another example of a combination of simple linkages. It is made up of a slider-crank mechanism (links 2 and 3 and the slider at D) and a sliding contact mecha-

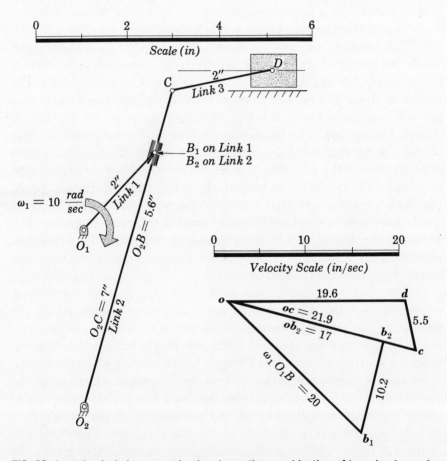

FIG. 23. A mechanical shaper mechanism is another combination of two simple mechanisms. The velocity diagram is constructed as usual. To find the magnitude of *oc*, however, we must use velocity *ob_2* and the proportionality of link 2 (O_2C) to O_2B_2.

122

nism (links 1 and 2 and a slider at B moving along link 2). When the mechanism is operating, the angular velocity of link 1 is essentially constant.

Beginning with the velocity of point B at the end of the crank, we find the velocity of a common point on link 2. The velocity of point C at the end of link 2 is found by forming the velocity image of link 2. The solution is completed by examining the mechanism formed by links 2 and 3 and the slider at D (a slider crank of unusual proportions).

A detailed solution follows for the instant shown with the angular velocity of link 1 equal to 10 rad/sec clockwise.

Step 1. Select a reasonable velocity scale and draw velocity vector $ob_1 = \omega_1 O_1 B_1 = 20$ in/sec perpendicular to link 1 (downward and to the right), as shown in Fig. 23.

Step 2. Draw trial vector ob_2 perpendicular to link 2 and trial vector $b_1 b_2$ parallel to link 2, locating b_2.

Step 3. Use the proportion $oc/ob_2 = O_2 C/O_2 B_2$ to locate point c on the velocity polygon.

Step 4. Draw trial vector od from o parallel to the path of the slider D, and trial vector cd from c perpendicular to link CD, locating velocity point d. The velocity of D (the shaper tool velocity) is 19.6 in/sec to the right at the instant shown, as given by the scaled vector od. When angular velocity ω_1 is constant and clockwise, the average velocity of point D is greater when D moves to the left than when D moves to the right. This is the quick-return feature of the shaper which insures a slow powerful cutting stroke and a quick return. The stroke length (distance between extreme positions of D) is varied by adjusting the length of link 1. Since this adjustment affects the velocity of D, it may be necessary to compensate by changing the angular velocity of link 1 at the same time.

Beam Pump

The four-bar and slider crank mechanism combination of Fig. 24 forms a *beam pump*. Connecting rod (4) moves in a straight-line path practically along its own axis and the rod may be made very long. If we know the angular velocity of crank 1, it is a simple matter to construct velocity polygon *obc*. Then velocity image *cod* is drawn similar to CO_3D on link 3. The velocity polygon is completed by locating point *e* corresponding to the slider. Slider velocity is given by vector *oe*.

Mechanism

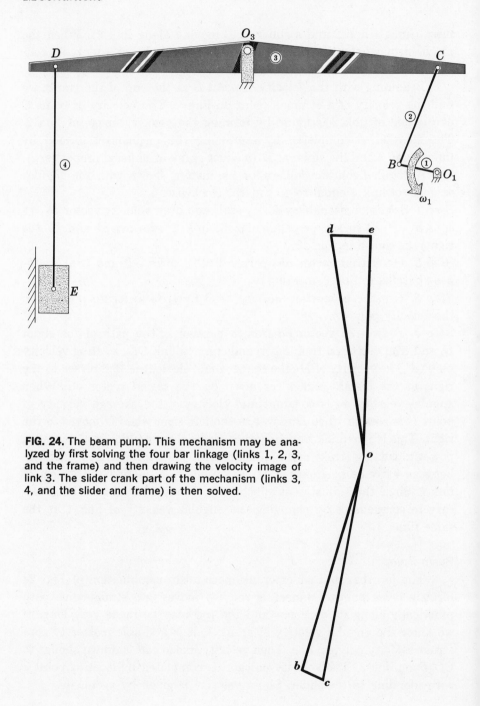

FIG. 24. The beam pump. This mechanism may be analyzed by first solving the four bar linkage (links 1, 2, 3, and the frame) and then drawing the velocity image of link 3. The slider crank part of the mechanism (links 3, 4, and the slider and frame) is then solved.

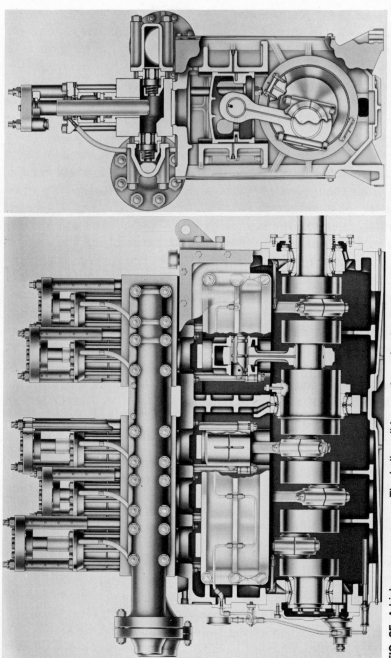

FIG. 25. A high pressure pump. The in-line slider crank mechanism is basic to several types of machines. In this case, five slider crank mechanisms are used to produce a continuous flow at up to several thousand pounds per square inch. At any instant each linkage is at a different point in its stroke. As seen in the end view (right), the crank drives the connecting rod which moves the crosshead. "Trombone" side rods connect the crossheads to the plungers which enter the top of the cylinder. (Ajax Iron Works)

Mechanism

Multiple Slider Crank Mechanisms

A single-cylinder, internal combustion engine is an adequate power plant for a lawnmower or model airplane. Power output, however, is limited by cylinder size. If we were to design a single-cylinder engine with a capacity of several hundred horsepower, the piston, connecting rod, and crank might be unreasonably large. At full speed, inertia forces could be a serious problem. Furthermore, the single power stroke per revolution in the case of a two-stroke-cycle engine (or one power stroke for each two revolutions in the case of a four-stroke cycle engine) might cause unacceptable fluctuations in speed, even when a flywheel is used. A pump or air compressor poses the same problems, particularly when high capacity or uniform output is called for. The solution is a design with several separate cylinders which might be in-line (with parallel axes) or in a V-arrangement (two separate banks of cylinders at an angle to one another).

The multi-cylinder high pressure pump shown in front and end section views in Fig. 25 is an almost trivial example of a mechanism combination (if we consider only the slider crank linkages). Similarly, Fig. 26 is a sketch representing two cylinders of a V-block engine or pump. When we have drawn the velocity polygon for links 1, 2 and the slider at C, it is only necessary to note that the velocity of D has the same magnitude as the velocity of B as we complete the polygon.

Ordinarily, all of the slider-crank linkages in a multi-cylinder engine are identical except for instantaneous link orientation. For example, we might examine piston velocity as a function of crank position for a single piston of an eight cylinder engine. If crankshaft speed is maintained, the results would apply equally to the other pistons, the only difference being the individual cylinder orientation and the phasing (timing) of the motion.

Conventional Slider Crank Designs. In Figs. 25 and 26 each connecting rod is attached to a *separate* crank pin. In the typical automotive engine this is usually the case; the crank pins of Fig. 26 thus correspond to *crankshaft journals*.

There are, however, several variations of the crank-connecting rod arrangement. Fig. 27A shows an alternate configuration for a two-cylinder engine, with both connecting rods (BC and BD) attached to a *single* crank pin, B. A practical example of this alternate arrangement is shown in the cutaway view of the two-stage, V-type compressor in

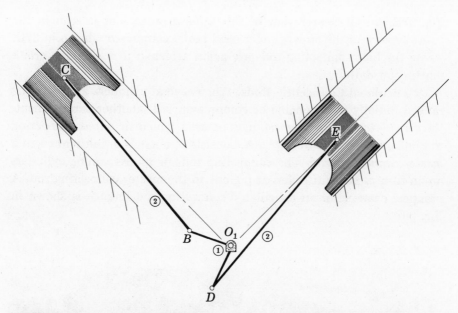

FIG. 26. A typical multi-cylinder engine or compressor configuration. This V-design shows two slider crank linkages on a common crankshaft, but with separate crank pins.

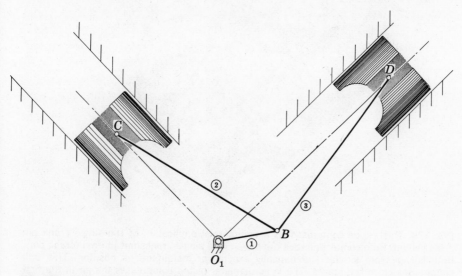

FIG. 27A. Note that in this variation of the crank-connecting rod arrangement, both connecting rods are attached to a *single* crank pin.

Mechanism

Fig. 27B. A still clearer view of this same arrangement is seen in the cutaway view of the four-cylinder semi-radial compressor shown in 27C, where the four connecting rods are again attached to a common crank pin (or journal).

Articulated Connecting Rods. When several cylinders are to be arranged radially in an engine or compressor, still another arrangement, the *articulated connecting rod*, may be used. The articulated connecting rod linkage, sketched in Fig. 28A, consists of a single crank pinned to a *master connecting rod*. The connecting rods of the remaining cylinders are in turn pinned (at different points) to the master connecting rod. A practical example of an articulated connecting rod linkage is shown in Fig. 28B.

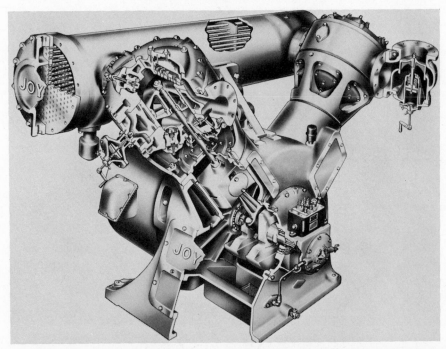

FIG. 27B. This V-type compressor is a commercial application of the single crank pin arrangement. Both connecting rods are driven by a single crankshaft journal (crank pin). Both linkages are similar kinematically except for instantaneous position. This unit compresses air in two stages. The large diameter piston compresses the air in the first stage and cools it. The cooled air is then brought to still higher pressure by the small (upper) piston in the second stage. (Joy Mfg. Co.)

FIG. 27C. This *semi-radial compressor* also employs a single crank pin. (Joy Mfg. Co.)

While the articulated connecting rod linkage and the single crank pin linkage of the semi-radial compressor of Fig. 27B appear to be very similar, the connecting rods of the semi-radial compressor must be placed in line with, or next to, each other whereas the articulated connecting rod linkage permits the connecting rods, and therefore the pistons, to lie in a single plane. The use of an articulated connecting rod therefore permits the design of a multi-cylinder engine with all of the cylinder centerlines in a single plane.

Analyzing Linkages through Trial and Error and Inverse Methods

For some mechanisms, the solution is not as straightforward as were the cases examined earlier. We may frequently find that step-by-step drawing of velocity vectors leads us to a point where a trial and error solution is suggested. Alternately, it may be more practical to use an

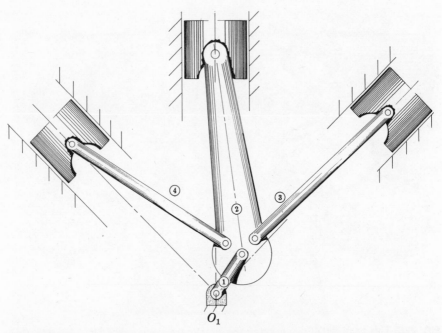

O_1

FIG. 28A. The *articulated* connecting rod. In this crank-connecting rod arrangement, the crank is pinned to a master connecting rod. The rest of the connecting rods are, in turn, pinned to the master rod.

FIG. 28B. Commercial application of an articulated connecting rod. The cylinder center-lines of the compressor shown, or those of an engine, can be arranged radially in a single plane perpendicular to the crankshaft axis for better balance. (Worthington Corp.)

130

inverse method, *i.e.,* to begin with the solution and work the problem backwards.

Fig. 29B, which is an equivalent linkage for the variable stroke pump shown in Fig. 29A, is a problem of the trial and error type. Link 4 of Fig. 29B is an equivalent link; in the actual pump, point D represents the pin in the guide block riding in a curved track (of radius O_4D). Stroke length (the length of the path of E) may be varied from zero to a maximum value by tilting the curved track, which is equivalent to changing the location of point O_4. The control mechanism may be manually operated or may incorporate an air operated plunger (not shown) to rotate the track automatically in response to a remote signal.

Trial and Error Method

Suppose it is necessary to find the velocity of the piston of the mechanism in Figs. 29A and B when the velocity of crankpin B is 100

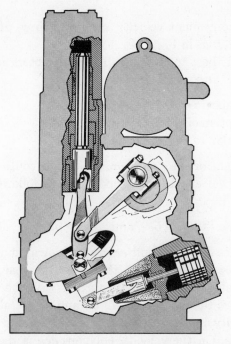

FIG. 29A. A variable stroke pump. This pump is identical to the pump shown in Chapter One. Here, the adjustment cylinder is set so that the stroke transformer provides a maximum plunger stroke. (Ingersoll-Rand Co.)

Mechanism

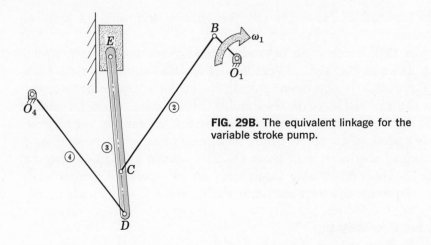

FIG. 29B. The equivalent linkage for the variable stroke pump.

in/sec with crank O_1B rotating clockwise. A *trial-and-error* procedure follows:

Step 1. Select a convenient velocity scale and draw $ob = 100$ in/sec perpendicular to O_1B as in Fig. 29C.

Step 2. It is usually best to indicate all known vectors and vector directions on the sketch. Draw trial vectors

od perpendicular to O_4D;
oe in the direction of sliding (vertical); and
bc perpendicular to BC (bc is added to ob).

Step 3. In a straightforward problem, we would continue the polygon by finding another velocity point, say point c. The following vector equations might be used:

$$oc = ob + bc \quad \text{and} \quad oc = oe + ec.$$

But the magnitudes of bc, oe and ec are unknown, and the magnitude and direction of oc are unknown; there are too many unknowns to utilize the equations. A similar problem exists with the vector equation $oc = od + dc$ since the magnitudes of od and dc are also unknown.

Step 4. The velocity image relationship is the missing tool; with it, a solution is possible. On the velocity polygon, dce is the (straight-line) image of DCE, three points on rigid link 3. The relationship is used by noting that d, c and e lie on a line perpendicular to line DCE with c be-

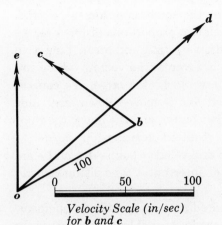

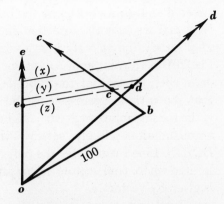

FIG. 29C. After a velocity scale is selected, the velocity polygon is begun.
However, the location of the velocity image *dce* is not immediately obvious.

FIG. 29D. Trial and error method of locating line *dce*. The third trial, line *z*,
satisfies the relationship *dc/de* =
DC/DE, with *c* between *d* and *e* since *C*
lies between *D* and *E*.

FIG. 29E. In the *inverse method of solution*, vector *oe* is drawn at an arbitrary
length, and the polygon is completed
without using a velocity scale. The scale
is then found by measuring *ob* (the only
magnitude we are given) on the polygon.

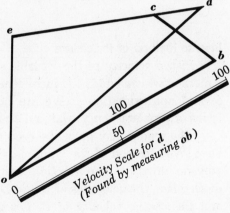

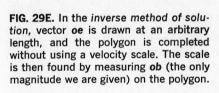

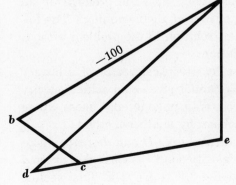

FIG. 29F. If the assumed sense of vector
oe is wrong, the vector magnitudes will
still be correct, but the orientation of the
polygon will be in error by 180°.

tween *d* and *e*, proportioning the line by the equation $dc/de = DC/DE$. Now that we have the direction and relative proportions of line *dce*, we may satisfy the velocity image condition by trial and error. Line *x* in Fig. 29D is the first approximation. It intercepts trial vectors *od*, *bc* and *oe* in such a way that the ratio dc/de would be too large. We can see that the ratio is decreased as the trial line is moved downward. Line *y*, the second approximation, is somewhat better, and the line *z*, the third approximation, closely satisfies the required relationship $dc/de = DC/DE$. Line *z* completes the polygon and velocity points *d*, *c* and *e* are located where trial vectors *od*, *bc* and *oe* intercept it. The piston velocity is given by vector *oe*.

Trial and error solutions are required more frequently in engineering practice than indicated by typical academic problem assignments. In the latter situation, a shortage of time favors the use of problems in which the answer is obtained directly. The reader should however be prepared for both types.

Inverse Method of Procedure

Piston velocity of the variable speed pump may also be found by a method which avoids the inconvenience and potential error of making several approximations. (We are not always so fortunate; for many types of problems, *only* trial and error solutions are known to exist.)

The reader may have observed in Fig. 29 that, had piston velocity been given instead of the crankpin velocity, we could draw the velocity polygon directly. The solution would proceed from the slider crank mechanism, the velocities of *E* and *D*, to the velocity of *C* by proportion and thence the velocity of *B*. Let us, then, solve the problem by an *inverse method*. (i.e., we assume the answer at the beginning.) The following steps constitute an entirely new solution to the problem without making use of the trial and error solution:

Step 1. Represent piston velocity *oe* by a vertical vector of arbitrary length, say $1\frac{1}{2}$ inches (Fig. 29E). We cannot give *oe* an actual velocity magnitude or select a scale since we would undoubtedly guess wrong unless we had already solved the problem by another method.

Step 2. Draw trial vectors *od* perpendicular to O_4D and *de* perpendicular to *DE* to locate velocity point *d*. Velocity point *c* is located between *d* and *e* on line *de* by using the proportion $dc/de = DC/DE$. Trial vectors *cb* perpendicular to *CB* and *ob* perpendicular to O_1B locate velocity point *b*, completing the polygon.

Step 3. Finally, the scale of the velocity polygon must be determined from the given data. In this problem, the velocity of the crankpin, *ob* = 100 in/sec. The length representing *ob* on the velocity polygon becomes 100 in/sec and all other vectors are scaled accordingly and labeled with their correct velocity magnitudes. Measurements taken directly from the velocity polygon give *oe/ob* = 0.58 from which piston velocity *oe* = 0.58 × 100 = 58 in/sec upward at this instant. When working a problem this way, we cannot expect the scale to be a round number and so it is necessary to use a slide rule to determine velocity magnitudes with which to label the velocity polygon.

In this particular example the angular velocity of link 1 is clockwise and it was clear at the start that the velocity of *E* would be upward. For some positions of this mechanism, it is impossible to determine the sense of piston velocity by inspection. Suppose we had guessed wrong this time and drawn *oe* downward in the velocity polygon. The result is shown in Fig. 29F, where *ob* is drawn downward and to the left (its orientation is in error by 180°). The measured length of *ob* on the polygon is equal to −100 in/sec and each of the vectors is given a negative value. For example, *oe* = −58 in/sec downward (i.e. 58 in/sec upward). Of course, the easiest way to rectify our error is to cut out the velocity polygon, rotate it 180° about point *o* and tape it back in place.

Velocity-Time Relationships

In each of the velocity problems considered up to this point, we have found velocities for a single mechanism position. One might ask how velocities vary through a complete cycle of motion. The question is answered, in most cases, by tedious repetitive drawing of velocity polygons. If many variations of a mechanism are to be considered, some time is saved by programming the work on a digital computer. Analog computers have also been used to analyze mechanisms. Alternately, a model of the proposed mechanism may be constructed to be examined during operation by high-speed motion pictures or other means. In a few cases, the simplicity of the mechanism permits a mathematical treatment.

Mechanism

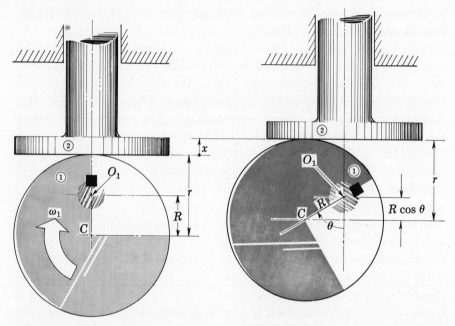

FIG. 30A. The cam, link 1, is formed by a circular disc of radius r and eccentricity R.

FIG. 30B. The follower, link 2, undergoes displacement x as the cam rotates through an angle Θ.

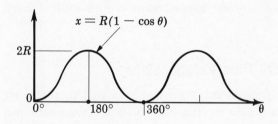

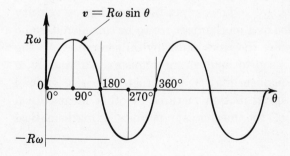

FIG. 30C. The displacement and velocity of the follower are plotted against cam rotation.

136

The eccentric cam with flat-face follower and the Scotch yoke are examples of mechanisms having simple mathematical representations. The *eccentric cam* of Fig. 30 is circular in form, but the center of the circle, C, is offset a distance R from the center of the camshaft, O_1. For circle radius r, the distance from cam shaft center to follower face is $r - R$ when the follower is at its lowest position. After the cam turns through an angle θ, Fig. 30B, the distance becomes $r - R \cos \theta$. Therefore, follower displacement during the interval is

$$x = r - R \cos \theta - (r - R) = R(1 - \cos \theta) \qquad (15)$$

for any value of θ where x is measured from the lowest position.

If this expression is differentiated with respect to time (see any elementary calculus text) we obtain follower velocity

$$v = R \, \omega \sin \theta. \qquad (16)$$

Velocity is given in in/sec for an eccentricity of R inches and a cam angular velocity of ω rad/sec. If ω is constant and if time t equals zero when the follower is at its lowest position, then θ may be replaced by ωt. The sine function is found on our slide rules and tabulated in many handbooks. We know that $\sin \theta$ (and therefore cam velocity) equals zero at $\theta = 0°$ and $\theta = 180°$. Furthermore, $\sin \theta$ reaches extreme values at $\theta = 90°$ and $\theta = 270°$, at which times $v = +R\omega$ and $v = -R\omega$ respectively. The motion repeats itself with every revolution of the cam shaft (every 360°).

Displacement and velocity are plotted in Fig. 30C for two revolutions of the cam shaft. Note that velocity is proportional to eccentricity R but independent of cam circle radius r. Since the follower face is always a constant distance r above point C, it moves as if it were riding on point C.

In the two-cylinder piston pump of Fig. 31, the cam raises and lowers a shaft with a piston at each end by acting alternately on two separate follower faces. The cam pushes against the upper follower face, lifting the shaft (upper piston) through 180° of cam rotation. Through the remaining 180° of cam rotation the cam acts against the lower follower face, forcing the shaft (lower piston) downward.

The *Scotch yoke* (Fig. 32) is kinematically equivalent to the eccentric cam considered above. In this case link 1, the driver, has a pin at point C on which the slotted follower, link 2, actually rides. Point C is

Mechanism

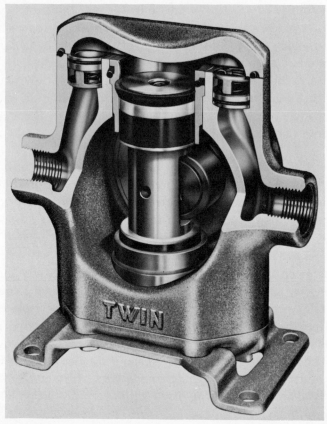

FIG. 31. A two cylinder cam-type piston pump. An eccentric cam (in the form of a sealed roller-type bearing) transmits power from crankshaft to follower (the piston drive). Piston location and velocity are the same as given for the eccentric cam except that the roller bearing eliminates sliding. (Hypro, Inc.)

a distance R from O_1, the axis of the driver. Measuring from the lowest position of the follower, displacement is again given by

$$x = R(1 - \cos \theta)$$

and velocity by

$$v = R\omega \sin \theta.$$

In this instance, graphical analysis gives us the above velocity relation-

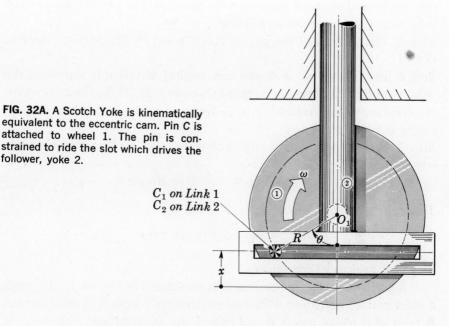

FIG. 32A. A Scotch Yoke is kinematically equivalent to the eccentric cam. Pin C is attached to wheel 1. The pin is constrained to ride the slot which drives the follower, yoke 2.

C_1 on Link 1
C_2 on Link 2

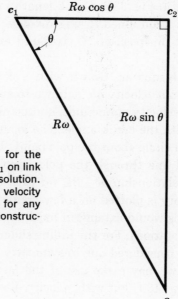

FIG. 32B. The velocity polygon for the Scotch Yoke. A common point (C_1 on link 1, C_2 on link 2) is the key to the solution. Note that the relative (sliding) velocity c_1c_2 is horizontal. The velocity for any angle θ is given by the above construction.

ship easily and we need not resort to calculus. The construction of the velocity polygon proceeds as follows:

Step 1. The velocity of the pin on link 1 is $oc_1 = R\omega$ perpendicular to O_1C.

Step 2. Trial vector oc_2 is drawn in a vertical direction to represent the velocity of link 2 (the common point C_2 on link 2). Then, the trial vector representing sliding velocity c_1c_2 is drawn in a horizontal direction, locating velocity point c_2.

Step 3. It is noted that velocity vectors oc_1 and c_1c_2 meet at an angle θ from which

$$oc_2 = oc_1 \sin\theta \quad \text{or} \quad v = R\omega \sin\theta.$$

The sliding velocity, incidentally, is given by

$$c_1c_2 = oc_1 \cos\theta = R\omega \cos\theta.$$

Graphical Velocity—Time Studies

A *graphical velocity-time study* is illustrated in Fig. 33. In this case, a slider crank mechanism with a connecting rod length L to crank length R ratio of three to one is the object of the examination. The crank is drawn in a series of angular positions with 15° intervals and each position is labeled as in Fig. 33B. Crank length may be arbitrary as long as the L/R ratio is maintained. Using dividers set to the connecting rod length, the wrist pin position, C, is found and labeled for each crank position.

Velocity polygons are drawn with a common pole point o as in Fig. 33C. Crank pin velocity ob is drawn to any convenient length which will represent a velocity of one unit, and point b for each crank position is subscripted with the crank angle. The locus of velocity points b (b_{15}, b_{30}, etc.) forms a circle about the pole point. The locus of velocity points c is a horizontal line through the pole point and velocity vector bc is located by the relationship $bc \perp BC$ for each crank position.

Slider velocity is plotted for a few crank positions in Fig. 33D. The graphical analysis would extend, in most cases, through an entire cycle (360° of crank rotation). For the in-line slider crank, only 180° of crank rotation need be considered due to symmetry. For crank angles between 180° and 360°, we may make use of the fact that the velocity plot is symmetrical about 180° but with velocity direction opposite what it was for the first 180° of rotation. In briefer form, $v(\theta) = -v(360° - \theta)$.

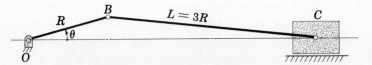

FIG. 33A. In-line slider crank mechanism, with $L/R = 3$.

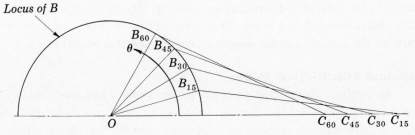

FIG. 33B. Sketches of the linkage for $\theta = 15°$, $30°$, $45°$, and $60°$. Subscripts of B and C refer to crank angle θ.

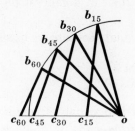

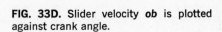

Velocity Scale (in/sec)

FIG. 33C. Velocity polygons are constructed for the above crank positions. The crank pin is arbitrarily given unit velocity (magnitude of 1).

FIG. 33D. Slider velocity *ob* is plotted against crank angle.

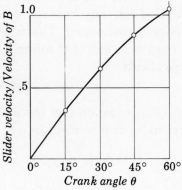

141

Mechanism

The plot, of course, repeats itself every 360°. For any crank length R and crank angular velocity ω rad/sec, actual piston velocity equals the velocity found above multiplied by ωR. For a velocity-time representation, θ is replaced by a function of time, for example $\theta = \omega t$ if angular velocity is constant.

The procedure outlined in the above paragraphs permits a design study to be carried out without actually specifying ω and the mechanism dimensions at the start. The curve obtained, however, is correct only for the specified crank length to connecting rod length ratio.

Analytical Velocity—Time Studies

An *analytical examination of the in-line slider crank mechanism* has some resemblance to the Scotch yoke considered above. In fact, the Scotch yoke can be considered a special case of the slider crank; a slider crank linkage with an infinite connecting rod. It is the connecting rod and the angle ϕ it forms with the slider path which complicates our analytical solution. Fig. 34 shows the in-line slider crank first in its extreme extended position, *top dead center*, and then in a general position with angular displacement θ of the crank.

Measuring piston displacement x from the original position, we have

$$x = R + L - (R \cos \theta + L \cos \phi)$$
$$= R(1 - \cos \theta) + L (1 - \cos \phi) .$$

While this expression appears simple, it contains two variables: crank angle θ, and connecting rod angle ϕ which in turn depends on angle θ. In our previous discussion of the slider crank, this was no problem since we used angles from a scale drawing of the mechanism. In the analytical solution, however, ϕ must be expressed in terms of θ before velocity is determined. This is accomplished by dropping a perpendicular from B to line O_1C forming two right triangles. The length of the perpendicular is

$$a = R \sin \theta = L \sin \phi.$$

Using this equation and the identity $\sin^2 \phi + \cos^2 \phi = 1$, we obtain exact slider displacement in terms of θ only:

$$x = R (1 - \cos \theta) + L (1 - \sqrt{1 - (R/L)^2 \sin^2 \theta} \,).$$

Slider velocity is obtained by differentiating x with respect to time.

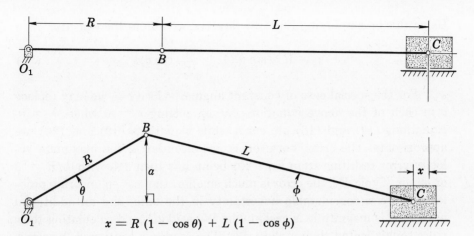

FIG. 34. In-line slider crank mechanism, shown in its extended position (*top*) and shown an instant later when the crank has moved through an angle Θ (*bottom*).

Angular velocity ω is the time rate of change in θ. Exact slider velocity is

$$v = R\,\omega\sin\theta \left(1 + \frac{R}{L}\ \frac{\cos\theta}{\sqrt{1 - (R/L)^2\sin^2\theta}} \right) \qquad (18)$$

We may now verify the fact that the Scotch yoke is a special case of the slider crank mechanism by substituting $R/L = 0$ in the above displacement and velocity equations to obtain Equations (15) and (16).

Using Equations (17) and (18), we may find slider displacement and velocity for any crank position and, if desired, plot x against θ, and v against θ or v against x. If we were to consider various ratios of R to L in order to determine the best design, the several plots would require many hours of work. In that case, it would be worthwhile to program the equations on a digital computer, using a system which would plot the results and relieve us of tedious repetitive work. Alternately, we may re-examine the equations in terms of the problem at hand. If the slider crank mechanism considered is a piston engine or piston pump for which the ratio of L to R is fairly large, say 3 or more, the following simplification is in order. The displacement equation is expanded by the binomial theorem, retaining only the terms:

$$x = R(1 - \cos\theta + \frac{1}{2}\ \frac{R}{L}\sin^2\theta). \qquad (19)$$

143

Using this or simplifying Eq. (18) directly, we obtain the velocity:

$$v = R \omega \sin \theta \left(1 + \frac{R}{L} \cos \theta\right). \tag{20}$$

For the special case of constant angular velocity ω, we may replace θ in each of the above equations by ωt, setting $t = 0$ when $\theta = 0$. Equations (17) and (18) are exact while Equations (19) and (20) are approximate. The error, however, is not often large; the maximum velocity error resulting from Eq. (20) being less than 2% with $L/R = 3$ or larger. Typically, the error is much smaller. In most engineering problems, there is considerable uncertainty in the data, and an additional error of this magnitude is acceptable. We seldom need calculating tools more sophisticated than a slide rule. The reader is cautioned, however, that the error in Equations (19) and (20) increases sharply with decreasing values of L/R and that the equations are useless when L/R is near unity.

EXAMPLE—PROBLEM 1: The in-line slider crank mechanism example considered earlier in this chapter will be used to illustrate the utility of the velocity equations, even though the L/R ratio is less than 3. Given data is repeated in Fig. 35 where: $R = 2$ in, $L = 3.76$ in, $\theta = 70°$, and $\omega = 10$ rad/sec.

Using these values in Equation (18), the exact equation, we have

$$v = 2 \ (10) \sin 70° \left(1 + \frac{2}{3.76} \frac{\cos 70°}{\sqrt{1 - (2/3.76)^2 (\sin 70°)^2}}\right)$$

$= 22.8$ in/sec (to slide rule accuracy)—the same value that was obtained graphically. From Equation (20), the approximate velocity equation, we obtain $v = 22.2$ in/sec, which is a fairly good approximation when one recalls that the L/R ratio is *not* within the recommended range for the approximate equation.

The words "exact" and "approximate" deserve a bit of clarification at this point. Equations (19) and (20) are approximate and cannot, in general, give us the exact solution because we have omitted terms. Equations (17) and (18) are exact, and so is the velocity polygon solution. The paradox of an "exact" velocity solution which is less accurate in fact than an "approximate" analytical solution may occur if the L/R ratio is fairly large and we carry out our analytical calculations to several

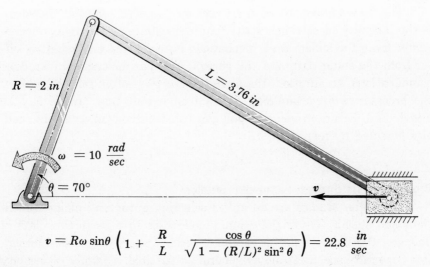

$$v = R\omega \sin\theta \left(1 + \frac{R}{L} \frac{\cos\theta}{\sqrt{1 - (R/L)^2 \sin^2\theta}} \right) = 22.8 \frac{in}{sec}$$

FIG. 35. This illustration of an in-line slider crank repeats Fig. 5. It is repeated to illustrate the relative difficulty and accuracy of the analytical solution.

significant figures, while the velocity polygon suffers inevitable graphical errors. The word "exact" refers to the *potential* exactness of the method without taking into account our limitations in graphics and computation. Furthermore, our solution accuracy can be no better than the accuracy of the "given" data, the crank velocity, linkage dimensions, and other data which define the problem.

In comparing the above analytical solution with the velocity polygon solution, it is clear that the analytical method will enable us to plot displacement and velocity against time or crank position with the least effort. Maximum and minimum values of velocity are obtained quickly by the methods of calculus. The velocity polygon method requires a scale drawing of the linkage for each position. An advantage of the velocity polygon, however, is the velocity image principle, by which we portray velocities for the entire linkage, rather than just for one point. We might, for instance, be interested in the velocity of a particular point on the connecting rod as discussed in the earlier section on the Velocity Image. The solution is immediate from the velocity polygon, while an analytical method requires a completely new analysis of the problem.

Mechanism

The major drawback of analytical mechanisms solutions, however, is the difficulty of setting up the required equations for many mechanisms. Even the slider crank mechanism in which the crankshaft is offset from the slider path and the general four-bar mechanism introduce complications. In addition, the analytical method often fails to portray the process we are examining to such an extent that errors may be undetected. Errors in velocity polygon construction, however, are usually detected by inspection.

Broad Analysis through Parameter Studies

Parameter studies are an aid in selecting optimum linkage dimensions and speeds. We might examine velocities in a particular class of linkages, the slider-crank for example, without specifying actual dimensions or crank speed. To be as general as possible, a family of velocity vs. crank angle curves can be plotted, each curve for a different ratio of connecting rod length L to crank length R. See Fig. 36. To normalize results, the product of crank angular velocity and crank length may be assigned a value of one. Then, all velocities will later be multiplied by the actual ωR value to obtain actual velocity.

The method of obtaining velocity-crank angle plots depends on the type of problem, precision required, and individual capabilities. Complicated linkages would suggest a velocity polygon approach. The availability of a digital computer would make an exact analytical method practical in many cases, particularly if a large number of points were to be plotted.

Fig. 36 is a family of curves of slider velocity vs. crank angle for an in-line slider crank mechanism. The $L/R = \infty$ curve is a sine wave, representing the actual velocity of a Scotch yoke mechanism, or the limiting velocity relationship for the connecting rod length many times greater than crank length. Note how closely the curve, $L/R = 7$, resembles the sine curve. To obtain curves for which the ratio of connecting rod length to crank length is near one, the exact analytical solution is preferred. For "hand" calculations, the approximate analytical solution would be satisfactory for curves where L/R was 3 or larger. The extra work of performing the exact calculation for all ratios of L to R would not be too time-consuming for a computer, however, and a single program would ordinarily suffice.

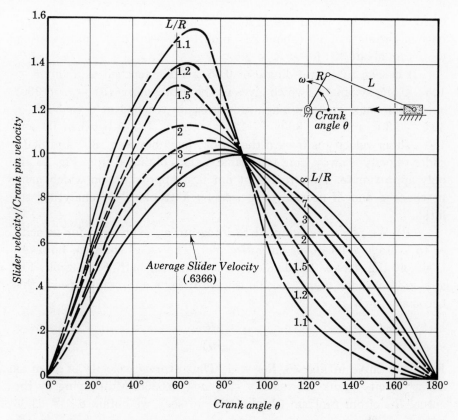

FIG. 36. The family of curves shown here represents an in-line slider crank mechanism *parameter study.* The *ratio* of slider velocity to crank pin velocity is plotted against the crank angle for various (increasing) *L/R* ratios. Slider velocity at any position of the mechanism is found by multiplying the ordinate (slider velocity/crank pin velocity) by the actual *Rω*.

EXAMPLE—PROBLEM 2: An in-line slider-crank mechanism has a crank length of 2 in, and a connecting rod length of 5.6 in. The crank rotates at a constant angular velocity of 50 rad/sec counterclockwise. (*A*) At what crank positions will the slider velocity be 65 in/sec? (*B*) Find average slider velocity for one stroke.

Solution: (*A*) Crank pin velocity is $R\omega = 2 \times 50 = 100$ in/sec. Desired slider velocity/crank pin velocity $= 65/100 = 0.65$.

For the mechanism, we are considering the ratio of connecting rod length to crank length is $L/R = 2.8$. Using Fig. 36, we note the values of

147

crank angle θ for which the $L/R = 2$ curve and the $L/R = 3$ curve have an ordinate of .65 (about 28° and 31° respectively). Interpolating, we obtain about 30° for $L/R = 2.8$.

It is seen that an ordinate of 0.65 is again reached at about $\theta = 123°$. Using symmetry, which gives us the expression $v\,(\theta) = -v\,(360° - \theta)$, the same velocity magnitude is again reached at $\theta = 360° - 30° = 330°$ and $\theta = 360° - 123° = 237°$. For θ between 0° and 180°, slider velocity is toward the crank; for θ between 180° and 360°, slider velocity is away from the crank. Values obtained from Fig. 36 are only approximate. They represent our first approximation which must be checked and, if necessary, revised by a graphical or analytical solution.

(*B*) We might be tempted to integrate an expression for velocity or to average values over an entire plot. The exact solution, however, is simply the stroke, 2*R*, divided by the time for half of one cycle. For any in-line slider crank mechanism with constant crank speed, this becomes

$$v_{av} = \frac{2R}{\pi/\omega}\,.$$

For every curve in Fig. 36, $R\omega = 1$. Thus average velocity is given as slider velocity/crank pin velocity $= 2/\pi = 0.6366$. Multiplying by the actual $R\omega$ of our problem (2 in $\times$ 50 rad/sec), we obtain $v_{av} = 63.66$ in/sec.

Centros and Other Graphical Methods of Velocity Analysis

Centros Defined

The velocity polygon is by no means the only graphical method of linkage analysis. Among other methods, the *centro* method has been, traditionally, of considerable importance. It consists of locating a point, *the centro*, which *is common to two links and has the same (vector) velocity in both*. The centro is then used to relate unknown velocities to known velocities. The pin connecting two links in a mechanism is obviously the centro of the two since it has the same velocity in both. See Fig. 37A.

If two bodies (two friction disks, for instance) roll on one another without sliding, then the instantaneous point of contact is the centro.

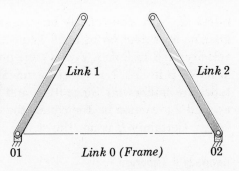

FIG. 37A. A centro is a point common to two links which has the same vector velocity in each link. The pins joining links 1 and 2 to the frame (link 0) are, respectively, centros 01 and 02 (zero velocity).

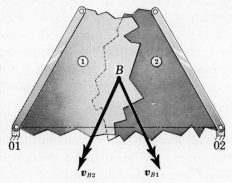

FIG. 37B. Three links have three centros, all of which lie on a straight line. To prove this theorem, let us assume that B, common to extended links 1 and 2, is the third centro. Vectors v_{B1} and v_{B2} violate the requirement for a centro that the velocity vector must be *identical* for both links. To meet this basic requirement, centro $\overline{12}$ cannot occur anywhere except on $\overline{01\ 02}$.

The centros just mentioned are *observed centros* and are to be located and labeled before any others are found by construction. The centro label will consist of the two link numbers, the smaller number first. The point having the same velocity in both link 0 and link 1, for example, will be labeled centro 01. The label 10 would apply to the same centro, but we will avoid duplication by always labeling this centro 01.

Since each pair of links has a centro, three links, which can form three different pairs, will have three centros. That is, links 0, 1 and 2 form three centros which we will label 01, 02 and 12. Fig. 37B shows three links including 0, the frame. There exist centros 01 (where link 1 is pinned to the frame), 02 (where link 2 is pinned to the frame) and 12 (which we will attempt to locate).

An arbitrary point B which does not lie on (line) $\overline{01\ 02}$ is selected as a possible location for centro 12. The bar on $\overline{01\ 02}$ will be used to represent a line in the mathematical sense (extending infinitely on both sides of the line segment between 01 and 02). Let us imagine an extension of links 1 and 2 so that B may lie in both. The velocity of B in link 1, v_{B1}, is perpendicular to $\overline{01\ B}$. Likewise, the velocity of B in link 2, v_{B2} is perpendicular to $\overline{02\ B}$. (The velocity magnitudes are unknown.) Since $\overline{01\ B}$ and $\overline{02\ B}$ are not parallel or colinear, v_{B1} and v_{B2} cannot be the same; the directions of v_{B1} and v_{B2} are different. Certainly B is not the centro 12.

Kennedy's Theorem

We can see from the above that centro 12 cannot be any point which does *not* lie on $\overline{01\ 02}$. A similar examination of the velocity direction of points lying on $\overline{01\ 02}$ shows that centro 12 may lie somewhere on $\overline{01\ 02}$. Considering the infinite extent of $\overline{01\ 02}$, there must be some point on it which has the same velocity magnitude as well as direction in both link 1 and link 2. Thus, we have Kennedy's Theorem (the three-link theorem) in a nutshell: *three links have three centros which lie on a line.*

Kennedy's theorem applies except in trivial cases (e.g., a linkage without any relative motion) but it does not assure us of finding all of the centros which exist in a theoretical sense. As for the original problem of actually locating centro 12, we have failed because there is a need for additional data (links 0, 1 and 2 do not actually form a mechanism). We are, however, now on our way to the solution of actual mechanism problems by the centro method.

Centros and Instant Centers

The mechanism of Fig. 38A has four links including the frame. There are six possible pairs formed by four numbers and, hence, six centros. They are observed centros 01, 12, 23 and 03; the remaining two centros, 02 and 13, must be located by construction. A procedure for finding the unobserved centros follows:

Step 1. The three link theorem will be used to draw a line on which centro 02 must lie. For the necessary three links, we must include links 0 and 2 since we are looking for centro 02; then, either of the remaining links will do. Using links 0, 2 and 1, we have centros 01 and 12 (both already labeled) and 02 (the unknown), all three on a line. Line $\overline{01\ 12}$ is drawn (of arbitrary length) and labeled 02 for our unknown centro.

Step 2. The three link theorem is used again to draw another line to

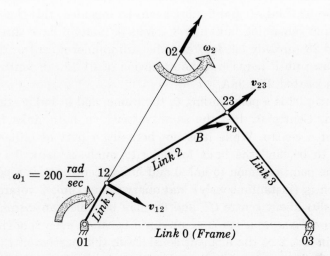

FIG. 38A. Locating unknown centro 02 using the three link (Kennedy's) theorem. Centro 02 is determined by the intersection of the extensions of $\overline{01\ 12}$ and $\overline{03\ 23}$. Since centro 02 is common to link 0 (the frame) and link 2 and has the same (zero) velocity in both, link 2 must rotate (instantaneously) about the centro. Therefore, centro 02 is called an *instant center.*

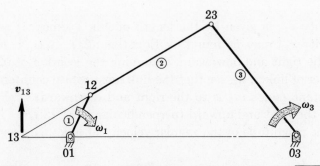

FIG. 38B. Unknown centro 13 is determined by the intersection of $\overline{01\text{-}03}$ and $\overline{12\text{-}23}$. Centro 13 (not an instant center) has the same *non-zero* velocity in links 1 and 3. The angular velocities of both links are inversely proportional to the distances from their respective fixed centers to the common centro.

Mechanism

locate centro 02. Links 0 and 2 must again be included, this time along with the other remaining link, link 3. Links 0, 2 and 3 have three centros, 03 and 23 (already labeled) and the still unknown centro 02. Line $\overline{03\ 23}$ is drawn until it reaches the extension of $\overline{01\ 12}$, at which point centro 02 is located, Fig. 38A.

Step 3. Centro 02 is a point in link 0, the frame, and in link 2, the connecting rod. Centro 02 has the same velocity in both links by the definition of a centro. While it is not actually a part of either, it is considered to be "in" the links for velocity analysis. Link 0 is fixed and thus the point common to link 0 and link 2, centro 02, is a point in link 2 which is (instantaneously) stationary. Thus, link 2 rotates (instantaneously) about centro 02, and 02 may be called an *instant center.* The word *instantaneous* is emphasized because, even though 02 is stationary in link 2 at the moment considered, the location of this stationary point changes continuously. For this reason, the notion of centros is a conceptual problem, hard to swallow for some.

Step 4. The location and application of instant centers is a method of velocity analysis in its own right, even though instant centers are merely a special case of centros. Since link 2 rotates about instant center 02, Fig. 38A, velocities of points on link 2 are proportional to their distances from 02. We may then state the ratio of velocities of points 23 and 12:

$$\frac{v_{23}}{v_{12}} = \frac{02-23}{02-12} \tag{21}$$

where $02-23$ and $02-12$ are distances scaled from the linkage drawing, Fig. 38A.

Velocity v_{12} is given by the length of link 1 times ω_1 and, using this, velocity v_{23} may be found by Equation (21). If ω_1 is clockwise, v_{12} is to the right and downward. Observing the location of 02, the instant center of link 2, we see that the link must rotate counterclockwise at this instant (since v_{12} is to the right and downward). Velocity v_{23}, then, is to the right and upward (perpendicular to $\overline{03\ 23}$.)

Step 5. The magnitude of the angular velocity of link 2 is given by

$$\omega_2 = \frac{v_{12}}{02-12}$$

where $02-12$ is the *actual distance* from point 12 to the instant center of link 2 for the full size mechanism. The velocity of an arbitrary point B on link 2 of Fig. 38A is given by

$$\frac{v_B}{v_{12}} = \frac{02-B}{02-12} \qquad (22)$$

where lengths $02-B$ and $02-12$ are scaled from the diagram.

Velocity v_B is perpendicular to $02-B$ and is to the right and upward, its sense determined in the same manner as for v_{23}.

Step 6. The angular velocity of link 3 follows immediately from the above calculations, but we will use centro 13 to complete the problem in order to illustrate further the centro method. Centro 13 is located in a manner similar to the procedure for locating centro 02. In this case, lines $\overline{01\ 03}$ and $\overline{12\ 23}$ both contain centro 13. Now 13 is a centro in the general sense, having the same non-zero velocity in links 1 and 3. Using that property, we have

$$v_{13} = \omega_1\, 01-13 \quad \text{and} \quad v_{13} = \omega_3\, 03-13$$

Equating these two expressions, we obtain

$$\omega_3\, 03-13 = \omega_1\, 01-13 \quad \text{or} \quad \frac{\omega_3}{\omega_1} = \frac{01-13}{03-13} \qquad (23)$$

which might be expressed in words as *angular velocities of two links are inversely proportional to distances from the respective fixed centers to the common centro.* To obtain Equation (23), which relates the angular velocities of links 1 and 3, it is not necessary to actually calculate v_{13}. In Fig. 38B, however, we see that v_{13} is upward when ω_1 is clockwise. Then, ω_3 is seen to be clockwise also. In general, when the common centro falls between the fixed centers of a pair of links, one link turns clockwise and the other counterclockwise; otherwise, both turn clockwise or both turn counterclockwise. The reader will observe that the pitch point for a pair of gears and the tangent point for a pair of friction disks represent the common centro. For these examples, the expression boils down to: *Angular velocities are inversely proportional to radii.*

Analyzing Basic Linkages Using Centros

The slider crank mechanism, Fig. 39, is solved by first examining the equivalent linkage shown in that figure. It is seen that the slider may be replaced by a link of infinite length perpendicular to the slider path. The slider moves in a horizontal path. Its motion can be duplicated by an equivalent link, link 3, which is vertical. Centro 03, the "fixed center" of the equivalent link, is shown an infinite distance below the slider path. (Centro 03 could, as well, have been located an infinite distance above the slider path, as long as the equivalent link 3 is perpendicular to the slider path.)

Observed centros 01, 12, and 23 are labeled on the sketch along with centro 03. Centro 02 is found by construction as in the four bar linkage described in Fig. 38, and the same equations apply. To find slider velocity in terms of crank pin velocity, we may use:

$$\frac{v_{23}}{v_{12}} = \frac{02-23}{02-12} .$$

For the velocity of an arbitrary point B on link 2 (*e.g.*, the center of gravity), we can use the formula:

$$\frac{v_B}{v_{12}} = \frac{02-B}{02-12} ;$$

and for angular velocity of link 2:

$$\omega_2 = \frac{v_{12}}{02-12} .$$

In the last equation, the reader is reminded that the dimension $02-12$ refers to the true distance between 02 and 12 on a full scale drawing. Then, ω_2 is given in rad/sec for v_{12} in in/sec. The dimensions in the first two equations may be to any scale as long as they are consistent.

It is clear from the equivalent linkage of Fig. 39 that the slider-crank mechanism is a four-bar linkage. In the above discussion, only five of the six centros for the linkage have been found. The remaining one, centro 13, is of interest because it gives us slider velocity directly from crank angular velocity. Using the three-link theorem with links 1, 2 and 3, we draw line $\overline{23\ 12}$ to locate centro 13. Applying the three-link theorem again, using links 0, 1 and 3 this time, centro 13 is located on line $\overline{03\ 01}$. Since 03 is located at an infinite distance from the slider, the line $\overline{03\ 01}$ must be drawn parallel to equivalent link 3 (perpendicu-

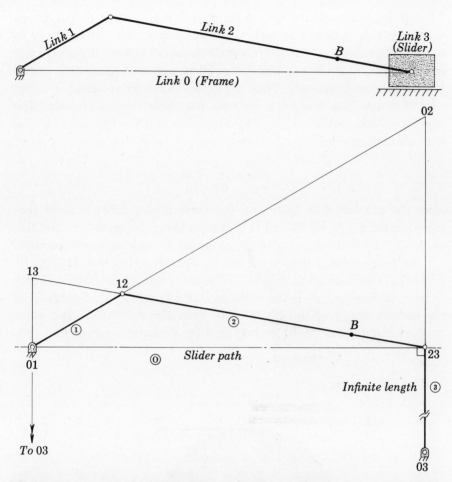

FIG. 39. To use centros to find velocities in a slider crank mechanism, an equivalent linkage must be used, where the slider is replaced by a vertical link of infinite length. The solution then proceeds as for a four bar linkage.

lar to the slider path); any other orientation would require that 03 be located at a finite distance from the slider. In Fig. 39 line $\overline{03\ 01}$, a perpendicular to the slider path, is extended upward until it intersects line $\overline{23\ 12}$, an extension of the centerline of link 2. Centro 13 is located at the intersection.

155

Mechanism

By definition, centro 13 is a point "in" both links 1 and 3. Given ω_1, the angular velocity of link 1, the velocity of the centro is $v_{13} = \omega_1\ 01-13$ where $01-13$ is the full-scale distance between the centro and crank center. Since link 3 translates, all points in it (including centro 13) have the same velocity. Thus, v_{13} is also the slider velocity.

Of course link 3 which represents the slider does not rotate. The angular velocity ratio (as given by Equation (23) for the more general four bar linkage) is:

$$\frac{\omega_3}{\omega_1} = \frac{01-13}{03-13} = 0$$

since the numerator is finite and the denominator infinite. Note that the equation $v_{13} = \omega_3\ 03-13$ is useless in this case; ω_3 is zero and distance $03-13$ is infinite, therefore giving us an indeterminate product.

Rolling contact is easily treated by the centro method. In Fig. 40, a wheel (1) rolls on the frame (0). The point having the same velocity in both (zero velocity) is the point of contact, centro 01. Centro 01 is the instant center of the wheel, and given the velocity of any point on the wheel (01 excepted) we may find the velocity of any other point.

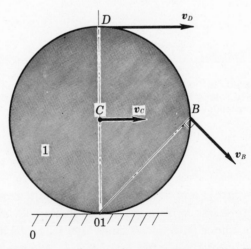

FIG. 40. Using the centro (instant center) to analyze rolling contact. The velocity of any point on the circle is proportional to its distance from the point of contact.

Using the relationship that velocities are proportional to distances from the instant center, we have

$$\frac{v_B}{v_C} = \frac{01-B}{01-C} \quad \text{and} \quad \frac{v_D}{v_C} = \frac{01-D}{01-C}. \tag{22}$$

If, as in Fig. 40, $01-C-D$ forms a diameter of the wheel with C the center, then the velocity of D is twice the velocity C. If $C-B$ is a radius perpendicular to $01-C$ then $v_B/v_C = \sqrt{2}$. In every case, velocity of a point on the wheel is perpendicular to the line between centro 01 and the point.

The Cam and Follower. The *cam and follower* present a new problem in the location of centros. Centros 01 and 02 are the fixed centers of the cam and follower respectively in Fig. 41. Using the three-link theorem, centro 12 is known to lie somewhere on line $\overline{01\ 02}$, but more information is needed to actually locate 12. The relative motion between cam and follower is sliding, having some resemblance to the motion of the slider relative to the frame in a slider crank mechanism. And in both cases the common centro lies on a line perpendicular to the relative motion. Thus, centro 12 is located at the intersection of the common normal through the point of contact and line of centers of cam and follower. By definition, centro 12 has the same velocity "in" links 1 and 2 from which:

$$v_{12} = \omega_1\, 01-12 = \omega_2\, 02-12$$

Using this equation, we see that the angular velocity ratio of follower to cam is inversely proportional to the distances from the common centro to the fixed centers:

$$\frac{\omega_2}{\omega_1} = \frac{01-12}{02-12}.$$

For the position shown, centro 12 does not fall between centros 01 and 02; therefore cam and follower both turn clockwise or both turn counterclockwise. Measuring the ratio of distances given by the above equation, we find the same angular velocity ratio as when this problem was solved by the velocity polygon method in a previous section. (Slight variations may be attributed to graphical error.)

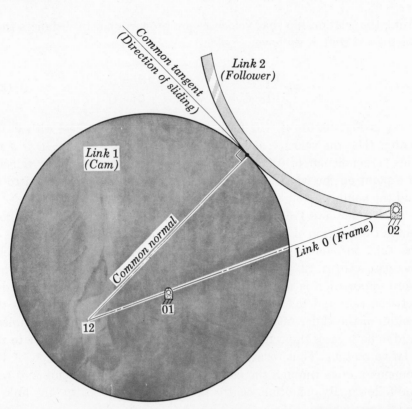

FIG. 41. The cam and follower analyzed by the centro method. Unknown centro 12 lies on the intersection of the line of centers and the common normal through the point of contact.

Spur Gears. *A pair of spur gears* has much in common with the cam and follower considered above. The use of centros in this case gives us some insight into gear design for a constant angular velocity ratio. In Fig. 42, centro 12 is located on the intersection of the line of centers and common normal through the point of contact of a pair of teeth. Angular velocity ratio is given by

$$\frac{\omega_2}{\omega_1} = \frac{01-12}{02-12}$$

and if the location of centro 12 is fixed in space (gears rotate on fixed shafts), the angular velocity ratio is constant. Here, of course, gears

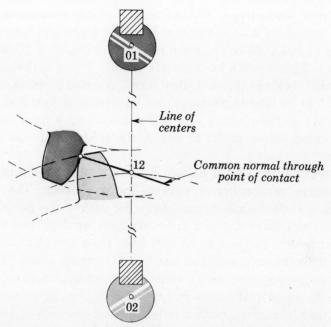

FIG. 42. A pair of gears analyzed by the centro method. Centro 12 is located at the intersection of the line of centers 01-02 and the common normal through the point of contact. This point of intersection is referred to as the *pitch point*.

and cams differ because a cam is usually designed to transmit cyclic motion to the follower. Except in a few instances a constant angular velocity ratio is a fundamental gear system requirement and each gear tooth form must be cut to ensure that centro 12 *is* fixed in space. An involute curve meets this requirement and is used almost exclusively. Involute curves will be discussed in detail in Chapter Four.

Centro 12 of Fig. 42 is called the *pitch point* and defines the pitch radius of a gear. The ratio $01-12/02-12$ represents the ratio of pitch radius of gear 1 to pitch radius of gear 2. When we say angular velocities are inversely proportional to diameters,

$$\frac{\omega_2}{\omega_1} = \frac{d_1}{d_2},$$

d_1 and d_2 refer to pitch diameters.

Shaper Mechanisms. The *mechanical shaper* mechanism (Fig. 43) may be considered a six-bar linkage when the frame and both sliders are counted as links. To begin, seven centros are observed (located by inspection). They are the fixed centers of links 1 and 2, three pin joints, the "fixed" center of the equivalent link 5 (located perpendicular to the path of 5 at an infinite distance) and the centro of link 2 and slider 4. By analogy to the problem of a slider moving on a fixed path, centro 24 is located perpendicular to link 2, the relative path, at an infinite distance.

Altogether the six-bar linkage has $n(n-1)/2 = 15$ centros, where n represents the number of links in the mechanism. The three link theorem is applied sixteen times, twice for each of the remaining eight centros. Using links 0, 1 and 2, for example, we draw line $\overline{01\ 02}$ since unknown centro 12 must lie on that line. Then using links 1, 2 and 4, line $\overline{14\ 24}$ is drawn to intersect line $\overline{01\ 02}$, locating centro 12. The procedure progresses until all 15 centros are located, treating centros at infinite distances in the same manner as with the slider crank mechanism. It may be convenient to arrange the link numbers in a circle as in Fig. 43 and draw lines between a pair of numbers when the corresponding centro is found. When a new line between two numbers would simultaneously complete two triangles with vertices at the link numbers, the links indicated may be used to apply the three link theorem. Occasionally, the two centro loci are colinear and a new attempt must be made. Fig. 43 also shows all 15 centros of the six-bar linkage with the procedure tabulated. It is not necessary to locate the centros in the order given however.

For a mechanism of the type just considered, we might be interested in the velocity of slider 5 in terms of the angular velocity of link 1. This is obtained directly through centro 15 since 15 may be considered a part of slider 5 and link 1. The velocity of any point in slider 5 is

$$v_5 = \omega_1\, 01-15$$

where $01-15$ represents the full-scale distance between centros 01 and 15.

An alternate method which requires the location of only a few centros follows:

Step 1. Let ω_1 be given. Centro 12 is located and used to obtain ω_2.

160

Centros Found by Three Link Theorem

Three	Three Centros		
Links	Known		Unknown
012	01	02	12
124	14	24	12
014	01	14	04
024	02	24	04
023	02	23	03
035	05	35	03
025	02	05	25
235	23	35	25
234	23	24	34
034	04	03	34
125	12	23	13
134	14	34	13
045	04	05	45
245	24	25	45
015	01	05	15
145	14	45	15

Observed
Centros

01
02
05
14
23
24
35

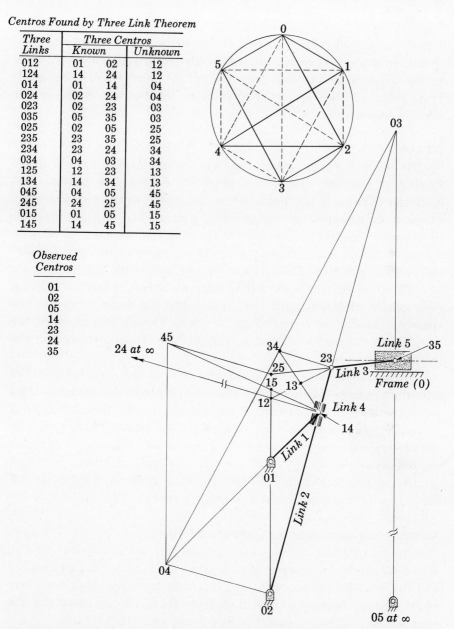

FIG. 43. Using centros to determine the velocities of a six bar linkage. Eight unknown centros must be determined using the three link theorem. Since keeping track of the centros may be confusing, an orderly procedure is necessary. A table like the one shown is recommended.

Mechanism

Step 2. Using ω_2, v_{23} is calculated.

Step 3. Centro 03 is then located and used to obtain v_{35}. Since both of the above procedures fail to give us relative velocities directly, they are not recommended when accelerations of the linkage are also required. Their major practical use is to serve as an independent check on our velocity polygon results.

Centrodes

As noted above, an instant center is instantaneously fixed in space. In general, however, the instant center will have a new position at a later time. That is, a new point will be designated as the instant center. Consider, for example, the case of rolling contact, Fig. 40. Instant center 01, the point instantaneously fixed in the rolling body, is a fixed point in space. An instant later, however, we must designate a new instant center 01 a little to the right of the present position (along the path of rolling).

The track on which the rolling body moves is the locus of all possible instant centers 01, and it may be called the *space centrode*. The space centrode is, of course, fixed in space. The circumference of the roller forms the locus of all instant centers 01 relative to the roller; it is called the *body centrode*.

In Fig. 38 we located the instant center of the connecting rod of a four bar linkage, labeling it 02. The space centrode for the connecting rod is the locus of all positions of 02 in space. It must be plotted for a succession of linkage positions, using the same constructions shown in the illustration. If we were to fix link 2 and let link 0 act as the connecting rod, we could plot the body centrode, the locus of instant center 02 relative to link 2. For any linkage, the body centrode appears to roll along the space centrode which is fixed in space.

Analyzing Linkages Using the Component Method

Another method of velocity determination, the *component method* is of more academic than practical interest. This method is based on the fact that velocity components *along* a straight rigid link are everywhere equal. The argument is simple: if components of velocity along the link were different at two points, the link would change in length.

In Fig. 44, the velocity of point C is given and the velocity of point B is to be found. Velocity v_c is broken into a component perpendicular to link 2 and one along link 2. The component of v_c along link 2 is

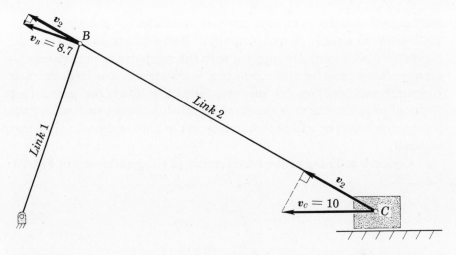

FIG. 44. The vector component method of linkage analysis. Since velocities *along* the link are everywhere equal, the component of v$_B$ along *BC* is equal to the component of v$_C$ along *BC*.

labeled v_2. The component of v_B which lies along link 2 must also be v_2. The direction of v_B is known to be perpendicular to link 1. Velocity v_B is made up of two components, v_2 along link 2 and another component perpendicular to link 2. Adding the components, v_B is found as in the illustration. It is seen that $v_2 = v_C$ times the cosine of the angle between v_C and v_2. Then $v_B = v_2$ divided by the cosine of the angle between v_2 and v_B or $v_B =$ approximately 8.7 in/sec at the instant shown in the figure for $v_C = 10$ in/sec.

For complicated linkages, the sketch may become cluttered with construction lines and lead to possible errors. For this reason, the component method is recommended only as a check on other velocity methods.

Analog Simulation

One may construct an electrical model of a mechanism or other physical systems using an electronic analog computer. Voltages in the computer represent velocities, displacements and other variables in the

163

Mechanism

mechanism; thus the computer circuitry simulates the mechanism (in a mathematical sense). Some computing elements are internal to the computer while others are supplied with the computer or purchased separately. *Since most of the computing elements are specified by their computational function (as summer, integrator, etc.), the user is not required to be an expert in circuitry.* He must, however, understand the mechanism which he wishes to simulate and be able to describe it mathematically.

Consider a sliding contact mechanism of the type shown in Fig. 23.

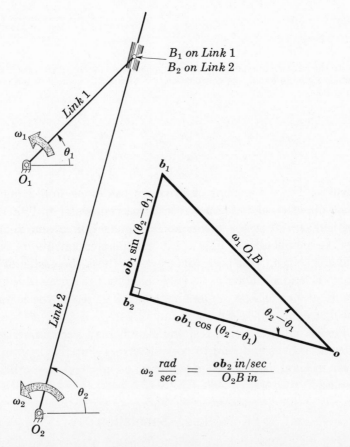

FIG. 45. Computer analysis of a sliding contact mechanism. In order to analyze the velocities of this mechanism with an analog computer, the velocities will have to be expressed as mathematical relationships. The data is fed to the computer which performs the mathematical steps for which it is programmed.

Only the part shown in Fig. 45 will be examined at this time. Let ω_1, the angular velocity of link 1 be given. We will write an expression for relative velocity b_2b_1 and angular velocity ω_2 and then discuss the analog computer solution. The velocity polygon is drawn beginning with the velocity of point B on link 1, $ob_1 = \omega_1O_1B$, where ob_1 is perpendicular to link 1. (The scale of the drawing is not important here since we are only developing a mathematical expression.) The polygon is completed by drawing the velocity of B_2, ob_2 perpendicular to link 2 and relative velocity b_2b_1 parallel to link 2. Since velocities ob_1 and ob_2 are respectively perpendicular to links 1 and 2, they form the angle, $b_1ob_2 = \theta_2 - \theta_1$. Furthermore, since link 2 is straight, angle ob_2b_1 is a right angle. Using the velocity polygon, and the above equations for ob_1 and b_1ob_2, the relative velocity becomes:

$$b_2b_1 = ob_1 \sin (\theta_2 - \theta_1) = \omega_1O_1B \sin (\theta_2 - \theta_1). \qquad (24)$$

Similarly, the velocity of point B on link 2 is:

$$ob_2 = ob_1 \cos (\theta_2 - \theta_1) = \omega_1O_1B \cos (\theta_2 - \theta_1) . \qquad (25)$$

Dividing this equation for the velocity of B_2 by the distance O_2B, we obtain the angular velocity of link 2:

$$\omega_2 = \frac{ob_2}{O_2B} = \frac{\omega_1O_1B \cos (\theta_2 - \theta_1)}{O_2B} . \qquad (26)$$

Solutions for the above two equations can be obtained with the analog computer circuitry as block-diagrammed in Fig. 46. This circuitry was developed in a paper by Timm who also determined displacements and accelerations as well as describing a procedure for solving four bar linkages.[6] Computing elements will be discussed briefly to introduce the basic concepts of analog computer-aided mechanism design. If the reader intends to personally simulate a mechanism as his first attempt at analog computer operation, he will need the additional help of an operator's manual or a text such as the one by James, Smith and Wolford.[7]

For the example we are considering, angular velocity ω_1 is to be given and thus a voltage representing ω_1 serves as input to the circuit. The symbol ω_1 on the circuit is a voltage signal equal to the actual angular velocity on the mechanism divided by some scale in radians/second/volt. For convenience, the input is taken as negative (in the lower

6. R. F. Timm, "Analog Simulation of Rigid Link Mechanisms," A.S.M.E. paper No. 66-*Mech*-28, 1966.

7. M. L. James, G. M. Smith, and J. C. Wolford, *Analog Computer Simulation of Engineering Systems* (Scranton: International Textbook Co., 1966).

165

Mechanism

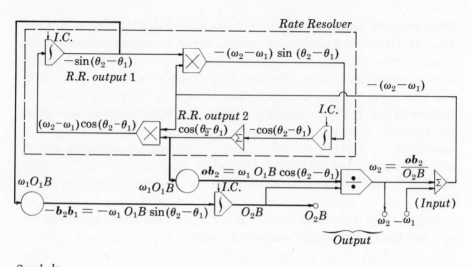

Symbols

I.C. (Initial Condition)

⬭ Attenuator   ▷ Divider   ▷ Integrator   ⊠ Multiplier   ▷ Summer

FIG. 46. *Analog simulation.* This circuit duplicates the sliding contact mechanism shown in Fig. 45. It is the circuit used by Timm to simulate sliding contact mechanism.

right of Fig. 46) and added to ω_2 in a summer. The circuitry of a summer is such that its output signal is the negative of the sum of the inputs: $-(\omega_2 - \omega_1)$. The output of the summer becomes the input to a rate resolver circuit consisting of integrators, multipliers and a summer, the latter element performing only a sign change. Signals within the rate resolver are shown after the variables are integrated with respect to time and multiplied, where these processes also result in a sign change.

The rate resolver has two outputs: $-\sin(\theta_2 - \theta_1)$ and $\cos(\theta_2 - \theta_1)$. The latter is multiplied by the constant $\omega_1 O_1 B$ using a potentiometer (attenuator) to form velocity ob_2 as in Equation (25). The other output, multiplied by $\omega_1 O_1 B$, forms relative velocity $-b_2 b_1$ (Equation 24). Now, $b_2 b_1$ is the time rate of change in distance $O_2 B$. Integrated, it forms the instantaneous value of $O_2 B$. This is one of the output signals, a voltage which may be plotted as a function of time and also scaled to give the actual distance in inches on the mechanism.

In each of the integrations, a constant voltage proportional to the initial condition must be applied at the I.C. (initial condition) terminal of the integrator. The appropriate initial condition for integration of $-b_2 b_1$ is a negative voltage proportional to the initial value of distance $O_2 B$ (both inputs change sign in the integrator circuit). Finally, the ob_2 signal is divided by $O_2 B$ to form the output signal ω_2 which is plotted as a function of time. The angular velocity scale converts this to actual angular velocity of link 2 at any instant.

Since the computer circuitry is overloaded by excessive voltages and because low voltages would reduce accuracy, signals must be attenuated or amplified (scaled) at several points within the computer circuit. Scaling depends on the actual system variables (lengths, velocities, etc.) and is not shown in the block diagram.

In the above example, we did not attempt to solve a problem by analog simulation which we could not solve by other methods. Fig. 45 includes the complete velocity polygon solution for the instant shown. By repeating the velocity polygon analysis for successive positions of the linkage, the angular velocity of link 2 may be plotted as a function of linkage position or time. In addition, the velocity polygon was used to specify the problem mathematically. Using Equations (24) through (26), together with the identities which precede these formulas, and an equation for distance $O_2 B$, we may obtain the same results analytically by hand calculations, desk calculator or digital computer.

If our problem is *analysis* of a linkage with set dimensions, any of the above methods can be used with about the same amount of total effort. *Design*, however, presents a different situation since we may wish to consider various linkage dimensions. Hand calculations and graphical solutions then become very expensive; the digital computer therefore becomes more attractive. The computer program may be used repetitively for a wide range of possible dimensions, particularly when the computer is integrated with a plotter.

The strength of analog simulation also lies in the design field since the designer may vary parameters (linkage lengths, etc.) simply by adjustment of a potentiometer as the solution is plotted before him. Since solutions are plotted in a few seconds and changes are made instantaneously, the designer may choose to optimize dimensions by taking advantage of the flexibility of analog computer simulation.

167

Kinematic Design for Specific Requirements

Often a mechanism must be designed to meet certain requirements as to displacement, velocity and acceleration. Cams provide the designer a maximum of flexibility in meeting such requirements. Other linkages, however, have certain advantages including the ability to transmit considerable force. But there may be no known linkage which will follow a given (arbitrarily chosen) displacement and velocity pattern. The best "fit" to the desired requirements is then determined by trial and error.

Let us specify the dimensions of a linkage to meet a simple set of requirements. Suppose a certain process requires rectilinear motion with a velocity between 75 and 100 in/sec during at least 15% of each cycle. The linkage is to be driven by a shaft which turns at 600 RPM. The requirements are not very rigid and therefore several mechanisms would be satisfactory, but we will consider the in-line slider crank mechanism which has already been examined in detail. Checking the curve representing $L/R = 3$ in Fig. 36, we see that this connecting rod to crank length ratio may be satisfactory. For that curve $v/R\omega$ ranges from about 0.8 to 1.05 during the interval from $\theta = 40°$ to $\theta = 110°$ (which is greater than 15% of one cycle). If we let $v/R\omega = 0.8$ correspond to $v = 75$ in/sec, when

$$\omega = \frac{2\pi}{60} \times 600 \text{ RPM} = 62.8 \frac{\text{rad}}{\text{sec}} \text{ then } R = \frac{v}{.8\omega} = \frac{75}{.8 \times 62.8} = 1.5.$$

At maximum velocity, $v/R\omega = 1.05$ or $v = 99$ in/sec (approximately) which is within the required range. The tentative solution, then is an in-line slider crank mechanism with crank length $R = 1.5$ in and connecting rod length $L = 3R = 4.5$ and the conditions are satisfied between crank angles of $\theta = 40°$ and $110°$ (approximately). Since the curves are only approximate, the next step is an accurate plot of velocity during the interval chosen.

For almost every practical design situation, the first step involves sketching of as many linkages as possible which might be suitable. The only limits are the designer's creativity and experience. Then, the motion characteristics of the linkages are analyzed, first to see that the displacement pattern meets all requirements, then to check velocity and acceleration. In most cases the velocity polygon is the preferred method of velocity analysis although it may be followed by an analytical approach or checked by another method.

Chapter

3

Acceleration:
Methods of Analysis

Introduction

In the first chapter, we considered the angular velocity and angular acceleration of a rotating link, and the velocity and acceleration of a point on a rotating link. In Chapter Two, we used the concept of relative velocity to complete velocity analyses of entire linkages. In the sections that follow, we will develop similar techniques for the acceleration analyses of complete linkages through the concept of relative acceleration. The reader may find it profitable to review briefly the normal and tangential acceleration section in Chapter One, and the relative velocity section of Chapter Two at this time.

Relative Acceleration

In order to solve acceleration problems, we must often consider the acceleration of one point relative to another, the *relative acceleration*. Consider link BC of Fig. 1A, which is not fixed at any point. If the acceleration of point B is known, we may find the acceleration of any point C on the link by adding *the acceleration of point C with respect to B* to the acceleration of B. (Recall that the addition of vector quantities requires that the vector sense be considered as well as the vector magnitude.) Symbolically, then, the acceleration of point C is given by the expression

$$a_C = a_B + a_{CB} \qquad (1)$$

where $\mathbf{a}_{CB}$, the acceleration of point C with respect to point B may be broken into its normal and tangential components:

$$a_{CB} = a^n_{CB} + a^t_{CB}. \qquad (2)$$

169

Mechanism

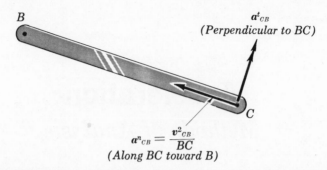

$$a^t_{CB}$$
(Perpendicular to BC)

$$a^n_{CB} = \frac{v^2_{CB}}{BC}$$
(Along BC toward B)

FIG. 1A. The acceleration of point *C* relative to point *B*, a_{CB}, is shown broken into its normal and tangential components. The vector representing the normal component, a^n_{CB}, lies along *BC* and is directed toward *B*; the vector representing the tangential component, a^t_{CB}, is perpendicular to *BC*. Since the angular acceleration α of the link is unknown, the magnitude of a^t_{CB} is also unknown (double arrowhead).

The procedure for finding the normal component of relative acceleration is similar to the method used in Chapter One to find the normal acceleration on a link with a fixed center. The normal acceleration was given by the formula: $a^n = v^2/R$. Similarly, the normal component of relative acceleration is given by the square of relative velocity v_{CB} divided by the distance between the points

$$a^n_{CB} = \frac{v^2_{CB}}{BC} = \frac{(bc)^2}{BC} \qquad (3)$$

and is directed along the line *BC* toward *B*. The term *bc* in Equation (3) is identical to v_{CB}; it refers to the actual vector velocity of *C* with respect to *B* expressed in in/sec. The tangential component of relative acceleration, a^t_{CB}, is perpendicular to *BC*. The magnitude of the tangential component depends on the angular acceleration of link *BC*. These relationships hold for any two points on the same rigid link, whether or not the link rotates about a fixed center.

EXAMPLE—PROBLEM 1: Let the velocity of *C* with respect to *B* in Fig. 1A be given as *bc* = 60 in/sec, where the length *BC* = 3 in. If the acceleration of *B* (a_B) is known, how is the acceleration of *C* found?

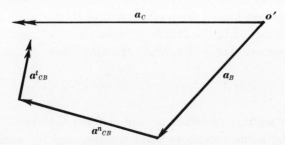

FIG. 1B. The absolute acceleration of point C is given by the vector sum: $a_C = a_B + a_{CB}$. The vectors can also be added by adding the normal and tangential components so that $a_C = a^n_B + a^t_B + a^n_{CB} + a^t_{CB}$. If the magnitude of a^t_{CB} (equal to $BC\ \alpha$) is unknown, an additional relationship will be needed to close the polygon and complete the solution.

Solution: The acceleration vector a_B is drawn to a convenient scale in Fig. 1B. Note that information on a_B must include its direction as well as its magnitude if it is to be drawn as a vector. To the head of a_B we add the scaled vector

$$a^n_{CB} = \frac{(bc)^2}{BC} = \frac{(60 \text{ in/sec})^2}{3 \text{ in}} = 1200 \text{ in/sec}^2$$

parallel to CB (pointing to the left and upward). As in the case of velocity vectors, the direction of the components of the relative acceleration vector will be taken directly from the orientation of the link BC in Fig. 1A.

If the angular acceleration α of the link is known, the tangential component of relative acceleration is given by

$$a^t_{CB} = \alpha\ BC \tag{4}$$

(perpendicular to BC with a sense determined by the sense of α), and may be scaled and added at the head of, and perpendicular to, a^n_{CB}. Otherwise, a^t_{CB} is added as a vector of unknown length as in Fig. 1B, its magnitude to be determined later by considering other constraints of the mechanism which includes link BC.

The absolute acceleration of a point C on the link is completely given by the vector sum

$$a_C = a_B + a_{CB} = a^n_B + a^t_B + a^n_{CB} + a^t_{CB}. \tag{5}$$

If a^t_{CB} were known and drawn to scale on the acceleration vector diagram, we could complete (close) the polygon by drawing $o'c'$ (alternate form of notation for a_C) from pole point o' to the head of a^t_{BC}, the last vector to be added to the diagram. Measuring $o'c'$ against the acceleration scale, we could then determine the magnitude of the acceleration of point C.

In the sections to follow we will *complete* solutions to problems of this type by using the above relationships, and by using still another vector relationship, the acceleration image. In Example Problem 1 we are concerned primarily with the *method* of solution.

The student should by this time be aware that an acceleration vector sum can be written in several different ways. This is possible because an acceleration vector can be represented by a single term or as the vector sum of its normal and tangential components. Thus, Equation (5) is merely the expanded form of Equation (1). Which expression is used to represent the vector sum will usually be determined by the nature of the given data. The student may find it convenient to add to an acceleration vector of known magnitude and direction the normal component of a second (unknown) vector, and then to add the tangential component to the normal component to complete the vector sum. (This was done in Fig. 1B.) Alternately, the student may find it necessary to add all of the individual normal and tangential components of the vectors involved to arrive at the desired sum. All of the expressions below refer to the same vector sum; they are equivalent expressions.

$$a_C = a_B + a_{CB}$$

$$a_C = a_B + a^n_{CB} + a^t_{CB}$$

$$a_C = a^n_B + a^t_B + a^n_{CB} + a^t_{CB}$$

$$a_C = a^n_C + a^t_C = a^n_B + a^t_B + a^n_{CB} + a^t_{CB}$$

The Acceleration Polygon: Analysis of Slider Crank Mechanisms

The acceleration polygon is analagous to the velocity polygon discussed in Chapter Two. The vector polygon provides us with convenient method of finding the magnitude of unknown vectors through their relationship to known (easily calculated) vectors. In this case, the vectors being considered are accelerations. The acceleration polygon is simply the graphical expression of the acceleration vector equation, Equation (5).

EXAMPLE—PROBLEM 2: Analysis of the slider crank mechanism with constant crank velocity. Fig. 2A shows a slider crank linkage which was examined in the preceding chapter. We want to find the acceleration of point C on the slider.

Solution: The method of solution is that of Equation (5)—to add the acceleration of C relative to B to the known acceleration of point B.

The velocity analysis of this mechanism has already been completed. The velocity polygon of Fig. 2B has been taken directly from Fig. 7 of Chapter 2 to save steps. The student should by this time be familiar with its construction.

We are considering the case in which the crank rotates at constant angular velocity. Since α, the angular acceleration of the crank, is thus zero the tangential acceleration of the crank pin will also be zero: $a^t{}_B = O_1 B \alpha_1 = 0$. Then, the total acceleration of point B is the normal component of acceleration, given by Equation (3):

$$a_B = a^n{}_B = \frac{v^2}{r} = \frac{(ob)^2}{O_1 B} = \frac{(20 \text{ in/sec})^2}{2 \text{ in}} = 200 \ \frac{\text{in}}{\text{sec}^2}$$

parallel to $O_1 B$ and directed toward O_1. See Fig. 2C. Note that we must identify the particular radius $(O_1 B)$ and velocity (ob) in each case; the general formula for normal acceleration, v^2/r, is inadequate for these problems since we will deal with several different radii and velocities in analyzing a given mechanism.

In this problem, we are required to find the acceleration of point C, given the velocity of point B. The acceleration equation for the slider crank mechanism is similar to the velocity equation. The accelerations are related by Equation (5)

$$a_C = a^n{}_B + a^t{}_B + a^n{}_{CB} + a^t{}_{CB}$$

for the general case of the slider crank mechanism. The formula provides us simultaneously with a convenient list of all of the acceleration vectors to be determined and the order in which the vectors should be added in the acceleration polygon.

173

Mechanism

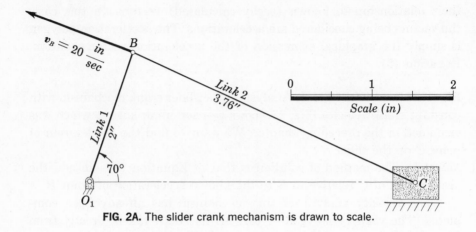

FIG. 2A. The slider crank mechanism is drawn to scale.

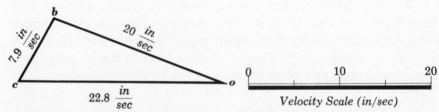

FIG. 2B. After a suitable velocity scale is selected, the velocity polygon for the slider crank linkage is drawn.

Before constructing the actual acceleration polygon, it will prove helpful to first note the acceleration vector directions which are apparent from the linkage drawing, Fig. 2A. After noting the linkage orientation, the restraints on the mechanism, and the given data, we can readily identify the presence and the direction of the following acceleration vectors, Fig. 2C:

a_C along the horizontal path to which the slider is constrained,

a^n_B parallel to O_1B and toward fixed point O_1,

$a^t_B = 0$, since crank O_1B rotates with constant angular velocity,

a^n_{CB} parallel to link BC and directed toward B, and

a^t_{CB} perpendicular to link BC (pointing upward and to the right).

174

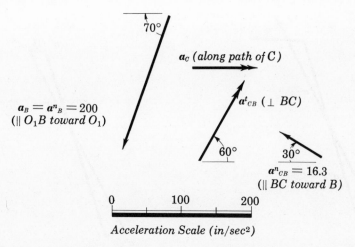

a_C *(along path of C)*

a^t_{CB} $(\perp BC)$

$a_B = a^n_B = 200$
$(\parallel O_1 B \text{ toward } O_1)$

60°

70°

30°

$a^n_{CB} = 16.3$
$(\parallel BC \text{ toward } B)$

0   100   200

Acceleration Scale (in/sec²)

FIG. 2C. After a suitable acceleration scale is selected, the directions of the various acceleration components are identified by inspecting the linkage orientation. Where vector magnitudes can be determined (with the aid of the velocity polygon and link lengths) the vectors are drawn to scale. Where the vector magnitudes are unknown, they are drawn with double arrowheads.

The procedure for constructing the acceleration polygon is similar in some ways to the velocity polygon procedure. The first step, Fig. 2C, includes selection of an acceleration scale which will result in an acceleration polygon of reasonable size. Of course, the accelerations are not all known at this time, but it may be assumed that they are of the same order of magnitude as a_B, the acceleration of the crank pin. When the student begins the step-by-step construction of the acceleration polygon, Figs. 2D and E, he will find that checking the vectors of the polygon against Fig. 2C will help to insure the correct orientation of the polygon.

In Fig. 2D the vector a^n_B has already been drawn. The tangential acceleration of the crank pin is zero in the special case under consideration, eliminating the term a^t_B from Equation (5). (Note: It does not necessarily follow that the tangential acceleration of C with respect to B is likewise zero; in fact, it will be shown that a^t_{CB} is quite large in this example.) Since $a^t_B = 0$, we see from Eq. (5) that a^n_{CB}, the normal acceleration of C with respect to B must be evaluated next. The normal acceleration of C with respect to B will lie along the connecting link BC,

175

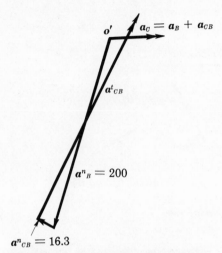

FIG. 2D. The acceleration polygon is begun. The order in which the vectors are added is indicated by Eq. (4).

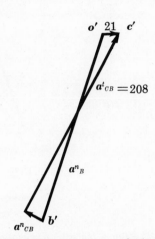

FIG. 2E. Accelerations a_C and a^t_{CB} are scaled directly from the acceleration polygon.

TABLE 1. VECTOR TABULATION FOR THE ACCELERATION POLYGON OF A SLIDER CRANK MECHANISM WITH UNIFORM CRANK VELOCITY, FIG. 2.

Vector	$a_C =$	a^n_B	$+ a^t_B$	$+ a^n_{CB}$	$+ a^t_{CB}$
Vector Magnitude	?	$\dfrac{(ob)^2}{O_1 B}$	$\alpha_1 O_1 B$	$\dfrac{(bc)^2}{BC}$	?
Vector Direction	‖ path of C	‖ $O_1 B$ toward O_1	$\perp O_1 B$	‖ BC toward B	$\perp BC$
Vectors Used to Construct Polygon	?	$200 \dfrac{\text{in}}{\text{sec}^2}$	0	$16.6 \dfrac{\text{in}}{\text{sec}^2}$	?

directed toward B. The formula (4) for the normal component of relative acceleration is $a^n{}_{CB} = v^2{}_{CB}/r$, where v_{CB} can be taken from the velocity polygon of Fig. 2B. The radius, r, is the length of the connecting rod BC. Thus

$$a^n{}_{CB} = \frac{v^2{}_{CB}}{r} = \frac{(bc)^2}{BC} = \frac{(7.9 \text{ in/sec})^2}{3.76 \text{ in}} = 16.6 \frac{\text{in}}{\text{sec}^2}.$$

Vector $a^n{}_{CB}$ is then drawn to scale and added at the head of vector $a^n{}_B$ (Fig. 2D), parallel to BC and is directed toward point B. The final vector, $a^t{}_{CB}$, is added at the head of and perpendicular to $a^n{}_{CB}$ to complete the vector sum of Equation (5). A double arrowhead is used, Fig. 2D, to indicate that the length of $a^t{}_{CB}$ is not yet known. The sum $a^n{}_B + a^n{}_{CB} + a^t{}_{CB}$ represents the total acceleration of C; the true direction of the acceleration of C is horizontal. (The direction of C was obvious at the onset and was drawn as a horizontal vector in Fig. 2C.) We therefore draw a_C horizontally (to the right to close the polygon) from pole point o' in the acceleration polygon, Fig. 2D, again using a double arrowhead since the magnitude of a_C is unknown. Both vectors a_C and $a^t{}_{CB}$ end where they intersect, a point which we label c'. Measuring the lengths of each on the acceleration scale we find that

$$a^t{}_{CB} = 208 \frac{\text{in}}{\text{sec}^2} \text{ upward and to the right, and}$$

$$a_C = 21 \frac{\text{in}}{\text{sec}^2} \text{ to the right, as shown in Fig. 2E.}$$

If greater accuracy is required we may compute the exact angles and use trigonometric functions.

Knowing the length BC and the tangential acceleration of C with respect to B, we can also find the angular acceleration of the connecting link, link 2. From the formula for tangential acceleration, $a^t = r\alpha$, we obtain

$$\alpha_2 = \frac{a^t}{r} = \frac{a^t{}_{CB}}{BC} = \frac{208 \text{ in/sec}^2}{3.76 \text{ in}} = 55 \frac{\text{rad}}{\text{sec}^2}.$$

The method for finding the direction of α_2 is similar to the method for finding the direction of ω. Tangential acceleration $a^t{}_{CB}$ is placed at C on link BC as in Fig. 2F. We see immediately that α_2 is counterclockwise (opposite the direction of ω_2 found in the preceding chapter). Thus, at

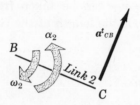

FIG. 2F. Knowing the tangential acceleration of C relative to B, a^t_{CB}, and knowing the length of the link BC, we can easily find the angular acceleration of the link.

this instant, the angular acceleration α_2 is opposing the angular velocity ω_2, which means that ω_2 is decreasing. The reader will recall that ω_1, the angular velocity of the crank, is constant in this example.

Let us now review the above steps for finding accelerations on the slider crank mechanism, Fig. 2.

Step 1. Draw the linkage to scale. Draw the velocity polygon ***obc*** representing the solution to the vector equation

$$v_C = v_B + v_{CB} \quad \text{or} \quad oc = ob + bc.$$

Step 2. Solve the general acceleration vector equation, Eq. (5), for the slider crank mechanism

$$a_C = a_B + a_{CB} = a^n_B + a^t_B + a^n_{CB} + a^t_{CB}$$

graphically as demonstrated in Table 1.

Step 3. The acceleration of B is labeled ***o'b'***. The "prime" used with the lower case bold face letters indicates that the vector is an acceleration and not a velocity. In this case, $a^t_B = 0$ since $\alpha_1 = 0$, from which $a_B = a^n_B$ only. To a_B, we add vectors a^n_{CB} (the magnitude is found with the aid of the velocity polygon) and a^t_{CB} (drawn perpendicular to BC and of unknown magnitude). The intersection of a_C and a^t_{CB} completes the polygon and determines the magnitude of each.

Step 4. The acceleration vectors have been identified by their components (e.g., a^n_B and a^t_B) and by an acceleration polygon notation patterned after the velocity polygon notation. For the linkage considered above:

$a_B = o'b'$

$a_{CB} = b'c'$. Although not shown in the acceleration polygon, the normal and tangential components of a_{CB} could be replaced by a single vector representing their sum, and extending from b' to c' ($b'c'$).

$a_C = o'c'$

Note the reversal of letters in acceleration polygon notation: Acceleration a_{CB} becomes $b'c'$, just as velocity v_{CB} becomes bc in velocity polygon notation. The acceleration polygon will be used to advantage later when we consider the acceleration image.

EXAMPLE—PROBLEM 3: The acceleration analysis of the slider crank linkage with angular acceleration of the crank. Find the accelerations for the linkage of Fig. 3. Given data is the same as that for the preceding problem except that link 1 does not have a constant angular velocity, but instead accelerates at a rate $\alpha_1 = 40$ rad/sec^2 counterclockwise.

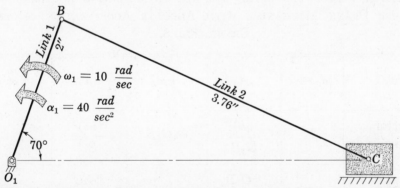

FIG. 3A. The mechanism of Fig. 2 is redrawn. This time, the crank is given an angular acceleration instead of constant angular velocity.

FIG. 3B. The addition of an angular acceleration does not affect the velocity polygon for the instant considered.

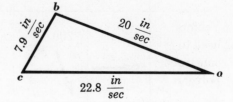

Solution: The addition of an angular acceleration has no effect on the instantaneous velocity readings so that the velocity polygon remains unchanged. We will again use Equation (5). In this case, however, the tangential acceleration of point B does not equal zero:

$$a^t_B = \alpha_1 O_1 B = (40 \ \frac{\text{rad}}{\text{sec}^2}) \ (2 \ \text{in}) = 80 \ \frac{\text{in}}{\text{sec}^2}.$$

For convenience, the terms of the acceleration equation are tabulated below (Table 2).

We can now construct the acceleration polygon. Beginning at an arbitrary pole point o' in Fig. 3C, we draw a^n_B to scale and add a^t_B at the head of a^n_B. The sum $a^n_B + a^t_B$ forms a_B (or $o'b'$). Thus, the head of a^t_B is labeled point b'. Next, the two components of relative acceleration are added: first a^n_{CB} starting at b' and, to it, a^t_{CB} (of unknown length). Finally, the length of a_C is found by drawing vector a_C hori-

TABLE 2. VECTOR TABULATION FOR THE ACCELERATION POLYGON OF A SLIDER CRANK MECHANISM WITH ANGULAR ACCELERATION OF THE CRANK, FIG. 3.

Vector	$a_C =$	a^n_B	$+ a^t_B$	$+ a^n_{CB}$	$+ a^t_{CB}$
Vector Magnitude	?	$\dfrac{(ob)^2}{O_1 B}$	$\alpha_1 O_1 B$	$\dfrac{(bc)^2}{BC}$	?
Vector Direction	∥ path of C	∥ $O_1 B$ toward O_1	⊥ $O_1 B$	∥ BC toward B	⊥ BC
Vectors used to construct polygon	?	$200 \ \frac{\text{in}}{\text{sec}^2}$	$80 \ \frac{\text{in}}{\text{sec}^2}$	$16.6 \ \frac{\text{in}}{\text{sec}^2}$	?

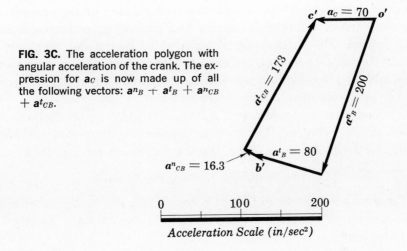

FIG. 3C. The acceleration polygon with angular acceleration of the crank. The expression for a_C is now made up of all the following vectors: $a^n_B + a^t_B + a^n_{CB} + a^t_{CB}$.

zontally (as in the previous example, the slider is physically restricted to horizontal motion) until it intersects the vector a^t_{CB}. The point of intersection determines the magnitudes of a^t_{CB} and a_C; it is labeled c'.

Scaling the vectors in Fig. 3C, we obtain the slider acceleration

$$a_C = 70 \ \frac{\text{in}}{\text{sec}^2} \quad \text{to the left,}$$

and the tangential component of relative acceleration

$$a^t_{CB} = 173 \ \frac{\text{in}}{\text{sec}^2} \quad \text{upward and to the right.}$$

From the latter acceleration, we can also obtain the angular acceleration of the connecting rod

$$\alpha_2 = \frac{a^t_{CB}}{CB} = 46 \ \frac{\text{rad}}{\text{sec}^2} \quad \text{counterclockwise.}$$

Acceleration Image

In the above example problem, we determined the accelerations of the crankpin B and the slider C. We may also wish to find the acceleration of another point on the crank or connecting rod. The acceleration of the center of gravity, for example, would be needed to make a dynamic analysis of a link, or in a more complicated linkage, an intermediate point on a link which serves as a connecting point would be investigated. The acceleration polygon alone cannot determine the acceleration of such a point. We must therefore resort to the image method (similar to the velocity image method) in order to find the acceleration of a point which does not lie on line *BC*.

Consider any three points *B*, *C* and *D* which lie on the same rigid link shown in Fig. 4A. Let the link have an angular velocity ω_2 and an angular acceleration α_2. Then, the magnitudes of accelerations are:

$$a^n{}_{CB} = \omega_2{}^2 BC \quad \text{and} \quad a^t{}_{CB} = \alpha_2 BC \ .$$

The total acceleration of *C* with respect to *B*, a_{CB}, is the vector sum of its normal and tangential components. Its magnitude is given by the expression

$$a_{CB} = b'c' = \sqrt{(a^n{}_{CB})^2 + (a^t{}_{CB})^2}$$
$$= \sqrt{(\omega_2{}^2 BC)^2 + (\alpha_2 BC)^2}$$

from which

$$b'c' = BC \sqrt{\omega_2{}^4 + \alpha_2{}^2}.$$

Similarly, the other relative acceleration magnitudes for the connecting rod are

$$b'd' = BD \sqrt{\omega_2{}^4 + \alpha_2{}^2} \ \text{and}$$
$$c'd' = CD \sqrt{\omega_2{}^4 + \alpha_2{}^2}$$

from which we obtain the convenient *acceleration image* relationships:

$$\frac{b'd'}{b'c'} = \frac{BD}{BC} \ , \quad \frac{c'd'}{b'c'} = \frac{CD}{BC} \ , \quad \text{and} \quad \frac{b'd'}{c'd'} = \frac{BD}{CD} \ . \tag{6}$$

Equations (6) may be summarized by stating that triangle *b'c'd'* (the acceleration image of *BCD*) is similar to triangle *BCD* for any points *B*, *C*, and *D* on the same rigid link. The angle relationship between a line connecting two points on a rigid link and their relative acceleration depends on the angular acceleration α and the angular velocity ω, and is the same for any pair of points on the same rigid link. In the example problems which follow, we will utilize this relationship without having to calculate α and ω.

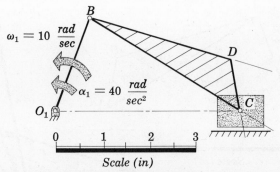

FIG. 4A. The slider crank mechanism of Fig. 3 is repeated here. The dimensions of the linkage and the motion of the crank remain unchanged. We are interested in finding the acceleration of any point *D* on the connecting rod other than points *B* and *C*.

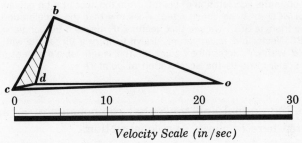

FIG. 4B. The velocity polygon for the slider crank mechanism, showing the velocity image of the connecting rod.

EXAMPLE—PROBLEM 4: Three points, *B*, *C*, and *D*, lie on the rigid link in Fig. 4A, but do not lie on a straight line. Using the acceleration image method, find the acceleration of point *D* of the mechanism, using the data and the scales given on the illustration.

Solution: This problem and the problem of Fig. 3 are identical except for the addition of an arbitrary point, *D*. The velocity polygon, including the velocity image, is constructed (Fig. 4B) as described in Chapter Two. The acceleration polygon *o′b′c′* (Fig. 4C) is taken directly from

Mechanism

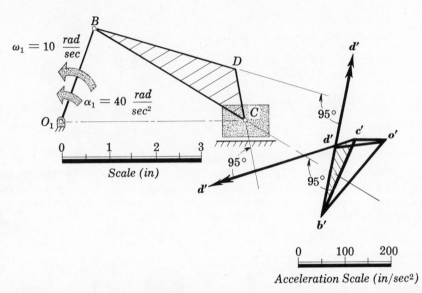

FIG. 4C. To obtain the acceleration of point D from the acceleration polygon, the acceleration image of BCD must be constructed. We know that the acceleration image will be *similar* to the triangle BCD. We see that vector $c'd'$ makes a 95° angle with the orientation of link BC. Vector $b'd'$ is, therefore, drawn to form a 95° angle with CD. The intersection of $b'd'$ with $c'd'$ determines point d'. The length of $o'd'$, measured against the acceleration scale, gives us the acceleration of point D.

Fig. 3, but the normal and tangential components of a_B and a_{CB} have been omitted here to clarify the construction.

We observe in Fig. 4C that the relative acceleration vector $b'c'$ (forming one leg of the required acceleration image) lies in the direction of line BC rotated approximately 95° counterclockwise. Since the acceleration image $b'c'd'$ and link BCD are similar triangles, we know that each leg of the acceleration image will make a 95° angle with its respective side in the linkage drawing. Beginning at b', we construct the acceleration image by first drawing trial vector $b'd'$, its direction determined by rotating line BD 95° counterclockwise. Then, trial vector $c'd'$ is drawn from point c', its direction is also found by rotating line CD 95° counterclockwise. Point d' is thus determined by the intersection of trial vectors $b'd'$ and $c'd'$ as in Fig. 4C, completing triangle $b'c'd'$, the acceleration image of link BCD on the acceleration polygon. The acceleration of D is thus given by vector $o'd'$. Using the acceleration scale, we find that $a_D = o'd' = 113$ in/sec^2, slightly downward to the left.

184

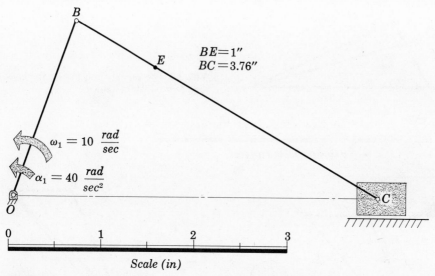

$BE = 1''$
$BC = 3.76''$

$\omega_1 = 10 \dfrac{rad}{sec}$

$\alpha_1 = 40 \dfrac{rad}{sec^2}$

Scale (in)

FIG. 5A. Fig. 3 is again repeated. We want to find the acceleration of a point *E* lying on line *BC*.

EXAMPLE—PROBLEM 5: In this problem we are required to find the acceleration of point *E*, which lies *on* the line *BC*, Fig. 5A.

Solution: Again, this problem and the problem of Fig. 3 are identical except for the addition of a point *E* along line (link) *BC*. We are again spared the necessity of constructing the velocity and acceleration polygons for the mechanism. In problems of this type, however, the student will make both constructions as a matter of course. See Figs. 5B and 5C. Construction of the velocity polygon is discussed in Chapter Two and the acceleration polygon *o'b'c'* is again taken directly from Fig. 3. This problem is simpler than the preceding problem because no additional construction is necessary after the acceleration polygon is constructed. Since point *E* lies on line *BC* we know that *e'* must lie somewhere on vector *b'c'*. A proportion similar to one of Equations (6) gives us the desired acceleration image relationship:

$$\frac{b'e'}{b'c'} = \frac{BE}{BC}$$

185

Mechanism

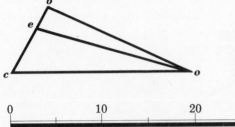

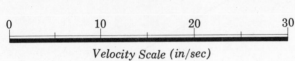

Velocity Scale (in/sec)

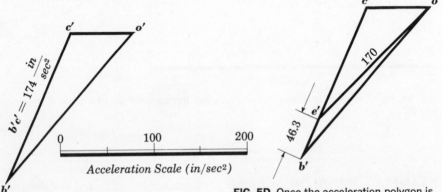

Acceleration Scale (in/sec²)

FIG. 5C. The acceleration polygon for the linkage at the instant shown.

FIG. 5D. Once the acceleration polygon is constructed, the position of **e′** (which must lie along **b′c′**) is quickly determined by the proportion **b′e′/b′c′ = BE/BC.** Drawing vector **o′e′** then gives us the magnitude and direction of the acceleration of E.

from which the acceleration of E relative to B is

$$b'e' = b'c' \; \frac{BE}{BC} \; = (174 \; \frac{in}{sec^2} \;) \; (\; \frac{1 \, in}{3.76 \, in}) = 46.3 \; \frac{in}{sec^2} \; .$$

This locates point e' on line $b'c'$. (Note that e' lies between b' and c' just as E lies between B and C). Vector $o'e'$ is then drawn to obtain the acceleration of E, as shown in Fig. 5D. Measuring $o'e'$ against the acceleration scale we obtain:

$$a_E = o'e' = 170 \; \frac{in}{sec^2} \quad \text{to the left and downward.}$$

186

The acceleration image principle discussed in Example Problems 4 and 5 (as well as the velocity image examined in Chapter Two) apply to a set of points on any rigid link, whether the link acts as a crank rotating about a fixed point or as a connecting rod. The only restriction is that the set of points considered must all lie on the same rigid link.

Analysis of the Four Bar Linkage

The acceleration analysis of a four bar linkage requires no new concepts. Referring to Fig. 6, for example, we may again relate accelerations by vector Equation (5)

$$a_C = a_B + a_{CB}$$

just as for the slider crank mechanism, but with one additional complication. Each of the above acceleration vectors will have, in general, both a normal and tangential component and the "long form" of Equation (5) should again be used:

$$a_C = a^n{}_C + a^t{}_C = a^n{}_B + a^t{}_B + a^n{}_{CB} + a^t{}_{CB}.$$

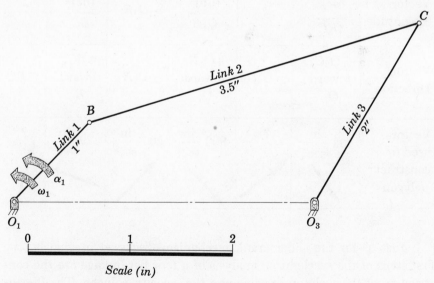

FIG. 6A. The skeleton drawing of a four bar linkage. We are again required to find the acceleration of point C using the relationship $a_C = a_B + a_{CB}$.

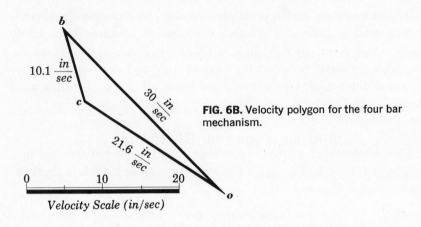

FIG. 6B. Velocity polygon for the four bar mechanism.

TABLE 3. VECTOR TABULATION FOR THE ACCELERATION ANALYSIS OF A FOUR BAR MECHANISM, FIG. 6.

Vector	a^n_C	$+ a^t_C$	$= a^n_B$	$+ a^t_B$	$+ a^n_{CB}$	$+ a^t_{CB}$
Vector Magnitude	$\dfrac{(oc)^2}{O_3C}$	?	$\dfrac{(ob)^2}{O_1B}$	$\alpha_1 O_1 B$	$\dfrac{(bc)^2}{BC}$	?
Vector Direction	$\parallel O_3C$, toward O_3	$\perp O_3C$	$\parallel O_1B$, toward O_1	$\perp O_1B$	$\parallel BC$, toward B	$\perp BC$
Vectors used to construct polygon	$233 \dfrac{\text{in}}{\text{sec}^2}$	?	$900 \dfrac{\text{in}}{\text{sec}^2}$	$200 \dfrac{\text{in}}{\text{sec}^2}$	$29 \dfrac{\text{in}}{\text{sec}^2}$	?

Just as for the slider crank mechanism discussed previously, the first steps of the acceleration analysis of a four bar linkage are the construction of the skeleton drawing and the velocity polygon. The dimensions taken from the scaled skeleton drawing (Fig. 6A) together with the velocities taken from the velocity polygon (Fig. 6B) allow us to calculate the normal components of acceleration of the links which, as we have seen, are usually the starting point for the acceleration polygon.

Acceleration vector directions and, where they can be determined, vector magnitudes are tabulated as in Table 3. The normal and tangential components of the acceleration vectors are, of course, along or perpendicular to the links. The magnitudes of the *normal* components are determined as already indicated. On the other hand, the magnitudes of the *tangential* components cannot be determined unless the total acceleration of a point, or the angular acceleration of the link and the distance of the point considered from the axis of rotation, is given. The magnitudes of the remaining components are therefore determined from the scaled acceleration polygon.

Again, while the acceleration vector table is not essential to the construction of the acceleration polygon, it is a convenient means of keeping track of the various vector components. It is a check list against which to compare the orientation of the acceleration polygon. This methodical approach helps to minimize confusion.

EXAMPLE—PROBLEM 6: Fig. 6A shows a four bar linkage for which an acceleration analysis will be made. The lengths of all of the links are indicated on the skeleton drawing. The crank has an angular velocity $\omega_1 = 30$ rad/sec and an angular acceleration $\alpha_1 = 200$ rad/sec^2.

Solution: The velocity polygon is constructed in Fig. 6B after selection of a suitable scale. The velocities are then indicated directly on the velocity polygon. The skeleton drawing, Fig. 6A, and the velocity polygon, Fig. 6B, give us the information needed to determine the normal components of acceleration. Given the angular acceleration of link 1, we can also calculate the tangential component of acceleration for point B. We can now put together our acceleration vector table (Table 3) and begin the construction of the acceleration polygon. Velocities *ob, oc* and *bc* are taken from the velocity polygon, Fig. 6B.

We will now construct the acceleration polygon, Fig. 6C, adding the vectors in the order indicated by Table 3. Beginning at the pole point o', we draw $a^n{}_C$ to the scale selected. To $a^n{}_C$ we add the trial vector $a^t{}_C$. The head of $a^t{}_C$ may be labeled c', but we do not as yet know the true magnitude of that vector. Again beginning at o', we add the

189

Mechanism

$$Calculations \qquad\qquad Measured\ Values$$

$$a^n{}_B = \frac{(ob)^2}{O_1B} = 900\ \frac{in}{sec^2}\ (\parallel O_1B\ toward\ O_1)$$

$$a^t{}_B = \alpha_1 O_1 B = 200\ \frac{in}{sec^2}\ (\perp O_1B,\ upward\ and\ to\ the\ left)$$

$$a^n{}_{CB} = \frac{(bc)^2}{BC} = 29\ \frac{in}{sec^2}\ (\parallel BC\ toward\ B)$$

$$a^n{}_C = \frac{(oc)^2}{O_3C} = 233\ \frac{in}{sec^2}\ (\parallel O_3C\ toward\ O_3)$$

$$a^t{}_{CB} = 930\ \frac{in}{sec^2}$$

$$a^t{}_C = 1110\ \frac{in}{sec^2}$$

$$a_C = 1130\ \frac{in}{sec^2}$$

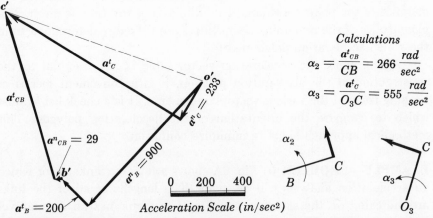

$$Calculations$$

$$\alpha_2 = \frac{a^t{}_{CB}}{CB} = 266\ \frac{rad}{sec^2}$$

$$\alpha_3 = \frac{a^t{}_C}{O_3C} = 555\ \frac{rad}{sec^2}$$

FIG. 6C. Acceleration polygon for the four bar mechanism. The presence of the many vectors makes a method of tabulation of the various vectors desirable to ensure correct vector addition and orientation.

vectors on the right side of Equation (5) in the order indicated. The sum $a^n{}_B + a^t{}_B = a_B$ (or $o'b'$); thus the head of $a^t{}_B$ is labeled b'. Adding the last two of the four vectors on the right side of the equation, which includes trial vector $a^t{}_{CB}$, we again obtain a_C (or $o'c'$). Point c' is located at the intersection of the trial vectors $a^t{}_C$ and $a^t{}_{CB}$, completing the polygon and determining in turn the magnitude of each tangential component. Thus, $a^t{}_C = 1110$ in/sec and $a^t{}_{CB} = 930$ in/sec^2. Using the acceleration scale, we can obtain the acceleration of point C:

$$a_C = a^n{}_C + a^t{}_C = o'c' = 1130\ \frac{in}{sec^2}$$

to the left and upward.

190

Using the tangential acceleration of point C, we can find the angular acceleration of link 3 (O_3C). From Equation (3), $a^t{}_C = r_3\alpha_3$, therefore

$$\alpha_3 = \frac{a^t{}_C}{O_3C} = \frac{1110 \text{ in/sec}^2}{2 \text{ in}} = 555 \ \frac{\text{rad}}{\text{sec}^2} \quad \text{counterclockwise.}$$

Similarly, the angular acceleration of link 2 (BC) is found using the same equation:

$$\alpha_2 = \frac{a^t{}_{CB}}{CB} = \frac{930 \text{ in/sec}^2}{3.5 \text{ in}} = 266 \ \frac{\text{rad}}{\text{sec}^2} \quad \text{counterclockwise.}$$

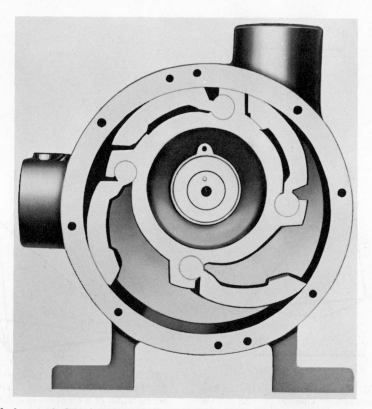

FIG. 7A. A curved-wing air pump. Air is carried from inlet to outlet by the curved wings which are held against the housing by acceleration forces. (Leiman Bros., Inc.)

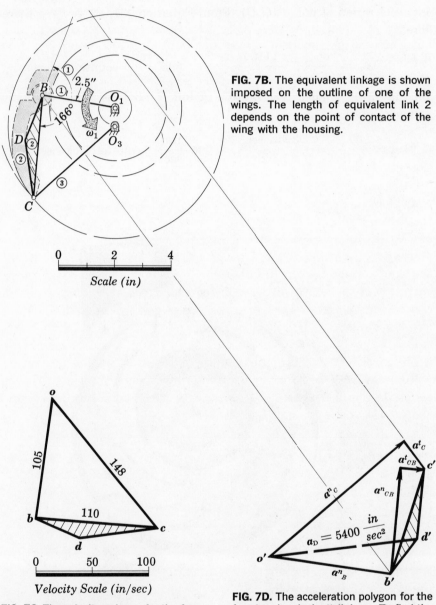

FIG. 7B. The equivalent linkage is shown imposed on the outline of one of the wings. The length of equivalent link 2 depends on the point of contact of the wing with the housing.

Scale (in)

Velocity Scale (in/sec)

FIG. 7C. The velocity polygon for the four bar (equivalent) linkage. To find the velocity of point *D* the velocity image of link 2 must be constructed.

FIG. 7D. The acceleration polygon for the four bar (equivalent) linkage. To find the acceleration of a point on link 2, the acceleration image of the link must be constructed.

Equivalent Linkages

Equivalent linkages are sometimes very useful in the acceleration analysis of actual mechanisms. Fig. 7A illustrates a commercially available curved-wing air pump, a mechanism which is obviously not a four bar linkage. The pump has four evenly spaced wings, but for purposes of analysis we need only consider the motion of one of these wings. The key to arriving at an equivalent linkage is to consider the forces acting on the mechanism and the restraints which restrict the mechanism to its specific path. These forces and restraints are replaced by links which are arranged so that the linkage duplicates the motion of the actual mechanism.

Fig. 7B shows only one of the four wings (dashed lines) and its equivalent linkage for the instant shown (solid lines). Link 1 represents the driver crank and link 2 the wing. Point O_3 is the geometric center of the housing, and link 3 represents the distance from the center of the housing to the point of contact between wing and housing. (Actually, the wing is restrained by the rotational force of the pump to follow the curvature of the housing. At the instant being considered this restraint can be considered a rigid link which forces point C to rotate about a circle of radius O_3C.) Link 3 does not exist on the actual pump, but it is essential to the equivalent linkage. Note that the equivalent linkage we have devised is the familiar four bar linkage, and the mechanism will be analyzed as such. In the following example problem, we will assign dimensions to the pump, assume a reasonable rotating speed, and analyze the acceleration of this mechanism.

EXAMPLE—PROBLEM 7: The pump shown in Fig. 7A rotates at a constant 400 RPM. The wing pins rotate about a circle of radius 2.5 in. The pump is shown drawn to scale. Find the angular acceleration of the wing and the acceleration of its center of gravity.

Solution: The equivalent linkage is drawn as shown in Fig. 7B. The lengths of links 2 and 3 are obtained from the scale to which the skeleton drawing is made.

The velocity polygon, Fig. 7C, is based on the given speed of 400 RPM and a given length of 2.5 in for link 1. The velocity polygon represents the solution to the vector equation

$$v_C = v_B + v_{CB} \quad \text{or} \quad oc = ob + bc.$$

Point D of our equivalent linkage represents the center of gravity of the curved wing. Equivalent link 2 (BCD) forms the velocity image bcd on the velocity polygon. (This example is intended only to illustrate principles of acceleration analysis; the convenient location of the center of gravity would not, in reality, correspond to the true center of gravity of the wing, and the dimensions used do not correspond to an actual pump.) The velocities of B and C and the relative velocity bc shown on the velocity polygon are obtained in the usual manner, and are used to construct the basic acceleration polygon $o'b'c'$ in the order tabulated below (Table 4).

The magnitudes of the normal accelerations as calculated for Table 4 indicate the need for an acceleration scale on the order of 1 in $= 2000$ in/sec². Since link 1 rotates at constant angular velocity (no angular acceleration), $a^n{}_B$ represents the total acceleration of point B, $o'b'$. Beginning with this acceleration, we draw $o'b'$ parallel to O_1B. To it, we add known relative acceleration $a^n{}_{CB}$ parallel to BC, and trial vector

TABLE 4. VECTOR TABULATION FOR THE ACCELERATION ANALYSIS OF THE AIR PUMP EQUIVALENT LINKAGE

Vector	$a^n{}_C$	$+ a^t{}_C$	$= a^n{}_B$	$+ a^t{}_B$	$+ a^n{}_{CB}$	$+ a^t{}_{CB}$
Vector Magnitude	$\dfrac{(oc)^2}{O_3C}$	?	$\dfrac{(ob)^2}{O_1B}$	$\alpha_1 O_1 B$	$\dfrac{(bc)^2}{BC}$	?
Vector Direction	$\parallel O_3C$ toward O_3	$\perp O_3C$	$\parallel O_1B$ toward O_1	$\perp O_1B$ when $\alpha_1 \neq 0$	$\parallel BC$ toward B	$\perp BC$
Vectors used to construct polygon	$6080 \dfrac{\text{in}}{\text{sec}^2}$	?	$4400 \dfrac{\text{in}}{\text{sec}^2}$	0 for $\alpha_1 = 0$	$3560 \dfrac{\text{in}}{\text{sec}^2}$	?

194

$a^t{}_{CB}$ perpendicular to BC, as shown in Fig. 7D. This completes the addition of the vectors on the right side of the equation.

Starting again at pole point o', we draw the known acceleration $a^n{}_C$ parallel to O_3C. To it, we add trial vector $a^t{}_C$ perpendicular to O_3C. The basic acceleration equation is satisfied when we locate c' at the intersection of the trial vectors $a^t{}_C$ and $a^t{}_{CB}$. The angular acceleration of the wing is then given by

$$\alpha_2 = \frac{a^t{}_{CB}}{CB} = 265 \, \frac{\text{rad}}{\text{sec}^2} \text{ counterclockwise}$$

using values for $a^t{}_{CB}$ and BC scaled from the illustration.

To find the acceleration of the center of gravity, D, we will have to construct the acceleration image of link 2. Points B,C, and the center of gravity, D, all lie on the same rigid link, permitting us to use the *acceleration image principle* to find a_D. Points b' and c' on the acceleration polygon are joined to form the image of BC. Using a protractor, we see that the orientation of $b'c'$ on the acceleration polygon is given by rotating BC on the skeleton linkage 166° counterclockwise. Similarly, BD and CD are rotated 166° counterclockwise to obtain the directions of $b'd'$ and $c'd'$ respectively. The acceleration image is thereby completed, locating d' at the intersection of $b'd'$ and $c'd'$. Vector $o'd'$ represents the total acceleration of the center of gravity of the wing, point D. Measuring vector $o'd'$ on the acceleration scale, we obtain

$$a_D = 5400 \text{ in/sec}^2 \text{ to the right and slightly upward.}$$

The construction used in the above problem (rotating the links to determine the position of the acceleration image) is equivalent to simply transferring angles BCD and CBD to the acceleration polygon (as angles $b'c'd'$ and $c'b'd'$ respectively). The acceleration image $b'c'd'$ is similar to the link BCD, identical except for size and orientation. However, it is not reflected, i.e., since we read BCD going around the link clockwise, $b'c'd'$ must appear in that same order, reading clockwise around the acceleration image.

The equivalent linkage which we have used to analyze the air pump of Fig. 7A is valid for any instant, so long as point C on the wing contacts the housing. It may not be used, however, for the portion of the cycle when point C leaves the housing (See the wing at the top of the mechanism in Fig. 7A.)

Analysis of Sliding Contact Linkages

Coriolis Acceleration

In the preceding sections we considered the acceleration of a slider moving along a fixed path (e.g., a piston in a cylinder) and we also considered the acceleration of a point on a rotating link (e.g., either of the pin joints in a four bar linkage). We will now look into the case of a link which slides along a rotating member. When these two conditions are met (a rotating path and a point which has a velocity relative to that path), there exists an additional acceleration component, Coriolis acceleration. Thus, the total acceleration of a point on the slider in Fig. 8 consists of

- (a) normal and tangential accelerations of a coincident point on the rotating link,
- (b) relative acceleration of the slider along the rotating link, and
- (c) *Coriolis acceleration* which will be shown to equal $2v\omega$ where v is the velocity of the slider relative to a coincident point on the rotating link and ω is the instantaneous angular velocity of the link.

Coriolis acceleration is a more difficult concept than normal and tangential acceleration. Its complete presentation requires a somewhat more sophisticated approach to vector analysis than that which we have been using. At this point, a rigorous presentation is not essential to the

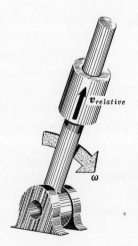

FIG. 8. Sliding contact along a rotating path. In this special case, an additional component of acceleration, *Coriolis acceleration*, is required to describe the motion of the slider.

correct use of Coriolis acceleration in solving problems with the acceleration polygon. The student may, however, examine the material on Coriolis acceleration found in Appendix A—Vectors if he wishes a more rigorous presentation than that offered in the following paragraphs.

It is important to recognize that the acceleration of a slider moving along a rotating path is not fully described by (a) and (b) above. A change in radius of the slider and a change in direction of the relative velocity vector produce the additional acceleration component referred to as Coriolis acceleration.

Fig. 9A shows a slider on a rotating link. In the first view (dashed lines) the slider is a distance r from the pivot. The velocity of a coincident point on the rotating link is $r\omega$. A second velocity vector, v, which represents the velocity of the slider relative to the rotating link, is added to velocity vector $r\omega$. A second view, representing the system an instant later, is superimposed on the first. For simplicity, ω and v are constant in magnitude for this problem. The later velocity vector sum includes the effect of a change in radius (vdt, the increase in distance of the slider from the pin in time dt), and a change in direction of the rotating link, ωdt.

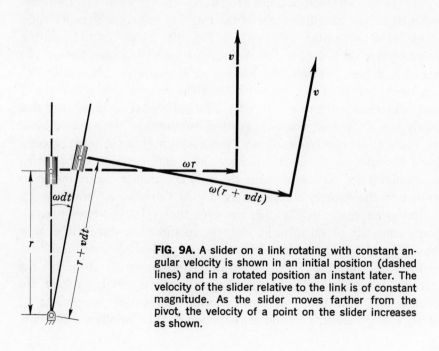

FIG. 9A. A slider on a link rotating with constant angular velocity is shown in an initial position (dashed lines) and in a rotated position an instant later. The velocity of the slider relative to the link is of constant magnitude. As the slider moves farther from the pivot, the velocity of a point on the slider increases as shown.

Mechanism

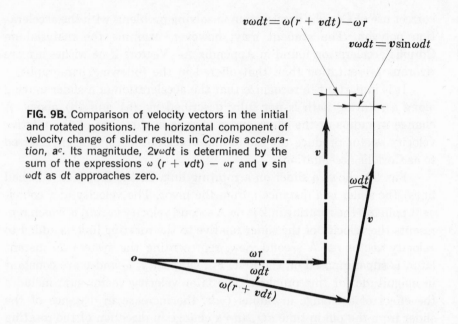

$$v\omega dt = \omega(r + vdt) - \omega r$$

$$v\omega dt = v\sin\omega dt$$

FIG. 9B. Comparison of velocity vectors in the initial and rotated positions. The horizontal component of velocity change of slider results in *Coriolis acceleration, a^c.* Its magnitude, $2v\omega dt$ is determined by the sum of the expressions ω $(r + vdt) - \omega r$ and **v** $\sin \omega dt$ as dt approaches zero.

Let us consider components of velocity change in a direction perpendicular to the initial position of the rotating link (i.e., velocity components in a horizontal direction) in Fig. 9B. In the initial position (shown by dashed lines), a point coincident with the slider, but on the rotating link, has a velocity ωr. During an infinitesimal interval dt the slider moves outward a distance vdt, and the corresponding velocity of a new coincident point is ω $(r + vdt)$. The horizontal component of this velocity is ω $(r + vdt)$ $\cos \omega dt$. For the infinitesimal time period however, $\cos \omega dt$ approaches unity and the above horizontal velocity component becomes $\omega r + \omega vdt$ (to first order differentials). Subtracting the original value, ωr, we obtain the velocity change ωvdt, one contribution to the velocity change referred to as Coriolis acceleration.

Referring again to Fig. 9B, we note that relative velocity **v,** although constant in magnitude, changes in direction during the time interval. In its initial position, relative velocity **v** has no horizontal component. After rotation, it has a horizontal component, given by the expression **v** $\sin \omega dt$. For an infinitesimal time interval, $\sin \omega dt$ approaches ωdt and thus we have another horizontal component of velocity change, ωvdt, a second contribution to the Coriolis acceleration.

198

The two vector velocity sums are compared in Fig. 9B. The total change in velocity in the direction perpendicular to the link is

$$2\,v\omega dt.$$

Dividing by the time interval dt, we obtain equation for the Coriolis acceleration

$$a^c = 2\,v\omega \qquad (7)$$

where v is the velocity of a point on the slider with respect to a coincident point on the rotating link and ω is the angular velocity of the link on which the slider travels. The direction of a^c is given by rotating the velocity vector 90° in the direction of ω. In this case, vector v is upward, ω is clockwise, and a^c is to the right.

As can be seen in the illustration, the velocity change also has a vertical component. It is the normal acceleration $a^n = \omega^2 r$ which is directed toward the center of rotation. If we permitted ω and v to vary in magnitude, two additional acceleration components would be present: $a^t = r\alpha$, perpendicular to the link, and relative acceleration a^r along the link. The above analysis is based on infinitesimal changes which take place during an infinitesimal time period, whereas Fig. 9 must depict finite changes in angles and velocities. Thus, the illustration is representative of the actual process, but not exact.

EXAMPLE—PROBLEM 8: Link 1 in Fig. 10 has an angular velocity $\omega_1 = 20$ rad/sec clockwise. The velocity of point B_2 on the slider with respect to a coincident point on link 1 is $v_{B2B1} = 30$ in/sec. Find the Coriolis acceleration.

Solution: The Coriolis component of slider acceleration is given by

$$a^c{}_{B2B1} = 2\,\omega_1\,v_{B2B1} = 2\,(30\,\frac{\text{in}}{\text{sec}})(20\,\frac{\text{rad}}{\text{sec}}) = 1200\,\frac{\text{in}}{\text{sec}^2}\,.$$

The direction of $a^c{}_{B2B1}$ is found by rotating relative velocity vector v_{B2B1} in the direction of ω_1 (clockwise) by 90°. In this example, $a^c{}_{B2B1}$ is to the left and upward as shown.

Mechanism

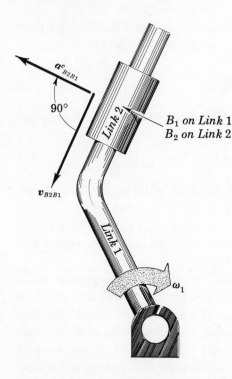

$a^c_{B_2B_1}$

$90°$

Link 2

B_1 on Link 1
B_2 on Link 2

$v_{B_2B_1}$

Link 1

ω_1

FIG. 10. Coriolis acceleration. The *direction* of Coriolis acceleration is found by rotating the relative velocity vector 90° in the direction of the angular velocity.

Using Coriolis Acceleration in Solving Sliding Contact Linkage Problems

The slider in the mechanism of Fig. 11A travels along link 1 which rotates. Thus, Coriolis acceleration is involved in an analysis of this linkage. To find the angular acceleration of link 1 in this problem, we will have to find the tangential acceleration of B_1. The acceleration polygon, which includes this time the Coriolis acceleration component, is again the method of solution.

Velocities were computed for this linkage in Chapter Two. The link numbers have been changed here to conform with the example in this section. We have from the velocity polygon (Fig. 11B):

$$v_{B1} = ob_1 = 11.7 \ \frac{\text{in}}{\text{sec}} \ \text{downward to the left}$$

$$v_{B2} = ob_2 = 36 \ \frac{\text{in}}{\text{sec}} \ \text{upward to the left}$$

$$v_{B2B1} = b_1b_2 = 34 \ \frac{\text{in}}{\text{sec}} \ \text{upward to the left.}$$

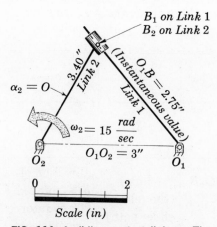

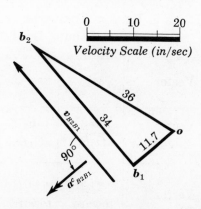

FIG. 11A. A sliding contact linkage. The acceleration analysis of the slider, in addition to determining normal and tangential accelerations, will require that we determine the relative and Coriolis accelerations.

FIG. 11B. The velocity polygon for the sliding contact linkage. When the direction of the relative velocity is determined, the direction of the Coriolis acceleration is found by rotating the relative velocity vector 90° in the direction of the angular velocity of the link on which the slider rides.

In solving for accelerations, we will express the acceleration of a point on the slider as the vector sum of the acceleration of a coincident point on link 1 *plus* the relative acceleration of the slider on the link *plus* Coriolis acceleration:

$$a^n_{B2} + a^t_{B2} = a^n_{B1} + a^t_{B1} + a^n_{B2B1} + a^t_{B2B1} + a^c_{B2B1}. \qquad (8)$$

In problems of this type several terms can often be eliminated from the equation, which simplifies the problems considerably. For the linkage of Fig. 11, the condition $\alpha_2 = 0$ eliminates the term a^t_{B2}. (If angular acceleration equals zero, there is no tangential acceleration.) The fact that link 1 (the relative path) is straight eliminates a^n_{B2B1}. (Since B_2 cannot rotate relative to B_1 there can be neither a relative angular velocity nor a normal component of relative acceleration).

We will now set up the vector table (Table 5) and proceed to solve for the remaining terms in the acceleration equation, Equation (8).

Since all vector directions are known and we require only two magnitudes, a^t_{B1} and a^t_{B2B1}, we are prepared to construct the acceleration polygon. Beginning at an arbitrary point o' on Fig. 11C, we draw a^n_{B2} to a convenient scale. Vector a^n_{B2} represents the total acceleration

201

TABLE 5. VECTOR TABULATION FOR THE ACCELERATION ANALYSIS OF A SLIDING CONTACT LINKAGE, FIG. 11

Vector	a^n_{B2}	$= a^n_{B1}$	$+ a^t_{B1}$	$+ a^t_{B2B1}$	$+ a^c_{B2B1}$
Vector Magnitude	$\dfrac{(ob_2)^2}{O_2B}$	$\dfrac{(ob_1)^2}{O_1B}$	?	?	$2(b_1b_2)\omega_1$
Vector Direction	$\parallel O_2B$ toward O_2	$\parallel O_1B$ toward O_1	$\perp O_1B$	$\parallel$ link 1 (the relative slider path)	direction of b_1b_2 rotated 90° counter-clockwise
Vectors used to construct polygon	$540 \dfrac{in}{sec^2}$ ↘	$50 \dfrac{in}{sec^2}$ ↘	? ↘	? ↘	$289 \dfrac{in}{sec^2}$ ↙

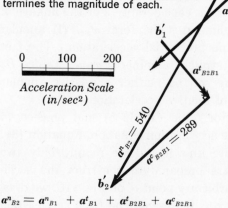

FIG. 11C. The acceleration polygon. After a^n_{B2}, a^n_{B1} and trial vector a^t_{B1} are drawn, we find that we must solve the problem "backwards." Starting at b'_2, a^c_{B2B1} is drawn to scale, with head at b'_2. Vector a^t_{B2B1} is drawn in the correct direction with its head starting at the tail of a^c_{B2B1}. The intersection of the trial vectors (the head of one with the tail of the other) determines the magnitude of each.

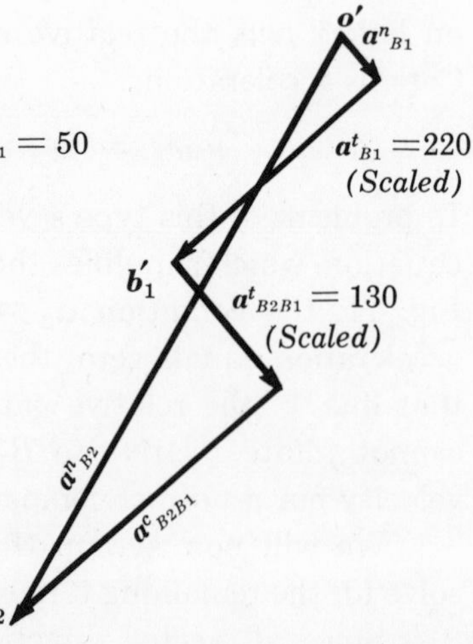

0   100   200

Acceleration Scale
(in/sec²)

$a^n_{B1} = 50$

a^t_{B1}

b'_1

a^t_{B2B1}

$a^n_{B2} = 540$

$a^c_{B2B1} = 289$

b'_2

$a^n_{B2} = a^n_{B1} + a^t_{B1} + a^t_{B2B1} + a^c_{B2B1}$

a^n_{B1}

$a^t_{B1} = 220$
(Scaled)

b'_1

$a^t_{B2B1} = 130$
(Scaled)

a^n_{B2}

a^c_{B2B1}

b'_2

FIG. 11D. The "cleaned-up" acceleration polygon. The trial vectors are measured against the acceleration scale and noted on the polygon.

of B_2 in this problem; the head of $a^n{}_{B2}$ is labeled b'_2. Then, working with the right side of the above equation and again beginning at o', we draw $a^n{}_{B1}$ and add trial vector $a^t{}_{B1}$.

It would be convenient to continue by adding $a^t{}_{B2B1}$, the next term in the equation, to the head of $a^t{}_{B1}$, but we do not know where to begin; the head of $a^t{}_{B1}$ has not been located. Instead, we observe that both sides of the equation represent $o'b'_2$, the acceleration of B_2. Then, the last term $a^c{}_{B2B1}$ may be put in its logical place, the head of $a^c{}_{B2B1}$ at point b'_2. Working backwards, the next to last term, trial vector $a^t{}_{B2B1}$, is placed with its head at the tail of $a^c{}_{B2B1}$. The intersection of the trial vectors locates the tail of $a^t{}_{B2B1}$ and head of $a^t{}_{B1}$ and we label that point b'_1. Fig. 11D shows the "cleaned up" acceleration polygon with scaled values of $a^t{}_{B1}$ and $a^t{}_{B2B1}$. Having obtained the tangential acceleration of B_1 the solution to the problem, the angular acceleration of link 1, is given by

$$\alpha_1 = \frac{a^t{}_{B1}}{O_1B} = \frac{220 \text{ in/sec}^2}{2.75 \text{ in}} = 80 \frac{\text{rad}}{\text{sec}^2} \cdot$$

Transferring tangential acceleration $a^t{}_{B1}$ to point B_1 on link 1, it is seen that α_1 is counterclockwise.

EXAMPLE—PROBLEM 9: The straight wing air pump (Fig. 12A) has four sliding vanes which are held against the housing by inertia forces. Let us examine a single vane (Fig. 12B) and find the acceleration of a point B on that vane.

Solution: The housing is circular and as long as the vane makes contact with the housing, the contact point will describe a circle. Thus, we may introduce (as we did in the equivalent linkage of Fig. 7) an artificial link 2 with its center at O_2 the center of the housing and its length equal to O_2B. The equivalent mechanism is shown in Fig. 12C where link 1 represents the vane guide with center of rotation O_1. Let the angular velocity of the vane guide be a constant value ω_1 (given).

Equation (8) is again the general equation for sliding contact problems of this type:

$$a^n{}_{B2} + a^t{}_{B2} = a^n{}_{B1} + a^t{}_{B1} + a^n{}_{B2B1} + a^t{}_{B2B1} + a^c{}_{B2B1}.$$

Mechanism

FIG. 12A. This straight wing air pump can be considered a sliding contact mechanism. This machine is used as a compressor or vacuum pump and is operated at 500-1500 RPM. Acceleration forces hold the four sliding vanes against the housing. (Leiman Bros., Inc.)

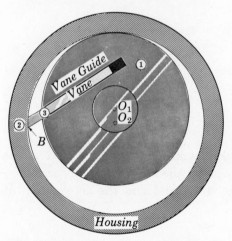

FIG. 12B. A single vane of the pump is examined. To arrive at an equivalent linkage for this mechanism, the motions and restraints must be clearly understood. Then, the rotor becomes link 1, the housing which limits the travel of the sliding vane becomes link 2, and the sliding vane becomes a slider at a fixed distance from O_2 and sliding along link 1.

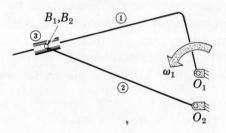

FIG. 12C. The equivalent linkage for the mechanism at the instant shown.

The given data for this problem differs only slightly from that given in the previous problem of Fig. 11. In this case angular velocity ω_1 is constant for the vane guide (link 1); the angular acceleration of B_1, α_1, is therefore zero and we can eliminate the term for the tangential acceleration, $a^t_{B1} = 0$. As in the preceding problem, because the path of B_2 relative to B_1 is straight (B_1 is on link 1 and B_2 slides along link 1), there is no relative rotation. We can therefore again eliminate the term for the normal component of relative acceleration from the above equation, $a^n_{B2B1} = 0$. In this problem, the angular acceleration α_2 of equivalent link 2 is unknown and the tangential component of acceleration for B_2, a^t_{B2}, will not, in general, equal zero.

TABLE 6. VECTOR TABULATION FOR THE ACCELERATION OF THE AIR PUMP EQUIVALENT LINKAGE, FIG. 12

Vector	a^n_{B2}	$+ a^t_{B2}$	$= a^n_{B1}$	$+ a^c_{B2B1}$	$+ a^t_{B2B1}$
Vector Magnitude	$\dfrac{(ob_2)^2}{O_2B}$	?	$\dfrac{(ob_1)^2}{O_1B}$	$2(b_1b_2)\omega_1$	?
Vector Direction	$\| O_2B$ toward O_2	$\perp O_2B$	$\| O_1B$ toward O_1	$\perp$ path of slider on link 1. (Found by rotating b_1b_2 90° in direction of ω_1.)	$\|$ path of slider on link 1.

Equation (8) can now be rewritten without the eliminated terms, as in Table 6. The components making up the acceleration polygon are handled most easily when added in the order indicated in the table. After we specify ω_1 and construct a velocity polygon, we may substitute in the above equations and construct the acceleration polygon for the straight wing air pump.

Analyzing Combinations of Basic Linkages

In most cases, mechanisms made up of six or more links may be broken down into simple basic linkages and solved in a straightforward manner for velocities and accelerations. As an example, let us find slider acceleration in the *toggle mechanism,* Fig. 13A. The velocity polygon, Fig. 13B, is constructed according to the methods given in Chapter Two. Using values from the velocity polygon, we will proceed to construct the acceleration polygon for *part* of the toggle mechanism, the four bar linkage made up of links 1, 2, 3 and the frame. If link 1 rotates at constant angular velocity, $a^t_B = 0$, and the by now familiar acceleration equation for a four bar mechanism, Equation (5), reduces to the equation shown in Table 7A. Noting the magnitudes of the accelerations as

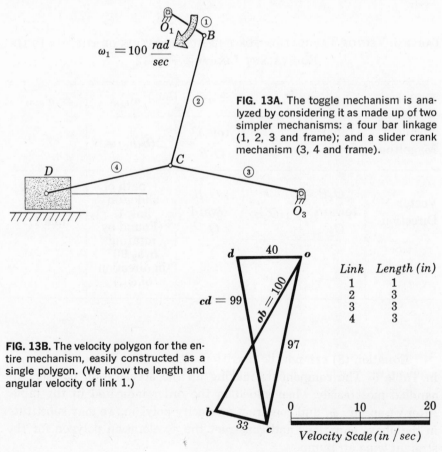

$$\omega_1 = 100 \, \frac{rad}{sec}$$

FIG. 13A. The toggle mechanism is analyzed by considering it as made up of two simpler mechanisms: a four bar linkage (1, 2, 3 and frame); and a slider crank mechanism (3, 4 and frame).

FIG. 13B. The velocity polygon for the entire mechanism, easily constructed as a single polygon. (We know the length and angular velocity of link 1.)

$cd = 99$

$ob \parallel 100$

40

97

33

Link	Length (in)
1	1
2	3
3	3
4	3

0   10   20

Velocity Scale (in / sec)

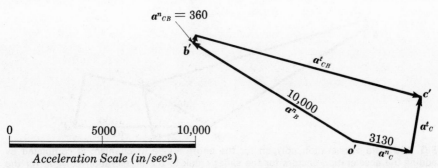

FIG. 13C. The acceleration polygon for the four bar linkage portion of the toggle mechanism.

TABLE 7A. PART ONE OF THE VECTOR TABULATION FOR THE ACCELERATION POLYGON FOR THE TOGGLE MECHANISM OF FIG. 13.

Vector	a^n_C	$+ a^t_C$	$= a^n_B$	$+ a^n_{CB}$	$+ a^t_{CB}$
Vector Magnitude	$\dfrac{(oc)^2}{O_3C}$	?	$\dfrac{(ob)^2}{O_1B}$	$\dfrac{(bc)^2}{BC}$	?
Vector Direction	$\parallel O_3C$ toward O_3	$\perp O_3C$	$\parallel O_1B$ toward O_1	$\parallel BC$ toward B	$\perp BC$
Vectors used to construct polygon	$3130\ \dfrac{in}{sec^2}$	?	$10{,}000\ \dfrac{in}{sec^2}$	$360\ \dfrac{in}{sec^2}$	?

indicated in Table 7A, a convenient scale is selected. An acceleration polygon is drawn for the four bar linkage made up of links 1, 2, 3 and the frame, using the above vectors. See Fig. 13C. The two unknown tangential components, a^t_C and a^t_{CB}, may then be scaled from the completed polygon.

207

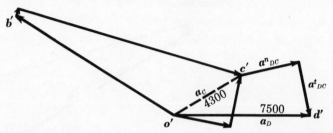

FIG. 13D. The acceleration polygon for the entire toggle mechanism is completed by adding the acceleration vectors for the slider crank to the acceleration polygon for the four bar mechanism.

TABLE 7B. PART TWO OF THE VECTOR TABULATION FOR THE ACCELERATION POLYGON FOR THE TOGGLE MECHANISM OF FIG. 13.

Vector	$a_D =$	a_C	$+ a^n_{DC}$	$+ a^t_{DC}$
Vector Magnitude	?	vector $o'c'$ already found (Fig. 13C)	$\dfrac{(cd)^2}{CD}$	?
Vector Direction	along slider path	See Fig. 13C	$\parallel CD$ toward C	$\perp CD$
Vectors used to construct polygon	? ⟶	$4300 \dfrac{\text{in}}{\text{sec}^2}$ ⟋	$3270 \dfrac{\text{in}}{\text{sec}^2}$ ⟋	? ↓

To complete the acceleration analysis we must now consider the rest of the mechanism—the slider crank made up of links 3, 4 and the frame. We can set up the general equation for the slider acceleration, a_D, as equal to the acceleration of point C plus the acceleration of D with respect to C, which is simply Equation (5) again. The formula is given in Table 7B.

We can either construct a separate acceleration polygon for the slider crank part of the toggle mechanism to find a_D, or we can simply add to the polygon constructed in the first half of the problem. The latter method is usually more convenient. In this case, for example, the first vector of the slider crank acceleration polygon, a_C, has already been constructed in the four bar polygon, Fig. 13C. Adding these vectors to the acceleration polygon in Fig. 13C then, we find slider acceleration $a_D = 7500$ in/sec^2 to the right (measured on the completed acceleration polygon, Fig. 13D). Slider acceleration direction (*o′d′* on the acceleration polygon) is opposite the slider velocity direction (*od* from the velocity polygon); i.e., the slider is slowing down.

Limiting Positions

Limiting positions of the slider crank mechanism and the crank rocker mechanism were discussed in Chapter One. As the driver crank rotates continuously, the follower link (slider or driven crank) stops and changes direction at the limiting position. At the limiting position, the follower velocity is zero, but the follower acceleration, in general, is *not* equal to zero. When analyzing linkages at their limiting positions, it is important to obtain the relative velocities for use in the acceleration equation.

Consider, for example, the in-line slider crank mechanism, (Fig. 14A) with the crank rotating at a constant angular velocity ω. In the limiting position, Fig. 14B, crank pin velocity is given by *ob* $= \omega R$, perpendicular to O_1B (downward). In forming the velocity polygon for the linkage at its limiting position, Fig. 14C, we note that relative velocity *bc* is colinear with velocity *ob* since the crank (O_1B) and connecting rod (*BC*) form a straight line. Point *C* travels only in a horizontal path, therefore velocity point *c* must lie at pole point *o* to cor-

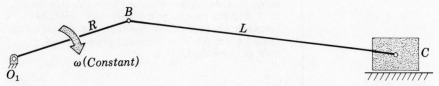

FIG. 14A. The in-line slider crank mechanism. The crank *R* rotates at constant angular velocity, ω.

Mechanism

rectly position bc perpendicular to BC. The velocity polygon tells us what we already knew: the velocity of the slider is zero. In addition, it gives us the relative velocity:

$$bc = \omega R \text{ (upward).}$$

If the crank has a constant angular velocity, the acceleration equation for the slider may be written as shown in the acceleration table, Table 8. But the last vector, a^t_{CB}, is clearly inconsistent with the acceleration equation since there are no vertical acceleration components. Therefore, $a^t_{CB} = 0$, and our vector equation becomes the simple scalar equation

$$a_C = a^n_B + a^n_{CB} = \omega^2 R \left(1 + \frac{R}{L}\right) \tag{9}$$

for the limiting position with the mechanism extended. See Fig. 14D. When the slider is at or near to the extreme right position, slider acceleration is to the left, as shown in the acceleration polygon. For crank angular acceleration $\alpha \neq 0$, we must include the tangential acceleration $a^t_B = \alpha R$ which is balanced by the equal and opposite vector a^t_{CB}. Equation (9) holds for the limiting position shown in Fig. 14B, for constant or variable crank angular velocity.

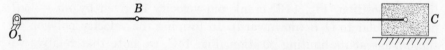

FIG. 14B. The mechanism is shown in its extreme limiting position, where O_1, B, and C are colinear.

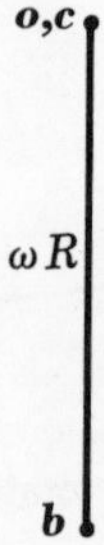

o,c

ωR

b

FIG. 14C. Velocity polygon at the instant the mechanism is in its limiting position. Since the velocity of B, and the velocity of B relative to C, must be perpendicular to O_1BC, velocity points o, b, and c must be colinear. Furthermore, points o and c must be coincident.

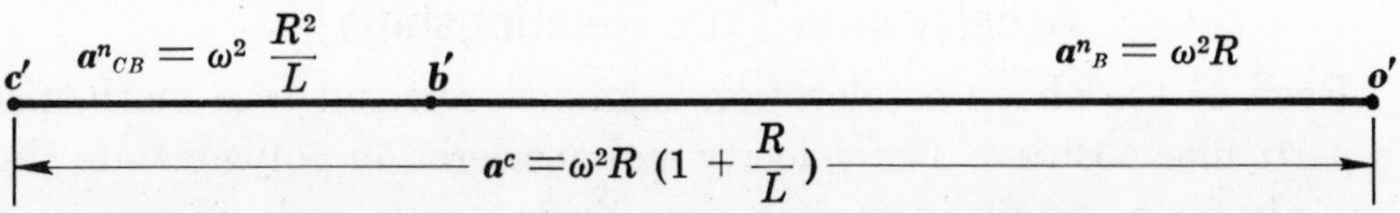

$$a^n_{CB} = \omega^2 \frac{R^2}{L} \qquad\qquad a^n_B = \omega^2 R$$

$$a^c = \omega^2 R \left(1 + \frac{R}{L}\right)$$

FIG. 14D. Acceleration polygon for the mechanism in its limiting position.

TABLE 8. VECTOR TABULATION FOR THE ACCELERATION ANALYSIS OF AN IN-LINE SLIDER CRANK IN A LIMITING POSITION, FIG. 14.

Vector	$a_C =$	a^n_B	$+ a^n_{CB}$	$+ a^t_{CB}$
Vector Magnitude	?	$\dfrac{(ob)^2}{R}$ or $\omega^2 R$	$\dfrac{(bc)^2}{BC}$	?
Vector Direction	along slider path	$\parallel O_1 B$ toward O_1	$\parallel BC$ toward B	$\perp BC$
Vectors used to construct polygon	? ⟵	$\omega^2 R$ ⟵	$\omega^2 \dfrac{R^2}{L}$ ⟵	? ↓

The other limiting position, with B and C at opposite sides of O_1, results in a slider acceleration

$$a_C = \omega^2 R \left(1 - \frac{R}{L}\right) . \tag{10}$$

When the slider is at or near its extreme left position, slider acceleration is to the right. The reader is reminded that Equations (9) and (10) were derived *exclusively* for the in-line slider crank mechanism in its limiting positions. The offset slider crank mechanism and other linkages will require separate analysis.

Acceleration-Time Relationships

Each of the above acceleration examples referred to a mechanism in a particular position. The velocity and acceleration polygons are thus valid only for a certain instant in time during each cycle of motion. If a graphical study of a mechanism is required, it is necessary to plot the results of a series of velocity and acceleration polygons. A sketch of the linkage and a velocity and acceleration polygon for each 30° of crank rotation may give enough data for a preliminary design study. If accurate results are required or if there are sudden changes in velocities, smaller intervals of crank rotation must be used. Symmetry should be considered wherever possible to reduce computational labor. As an example, consider the in-line slider crank linkage of Fig. 15, with constant crank speed. We need only to compute velocity and acceleration magnitude for one half of the cycle (180° of crank rotation) to completely describe the motion of this mechanism. We observe, of course, that velocity changes direction each half cycle. An acceleration-time plot for the slider is symmetric about either limiting position; the velocity-time plot is anti-symmetric about either limiting position. Most linkages (e.g. the offset slider or the crank-rocker mechanism) do not exhibit symmetry and must be examined for the entire 360° of crank rotation.

For design studies, it is convenient to normalize velocities and accelerations; this is done by letting crank angular velocity $\omega = 1$ and

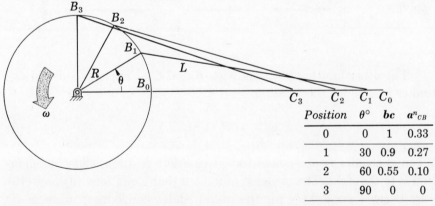

Position	$\theta°$	bc	a^n_{CB}
0	0	1	0.33
1	30	0.9	0.27
2	60	0.55	0.10
3	90	0	0

FIG. 15A. The acceleration of the slider crank mechanism is to be studied through a complete cycle. To facilitate the study, the velocities and accelerations are normalized: $R = 1$, $\omega = 1$.

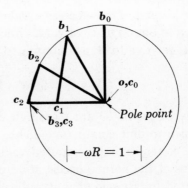

FIG. 15B. The velocity polygon. The locus of velocity points *b* is a circle of unit radius *ob* about the pole point. The respective values of *bc* are shown tabulated, together with the corresponding relative acceleration, for the angular positions considered.

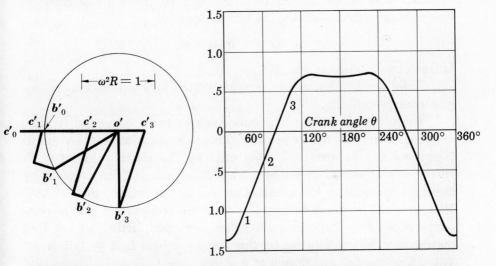

FIG. 15C. The acceleration polygon. The locus of acceleration points *b'* is again a circle of unit radius $o'b'$ about the pole point. Values for the relative acceleration are taken from the table in Fig. 15B. We are then able to plot the accelerations of point *C* against crank angle (or time) as shown.

crank length $R = 1$. In Fig. 15A point *B* represents the crank pin and *C* represents the slider. Subscripts 0, 1, 2 and 3 refer to crank angle $\theta = 0°$, $30°$, $60°$ and $90°$ respectively.

About pole point *o*, we draw a circle of unit radius, the locus of velocity points *b* ($ob = R\omega = 1$). See Fig. 15B. Velocity vectors ob_0, ob_1, etc., are drawn for each crank position, and then velocity points *c* are located. The successive values of relative velocity vectors *bc* are used to obtain a set of values for the normal component of acceleration of *C* relative to *B*, as determined from the equation

$$a^n{}_{CB} = \frac{(bc)^2}{BC}.$$

The values of *bc* are measured directly from the polygon since *ob* is drawn to unit length (one inch), and listed in tabular form along with the corresponding computed value of $a^n{}_{CB}$, as shown in Fig. 15B. The locus of the normal acceleration of point *B* on the crank, $a^n{}_B$, is represented by a circle of unit radius about the acceleration pole point *o'*. Thus, we have acceleration $a^n{}_B$ of constant magnitude and a convenient table of values for $a^n{}_{CB}$ for the positions being considered. The acceleration polygon is drawn solving the vector Equation (5)

$$a_C = a^n{}_B + a^n{}_{CB} + a^t{}_{CB}$$

for each crank position, Fig. 15C.

Slider acceleration a_C can now be plotted for each mechanism position considered, Fig. 15C.

The ordinate of the plot, crank angle, may be converted to time once we specify an angular velocity. True velocities are given by multiplying velocity vectors (ob_0, b_0c_0, etc.) by the actual value of ωR, where ω is measured in rad/sec. True slider acceleration is given by multiplying values on the acceleration plot by the actual values of $\omega^2 R$. It is seen on the graph in Fig. 15C that the acceleration plot is symmetric about $\theta = 180°$. Examining the graph still further, we see that maximum slider acceleration for this linkage (where $L/R = 3$) is $a_C = 4/3\ \omega^2 R$ to the left and occurs at $\theta = 0°$.

At the other limiting position, $\theta = 180°$, the slider acceleration $a_C = 2/3\ \omega^2 R$ to the right. Acceleration to the right peaks *before* $\theta = 180°$ if the ratio of connecting rod length to crank length is less than four. *It should be emphasized that the above results apply only to the in-line slider crank studied in Fig. 15, and are valid only for a L/R = 3 ratio and for a constant crank velocity.* Binford and Sampson give a detailed computer study of several thousand crank mechanisms with offset crankshafts.[8]

---

8. R. C. Binford and R. J. Sampson, "Slider Crank Charts for Offset Crankshafts," A.S.M.E. paper No. 66-Mech-39, 1966.

Slider accelerations may be obtained analytically by differentiating the velocity equation, as we saw in Chapter Two. Differentiating the approximate equation for the velocity of the slider of a slider crank mechanism

$$v_c = R\omega \sin \theta \left(1 + \frac{R}{L} \cos \theta\right)$$

we obtain

$$a_c = R\omega^2 \left(\cos \theta + \frac{R}{L} \cos 2\theta\right) . \qquad (11)$$

Equation (11) gives a positive value for a_c directed toward the crankshaft, and negative when a_c is directed away from the crankshaft. It is valid for the in-line slider crank when crank speed is constant and the ratio L/R does not approach a value of one, say L/R greater than or equal to three.

Dynamics of Linkages

Kinematics treats motion without considering the associated forces. The study of mechanisms is, traditionally, a study of the kinematics of machinery—the motion of linkages, but not the forces which cause the motion or arise from it. The study of the relationship between force and motion is called *Dynamics*. Since the areas of kinematics and dynamics are so closely related, an introduction to the terminology and methods of dynamic analysis is provided in Appendix B.

Chapter
4

Cams:
Design and Analysis

Introduction

Perhaps the simplest method by which a body can be given a certain prescribed motion is to make use of a cam and follower. A cam is a mechanism or machine which causes another body, known as the follower, to conform to a definite path of motion.

Since the cam mechanism has its motion prescribed, it is a good example of kinematic synthesis. In other words, rather than analyzing a mechanism to determine its motion, cams have a predetermined motion, and the analysis consists of designing the cam to give the desired motion. It is possible to obtain almost any type of follower motion by proper design of the cam. However, practical design considerations often necessitate modification of desired follower motions.

A great variety of cam types are available. Some of the more commonly used cams are shown in Fig. 1. Practical applications for cam mechanisms are numerous; one of the better known applications is the timing system used in automotive engines. See Fig. 2.

A cam mechanism usually consists of a cam (the driver), the follower (the driven element), and the frame (the support for the cam and follower). Among the common types of cam followers are: the knife-edge, flat-face, roller, pivoted, conical and offset types.

Disc Cam Designs for Basic Follower Types and Motions

Disk Cam with Reciprocating Knife-Edge Follower and Uniform Velocity

In order to understand cam terminology and design, it is necessary to consider the various types of cams, cam motions, and cam followers.

Slide Bar Cam

External-Barrel, Double-Track Cam

Helix Barrel Cam

Internal-Barrel Cam

Barrel Cam

Mirror-Image Conjugate Cam

Typical Three-Dimensional Cams

FIG. 1. A few of the infinite variety of cams available. (Commercial Cam Co.) Three-dimensional cams are also widely used. (Parker-Hartford Corp.)

Mechanism

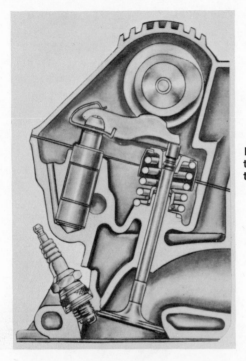

FIG. 2. Cams are used to operate the intake and exhaust valves of a modern automotive engine. (General Motors Corp.)

To begin, consider the design of the simplest cam, a *disk cam*, which is to give a prescribed motion to a reciprocating knife-edge follower. The follower center line coincides with the center line of the cam.

Let us now assign a specific set of movements to the follower. The follower is to rise 1½ inches with constant velocity in 120° of cam rotation, then remain at that height for another 120° of cam rotation, and finally, return to the initial position with constant velocity. The motion is to repeat this pattern with every camshaft revolution.

In the design of an actual cam, the points representing changes in velocity would be modified to provide reasonable values of acceleration. Later in this chapter, we will investigate the various motions in order to determine which give the best operating characteristics.

It should be clear that the follower motion could have been described in terms of the time in seconds rather than degrees of cam rotation. In other words, the follower is to rise 1½ inches in ⅙ of a second, dwell (remain at rest) for ⅙ second, and return to the initial position in

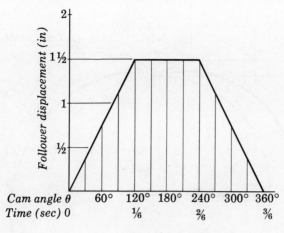

Cam displacement

FIG. 3. Displacement diagram. The diagram is a plot of follower displacement, in inches, versus cam displacement in degrees or time units of seconds. The cam takes ½ second to make 1 revolution, rotating at a constant speed of 2 rev/sec, or 120 RPM. The follower rises during the first 120° of cam rotation, dwells from 120° to 240°, and returns in the interval from 240° to 360°.

$\frac{1}{6}$ of a second. If the cam is made to rotate at a constant velocity of two revolutions per second, then one revolution of the cam will occur each half second. The motions, whether described in terms of cam angle or seconds, are thus seen to be the same.

Displacement Diagram. Fig. 3 shows a plot of follower displacement versus cam angle and time. Follower displacements are usually longitudinal displacements expressed in inches, while cam displacements are angular displacements measured in degrees or time units. The plot of follower displacement is usually drawn to scale, with follower displacement plotted along the ordinate and cam displacement (seconds) or degrees plotted along the abscissa. The motion of the follower can be described as a rise during the first 120°, a *dwell*, or rest, during the next 120°, and a return during the final 120° of rotation.

Cam Layout. Fig. 4 shows the layout of the corresponding cam. The initial position of the follower is at point 0, and coincides with point 0′ on the cam. The distance from point 0′ to the center C of the cam is the radius of the *base circle* of the cam. The size of the base circle de-

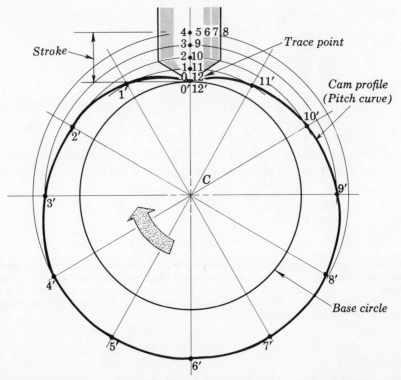

FIG. 4. Cam layout. The knife-edge follower shown is to be given the displacement motion of Fig. 3. The cam is rotating clockwise, while the follower is stationary. The cam profile is obtained by assuming that the cam is stationary, and that the follower rotates in the counterclockwise direction.

pends on several factors. In practice, the size may be limited by the space available in a given machine, the stresses developed, the velocities, and the accelerations.

The displacement diagram is the starting point for the design of the cam. The displacement diagram, Fig. 3, is divided into an equal number of intervals. In this case, 12 intervals were chosen, since 12 divided into 360° gives convenient intervals of 30°. In an actual cam design, since more accuracy is necessary in determining the cam profile, a larger number of divisions are used. The follower displacements, 0 to 12, taken from the displacement diagram, are then laid off along the follower center line in Fig. 4. The cam circle is also divided into 12 equal parts. Each radial line is 30° apart.

The next step in the procedure is to swing arcs from the numbered points on the follower, using the center of the cam, *C*, as the center of rotation. The intersections of these arcs with their respective radial lines on the cam, determine the points through which the cam profile will pass. In other words, the arc from point 1 on the follower center line intersects the 30° radial line at point 1′, the arc from point 2 intersects the 60° radial line at point 2′, etc. The cam profile is then completed by drawing a smooth curve through the points 0′ to 12′.

The assumption made here is that the cam remains stationary, while the follower rotates about the cam in the opposite direction. The results obtained, by using this assumption, are exactly the same as those for the true situation. This assumption is always made in cam layouts, because it makes the obtaining of the cam profile much simpler.

As the cam rotates clockwise through 120° (points 0′ through 4′), the follower rises 1½ inches. During the next 120° of rotation (points 4′ through 8′), the follower remains at the same height. Finally, during the last 120° of rotation (points 8′ through 12′), the follower returns to its initial position.

Basic Cam Terms. Some of the important procedures and terms, illustrated by the example of Fig. 4, should be discussed at this point. The greatest distance through which the follower moves (in this case the distance from points 0 to 4) is known as the *total follower travel*, the *stroke*, or the *throw*. The tip of the knife-edge, point 0, is known as the *trace point*. The *pitch curve* is the curve along which the trace point moves if the cam were stationary and the follower rotated. *For the knife-edge follower, the pitch curve and the cam profile are the same.* The follower motion used in the example is known as *uniform motion*. In other words, the follower rises and returns with constant velocity. The question of how to determine follower velocity and acceleration, as well as what effects they have on the follower, is an extremely important one, and will be discussed in detail in succeeding sections.

When a disk cam (a circular cam with an offset axis) is used, the follower is usually kept in contact with the cam surface by means of a spring force. Occasionally, when the follower motion is along a vertical line, the force of gravity is sufficient to maintain the contact during the return portion of the motion. However, great care must be exercised in the design of cams to ensure contact at all times between cam and follower.

Finally, the knife-edge follower discussed in this example is rather limited in its applications. Because the point contact between cam and follower results in large stresses and a great deal of wear, knife-edge followers are used only when the application involves very light service.

Disk Cam with Reciprocating Roller Follower and Simple Harmonic Motion

The problem, this time, will be to design a disk cam which is to translate a *reciprocating roller follower* with simple harmonic motion. The follower is to rise 1½ inches during the first 180° of cam rotation, and return to the initial position during the last 180° of cam rotation. A roller follower consists of an arm, which is constrained to move vertically, at the end of which a roller is attached by means of a pin. As the cam rotates, the roller rolls on the cam profile and causes the arm to translate.

The roller follower accomplishes pretty much the same thing the knife-edged follower does. The roller follower, however, greatly reduces wear because the contact is one of rolling rather than sliding. The roller follower is much preferred over the knife-edge follower in most applications. Before continuing with the example, it would be well to briefly discuss simple harmonic motion.

Harmonic Motion. Fig. 5 shows a point P, moving with constant angular velocity, at a radius r about a fixed point O. For every position of its orbit, point P can be projected onto the vertical diameter, AB. The projections of the successive positions of point P on AB are labeled P'. For example, when point P *is at position* P_1, the projection is P_1', when it is at P_2, the projection is P_2', etc. The motion of the projected points on AB (the P''s) as point P rotates about O, is simple harmonic motion. In other words, the path of motion traced out by points P_1' to P_{12}' is simple harmonic motion. It should be clear from considering the figure, that as point P continues to rotate about point O, the motion of P' keeps repeating itself. As we shall see later in this chapter, the equation for simple harmonic motion is

$$a = -\omega^2 r \sin \omega t,$$

where a is the acceleration in in/sec², ω is the angular velocity of point P in rad/sec, and r is the distance from point P to the fixed point O.

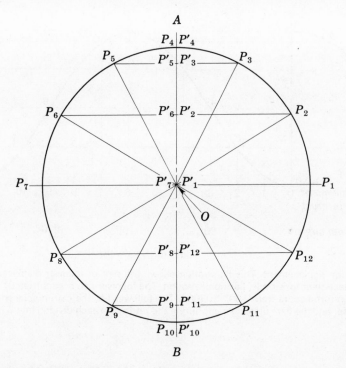

FIG. 5. Point *P* is a point moving at a constant rate in a circular path about a fixed point *O*. The projections of point *P* onto the vertical diameter are labeled *P'*. The motion of these projections is simple harmonic motion.

Displacement Diagram. Returning to our consideration of the problem, Fig. 6 shows the displacement diagram for harmonic motion specified. The diagram has been divided into 12 equal intervals. This choice is convenient, not only for dividing the cam into equal intervals, 30° each, but also for obtaining the proper displacements to obtain simple harmonic motion.

The following procedure is used to draw the displacement diagram. The semicircle shown in the figure is drawn with a radius of ¾ inch to the left of the displacement diagram proper. It is then divided into 6 equal sectors of 30° each. Horizontal lines are then drawn, 1 to 6, through the points of the semicircle. The intersections of these lines with vertical lines drawn through points 1 to 6 on the abscissa of the displacement diagram, determine points 1' to 6' on the displacement

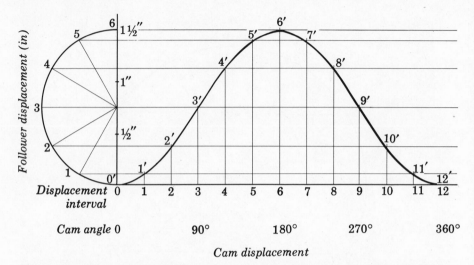

FIG. 6. Cam displacement. This illustration shows the plot of follower displacement vs. cam displacement for simple, harmonic motion. The follower rise occurs from 0° to 180°, while the return occurs from 180° to 360°. The follower lift, the cam displacement during the rise, and the cam displacement during the return are each divided into 6 intervals.

curve. A smooth curve drawn through points, 1′ to 6′, completes the desired displacement curve for the first 180° of cam rotation. A similar procedure is used to obtain the other (identical) half of the displacement curve.

To sum up, if the cam profile is designed using the displacement curve shown, the follower will rise 1½ inches, with simple harmonic motion, during the first 180° of cam rotation. The follower will then return 1½ inches, with simple harmonic motion, during the next 180° of cam rotation.

Cam Layout. The procedure followed in laying out the cam surface is similar to that used in the previous example. However, since a roller follower rather than a knife-edge follower is being used, there are some differences.

The cam layout for this example is shown in Fig. 7. The initial position of the follower is at point 0 (the pin connecting the roller to the follower rather than the point of contact between cam and roller), and coincides with point 0′ on the extension of the cam. A circle, the same size as the roller, is then drawn with 0′ as its center. The distance

224

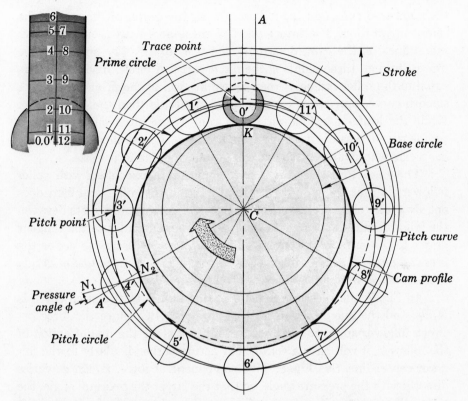

FIG. 7. The cam layout for a roller follower and the displacement of Fig. 6 is shown. The important terms illustrated in the figure are:

Stroke—maximum follower rise

Trace Point—reference point for follower displacement, located at roller center

Base Circle—smallest circle that can be drawn tangent to cam profile.

Pitch Curve—curve drawn through the center of the roller at the various positions around the circumference of the cam

Cam Profile—actual shape of the disk cam surface

Pressure Angle—angle between line of action of follower and a normal drawn to pitch curve

Pitch Point—that point on the pitch curve having the largest pressure angle

Pitch Circle—circle drawn through pitch point and having its center at cam center, C

Prime Circle—smallest circle, having its center at cam center, that can be drawn tangent to pitch curve

from point K to the center of the cam is the radius of the cam base circle.

As before, the follower displacements, 0 to 12, are laid off along the follower center line, beginning at the pin. Arcs are swung from the numbered points on the follower, using the center of the cam as the center of rotation. The intersection of these arcs with their respective radial lines on the cam, determine points 1' to 12'. The smooth curve drawn through these points is the *pitch curve*. A circle, having a radius equal to the roller radius, is then drawn at each of the primed points. A smooth curve, tangent to each of these circles, is then the cam profile. While the knife-edge follower had a cam whose pitch curve and cam profile were the same, it can be seen, from Fig. 7, that the roller follower has a cam whose pitch curve and cam profile are of different size.

The Cam Pressure Angle. A complication associated with roller followers is that the point of contact between the roller and cam does not always lie on the follower center line. The force which exists between the follower and the cam, acts along a line perpendicular to the tangent drawn to the surfaces in contact. It is, therefore, necessary to define the *pressure angle* of a roller follower as *the angle between the line of action of the follower and a normal drawn to the pitch curve.*

In Fig. 7, the pressure angle is ϕ, the normal to the pitch curve is $N_1 N_2$, and the line of action of the follower is $A'C$. Since the force between follower and cam does not act entirely along the line of action of the follower, it will have a component acting perpendicularly to the follower center line. See Fig. 8. This component of force, $F_n \sin \phi$, varies directly with the pressure angle, so that the larger the pressure angle, the larger the force. It is quite possible for the pressure angle to be large enough to result in a substantial lateral component of force. This component of force could cause the follower to jam in its bearings. It is, therefore, desirable to keep the size of the pressure angle as small as possible. However, the smaller the pressure angle, the larger the cam size. Since cam size is usually limited by space availability, a compromise with respect to the magnitude of the pressure angle is usually necessary. Most cams are designed with pressure angles less than $30°$.

Additional Cam Terms. The *pitch point*, Fig. 7, is that point on the pitch curve having the largest pressure angle. It should be clear from a consideration of Fig. 7, that the pressure angle does not in general remain constant as the cam rotates. While exact methods are available for determining the maximum pressure angle, sufficiently accurate results can usually be obtained by graphical methods, i.e., by drawing tangents to the pitch curve and measuring the angle. The location of the maximum pressure angle can also be approximated by considering

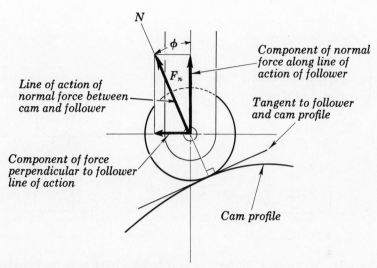

FIG. 8. The relationship between the contact forces and the pressure angle for a roller follower constrained to move vertically is illustrated.

the inflection points on the displacement diagram. An *inflection point* is the point where a curve changes from concave up to concave down and vice versa (points 3′ and 9′ of Fig. 6).

The *pitch circle*, Fig. 7, is defined as the circle drawn through the pitch point with its center at the cam center.

The last term to be defined for this example is the *prime circle*, Fig. 7, which is the smallest circle, having its center at the cam center, that can be drawn tangent to the pitch curve.

Disk Cam with Reciprocating Flat-Faced Follower and Cycloidal Motion

As another example of cam design, consider the problem of designing a disk cam which is to give a *reciprocating flat-faced follower* cycloidal motion. The follower is to rise 1½ inches during the first 180° of cam rotation and return to the initial point in the next 180° of cam rotation. The flat-faced follower, Figs. 9A and B, has the advantage of having a zero degree pressure angle. The side thrust present in roller followers is therefore not present in flat-faced followers. In addition, the contact points vary across its face, which means it does not develop the excessive wear present in knife-edged followers.

Although a flat-faced follower is usually made with a circular face,

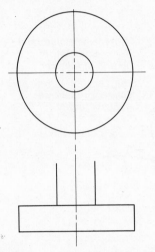

FIG 9A. A *circular* flat-faced follower.

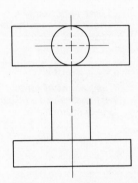

FIG. 9B. A *rectangular* flat-faced follower.

they are also made with rectangular faces. Fig. 9A shows a flat-faced follower with a circular face, while Fig. 9B shows a flat-faced follower with a rectangular face. In the problem now to be considered, the follower is to have a circular face.

Cycloidal Motion. A *cycloidal curve* is the path traced out by a point on a circle as the circle is rolled on a straight line. Fig. 10 shows such a cycloidal curve. As the circle of radius r rolls on the straight line, the point P traces out a cycloidal curve. While the mathematical equation for the cycloid could be used to plot the displacement diagram, the graphical method shown below is probably the simplest method.

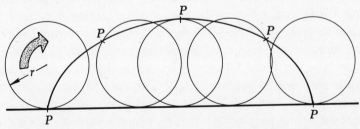

FIG. 10. Cycloidal motion. As the circle shown rolls on the straight line, a point P on its circumference traces out a cycloidal curve. The curve shown results when the generating circle makes one complete revolution.

Displacement Diagram. Let us consider a cam designed to give cycloidal motion to a follower. The displacement diagram shown in Fig. 11 is obtained by the following procedure. The ordinate (vertical axis), is divided into ½ inch intervals, while the abscissa (horizontal axis), is divided into 12 equal intervals of 30° each. Point A represents the maximum displacement of the follower, which occurs at 180° of cam rotation. A circle is now drawn with its center at 0, and having a radius equal to the maximum follower displacement (1½ inches) divided by 2π. In other words, the circumference of this circle is equal to the follower rise. The reason for doing this is that as this circle makes one revolution, a point on its circumference will move a distance equal to the rise of the follower.

Since the cam displacement between 0° and 180° has been divided into six equal intervals, the circle at 0 is also divided into six equal intervals (60° each). These intervals are numbered from 0 to 6. The points, 0 to 6, on the circumference of the circle are then projected onto

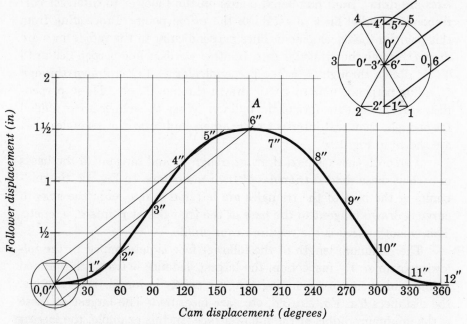

FIG. 11. The displacement diagram shown will give the follower a rise and return with cycloidal motion. The enlarged part of the diagram at the upper right illustrates the method of projecting the primed points.

the vertical diameter (horizontal lines are drawn through the points until they intersect the vertical diameter of the circle). The intersection points on the vertical diameter are numbered from 0′ to 6′.

Lines are next drawn through the primed points, parallel to line 0A, (the diagonal of the displacement diagram). The line through 0′ intersects the vertical line through 0° at point 0″, the line through 1′ intersects the vertical line through 30° at point 1″, etc. The smooth curve drawn through the double primed points is then the required displacement curve.

The *return* displacement curve, occurring between 180° and 360° of cam rotation, is a mirror image of the first half, and can therefore be drawn using the double primed points determined for initial displacement as shown in the figure.

Cam Layout. The next step in the solution is the drawing of the cam profile, shown in Fig. 12. The construction of the cam profile, through the step involving the determination of points 0′ through 12′, is exactly the same as the procedure discussed in the earlier examples. Arcs are drawn from numbered points on the follower to intersect corresponding radial lines to establish the prime points. Proceeding from this point in the development, lines perpendicular to the radial lines are drawn through the primed points. In other words, a line perpendicular to 0′C is drawn through 0′, a line perpendicular to 1′C is drawn through 1′, a line perpendicular to 2′C is drawn through 2′, etc. These perpendiculars represent the face of the follower. When these lines are extended far enough, they will intersect each other, and form the triangles that are shown in Fig. 12.

A smooth curve is next drawn through 0′, and tangent to the bases of each of these shaded triangles at their midpoints. In Fig. 12, the midpoints of the base of the triangles are lettered a, b, c, etc.; the smooth curve is drawn tangent to the base of the triangles at points a, b, c, etc. This smooth curve is the required cam profile.

The minimum length of the follower face is determined in the following manner. By inspection, the largest distance between the primed points and their corresponding tangent points is found. For example, the distances 0′a, 1′b, 2′c, 3′d, etc., are measured. The largest of these is the minimum radius of the follower face. In this example, the largest distance is 3′d. The radius of the follower is made slightly larger than this value, in order to ensure contact between follower and cam. This is

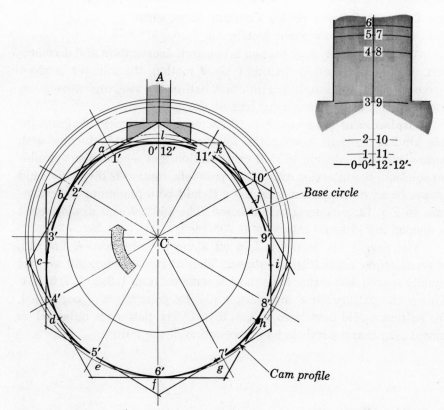

FIG. 12. The cam layout for a flat-faced follower having the cycloidal motion described in Figs. 10 and 11.

necessary because slight errors in graphical layout and manufacture might occur.

In the three previous examples, three different types of followers as well as three different types of motion were discussed. While construction procedures may vary for different types of followers, certain elements of cam layout, such as location of prime points, are fundamental to all constructions. These basic design procedures should be familiar to serious students of mechanisms. There are many other types of motion and followers in common use. These will be discussed shortly, but in much less detail. It should be clear that almost any kind of desired motion can be obtained by using an appropriately designed cam system.

Mechanism

Disc Cam with Follower Having Constant Acceleration and Deceleration, or Parabolic Motion

Another useful type of motion is constant acceleration and deceleration, or parabolic motion. In this type of motion, the follower is given a constant acceleration during the first half of the rise, and a constant deceleration during the second half of the rise.

Displacement Diagram. Fig. 13 shows a displacement diagram for this kind of motion. Assume the follower is to rise 1½ inches, with parabolic motion, during 160° of cam rotation. For a convenient graphical solution, the intervals into which parabolic motion is divided should always be an even number, and there should be a minimum of 6 intervals. In Fig. 13, 8 intervals will be used. The 160° of cam displacement is divided into 8 equal intervals of 20° each.

The rise of 1½ inches is laid off along the ordinate. A line $A0$, *at an arbitrary acute angle*, is drawn. The intervals on line $A0$ are not equally spaced, but rather have the following pattern, 1, 3, 5, 7, 7, 5, 3, 1. This is the pattern for 8 intervals, while if 6 intervals had been used, the pattern would have been 1, 3, 5, 5, 3, 1. The pattern is obtained by considering that a parabola has an equation of the form

$$y = kx^2$$

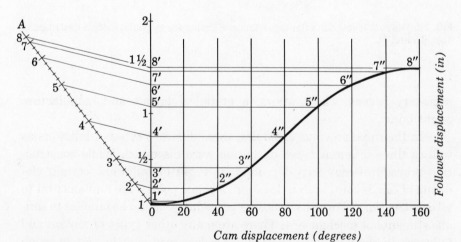

FIG. 13. The displacement diagram shown indicates that the follower is to have parabolic motion. The motion is constant acceleration between 0° and 80° of cam rotation and constant deceleration from 80° to 160°.

232

For $x = 1$, $y = k$; for $x = 2$, $y = 4k$; for $x = 3$, $y = 9k$; for $x = 4$, $y = 16\,k$; etc. Therefore, the first interval should contain one division, the second interval three equal divisions, the third interval five equal divisions, etc. The points 0 through 8 on line $A0$ are thus determined.

A line is then drawn from point 8 to the 1½ inch point on the follower displacement axis. Lines parallel to this one (which may or may not be horizontal) are then drawn through points 7, 6, 5, etc. The points 1′ through 8′ on the ordinate axis are thus determined. The points 0″ through 8″ are then obtained by the same procedure used in the previous examples. A smooth curve, drawn through the double primed points, is then the required displacement curve. The graphic construction of the cam follows next. Depending on the type of follower desired, the construction method will be one of the methods for the three types of followers described earlier.

Combination of Motions

A combination of motions is also very often used. A common combination is parabolic and constant velocity. It should be clear that the drawing of the displacement diagram for any combination of the motions discussed, would follow the same procedures shown.

Variations in Basic Follower Designs

Reciprocating, Oblique, Flat-Faced Follower

At this point, it would be well to briefly discuss other followers commonly used. A variation of the flat-faced follower discussed previously is the reciprocating *oblique* flat-faced follower shown in Fig. 14. The only difference in the cam layout is that when the primed points have been determined, instead of drawing a line through them at 90° to the radial line, a line at an angle (α) to the radial is drawn, as shown in Fig. 14. The layout procedure then follows exactly the one discussed earlier for flat-faced followers.

Oblique flat-faced followers are seldom used. They are useful for certain applications, however, because the tangent lines are at a different angle than those for 90° flat-faced followers, and a different cam profile would therefore result.

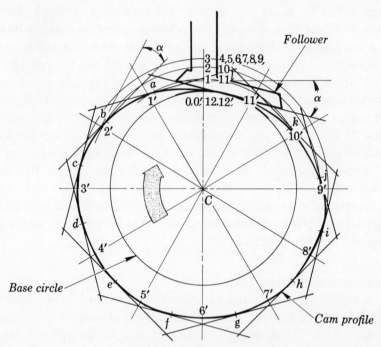

FIG. 14. The cam layout shown is for an *oblique*, flat-faced follower. The slight variation in the construction is due to the angle, α, of the follower face.

Reciprocating, Spherical-Faced Follower

Another similar follower is the reciprocating spherical-faced follower. This type of follower is shown in Fig. 15. Point 0 is the center of curvature of the follower face. The values from the displacement diagram are therefore laid off from 0. The primed points are obtained as usual, and circular arcs of radius $0B$ (the radius of curvature of the follower face) are drawn, using the primed points as the centers. The smooth curve drawn tangent to each of the arcs where they intersect their respective radial lines determines the required cam profile. The layout procedure just described is thus the same as that for the roller follower described in a previous section. The spherical-faced follower is very useful for applications where the cam profile is a steep curve. It is also often used as a secondary follower, as shown in Fig. 20 of this chapter.

234

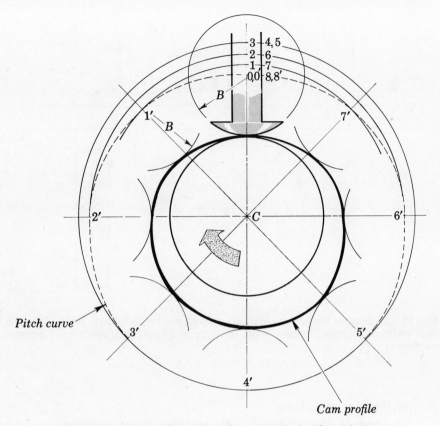

FIG. 15. The layout for the cam profile for a spherical-faced follower.

Reciprocating Mushroom Follower

Circular flat-faced followers are usually offset. In other words, the center line of the follower does not coincide with the center line of the cam. Fig. 16 shows front and side views of such a cam. The offset, which is shown in the side view, has the effect of causing the follower to *rotate*. This rotation results in a more equal distribution of wear over the follower face. This type of follower is known as a mushroom follower. The procedure for determining the cam profile is exactly the same as that for the flat-faced follower example shown previously.

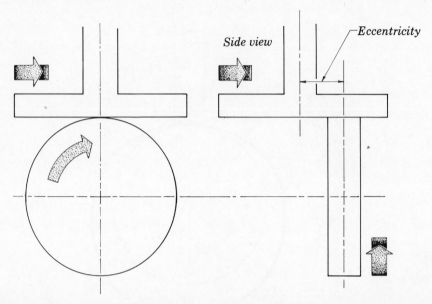

FIG. 16. The offset of the follower and cam axes causes the follower to rotate. The rotation results in equalized follower wear. This type of follower is known as a mushroom follower.

Pivoted, Flat-Faced Follower

The last of the flat-faced follower types to be considered is the *pivoted* flat-face follower. The motion of the follower for this case is not longitudinal translation, but rather is one of *angular* displacement.

This type follower is shown in Fig. 17. The cam center is at point C, while the follower is pivoted at the fixed point A_0. A circle of radius r', with center at A_0, is drawn so that the extension of the follower face will be tangent to this circle. The arc of radius r, with A_0 as the center, is the path along which the follower displacements, 0-6, are laid out. The angle α is the total displacement desired for the follower. The portion of the arc intercepted by the angle α is then divided into 6 intervals, chosen so as to give the required follower motion. The cam angle, during which this motion is to take place, is then divided into 6 equal angles.

A circle of radius CA_0, with C as its center, is now drawn. The angle β is the angle the cam will turn through while the follower moves from point 0 to point 1. Point A_1 on the pitch curve is thus located, and

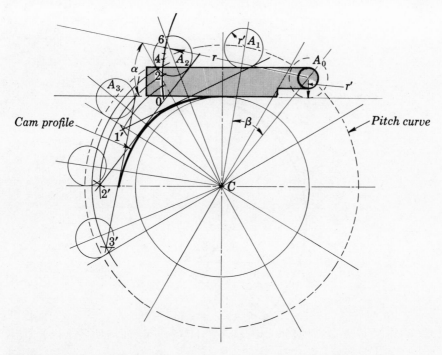

FIG. 17. The cam layout shown is for a pivoted, flat-faced follower. The angle, α, is the total (angular) displacement of the follower. The displacements are laid off along an arc rather than along a straight line.

a circle of radius r' is drawn. Point A_1 is the position the follower pivot point would have if the cam were stationary and the follower were rotating about it. An arc, with center at C, is drawn through point 1. Using A_1 as the center, another arc of radius r is drawn to intersect the arc drawn through point 1. This intersection is labeled 1'. A line through 1' tangent to the circle at A_1 is now drawn. This tangent line represents the position of the follower face for displacement 1.

The tangent lines for the other displacement points are obtained in a similar manner. The smooth curve drawn tangent to these tangent lines is then the required cam profile.

Reciprocating, Offset Roller Follower

A method to reduce the side thrust present in a roller follower, is

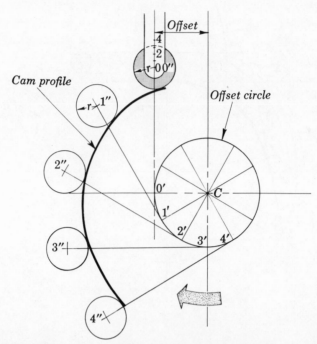

FIG. 18. The offset, reciprocating roller follower shown has less side thrust than an in-line roller follower. Points 0″-4″ are determined by drawing tangents to the offset circle at points 0′-4′, and laying off along these lines distances 0′1 from 1′, 0′2 from 2′, etc. Points 0″-4″ are then used as centers for circles having radii equal to the roller radius. A smooth curve drawn tangent to these circles is the required cam profile.

to offset the follower. In other words, the center line of the follower does not coincide with the center line of the cam. A follower of this type is shown in Fig. 18. The points 0 to 4 on the follower are the follower displacements for a given type of motion. The total displacement of the follower is to occur in 120° of cam rotation.

A circle, called the *offset circle*, is drawn with its center at *C* and with a radius equal to the distance between the cam centerline and the follower centerline. The 120° of this circle, during which the follower motion is to occur, is divided into 4 equal parts of 30° each. Then, points 0′, 1′, 2′, 3′, and 4′ are located, beginning on the horizontal axis of the offset circle.

Lines tangent to the offset circle (they are also perpendicular to the radial lines of the circle) are next drawn through the primed points. When the measured distance 0'1 is laid off along the tangent line from 1', point 1″ is located. The distance from 0' to 2 is then laid off from 2' to locate point 2″, etc. The double primed points, thus obtained, are used as the center of circles having the same radius as the roller radius (r). A smooth curve tangent to these circles is the required cam profile. It is worth repeating once again that in the examples worked out in this chapter only a few points are used to plot the motions and cam profiles, whereas in most actual cam designs many more points are required to produce the required accuracy.

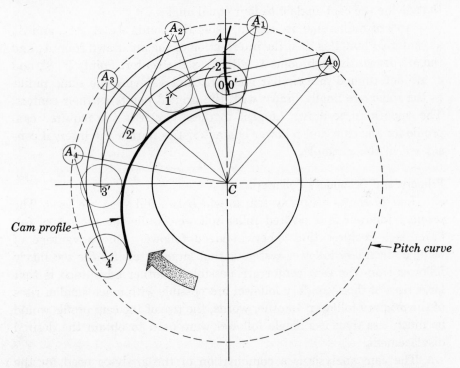

FIG. 19. A pivoted, roller follower. The interval of cam rotation, occurring during the follower rise, is again divided into 4 equal segments. Points A_1-A_4 are determined by the intersection of the equally spaced radial lines and the circle CA_0. Arcs of radius A_0O are drawn from points A_1-A_4. The intersections of these arcs with those drawn with cam center through points 1-4 determine points 1'-4'. Circles having radii equal to the roller radius are drawn with their centers at points 1'-4'. The smooth curve drawn tangent to these circles is the required profile for the part of cam considered.

Mechanism

Pivoted, Roller Follower

Another variation of the roller follower is the *pivoted* roller follower illustrated in Fig. 19. This design combines features of the roller follower and the pivoted flat-face follower. The follower pivots about the fixed point A_0. An arc of radius $A_0 0$ (the distance from the pivot pin to the roller pin) is drawn with A_0 as the center. Point 0 is the center of the roller, and the points 1, 2, 3, and 4 are the values for the desired follower displacement. The cam angle turned through while the follower moves from point 0 to point 4, is divided into four equal angles, beginning with line $A_0 C$. A circle, with its center at the cam center, is drawn through A_0, the fixed pivot point. Points A_1, A_2, A_3, and A_4 are the points on the pivot point circle through which pass the radial lines that divide the cam angle into four equal angles.

Arcs of radius $A_0 0$ are drawn, using the points A_1, A_2, A_3, and A_4 as centers. Point 1' is then the intersection of the arc drawn from A_1 and the arc drawn through point 1, with C as the center. Points 2', 3', and 4' are determined in a similar manner. Circles having the same radius as the roller are finally drawn with the primed points as their centers. The smooth curve drawn tangent to these circles is the required cam profile for the cam and follower characteristics during the interval considered in this example.

Primary and Secondary Followers

Fig. 20 shows a cam system in which two followers are used. The *primary* follower is a pivoted roller follower, while the *secondary* follower is a reciprocating spherical-edged follower. One advantage of using a secondary follower system is that large offsets for the secondary follower from the cam center are possible. Another advantage is that large rises of the secondary follower are possible with much smaller rises of the primary follower. In other words, the rise of the cam profile would be much less than if a single follower were used to obtain the desired displacement.

The cam analysis is a combination of the analyses used for the reciprocating spherical-edged follower and the pivoted roller follower. The required motion is plotted on a displacement diagram which is then used to determine the points 0 to 4 on the spherical-faced follower. The roller follower will move along the arc shown. The points 0' to 4' are determined by drawing lines through point A, tangent to the spherical-

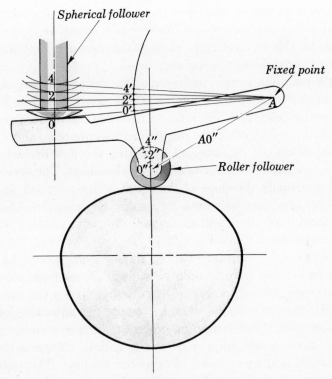

FIG. 20. The roller in contact with the surface is known as the primary follower. The arm to which the roller is attached actuates the spherical follower, known as the secondary follower. The spherical follower provides the motion desired in the problem. The displacements of the roller follower are therefore determined by the required spherical follower displacements.

edged arcs at points 0, 1, 2, 3, and 4. The intersections of these lines with the arc $A0''$ (the fixed distance between pivot pin A and roller pin $0''$) determine the points $0'$ to $4'$. The distance between $0'$ and $0''$ is then laid off from $1'$ to give $1''$, from $2'$ to give $2''$, etc. The cam profile can now be determined by the same procedure used for the pivoted roller follower.

Graphical Differentiation and Integration

The previous sections have dealt with the drawing of cam profiles to conform to a given displacement-time diagram. However, the velocity and acceleration characteristics of the follower often play an important role in choosing the motion the follower is to have. It is therefore desirable to be able to construct velocity-time and acceleration-time diagrams for the cam design being considered.

If the equation for the desired displacement is known, the mathematical procedure known as differentiation may be used to obtain the velocity and acceleration. The velocity equation can be obtained by taking the first derivative of the displacement equation, and the acceleration equation can be obtained by taking the first derivative of the velocity or the second derivative of the displacement. The derivative of a function is actually the slope of the graph of the function. It is therefore possible to obtain derivatives by a graphical procedure. The method, to be discussed shortly, involves drawing tangents to the curve of the function to be differentiated.

There are many instances where curves, which are to be differentiated, are obtained from recording oscillographs or from photographs. It is often very difficult to obtain the equation for a given curve. While numerical methods may be used to obtain the equation for such a curve, the graphical differentiation procedure does not require the curve equation. Another situation in which graphical differentiation is extremely useful is the processing of experimental data. This data is used to plot a curve, and the graphical method is applied to obtain the curve of the derivative.

The mathematical process of integration can be thought of as the procedure for obtaining the area under a given curve. As applied to cam design, the integration of an acceleration curve (determining the area beneath the curve) gives the velocity, and the integration of the velocity curve gives the displacement curve. In other words, the double integration of the acceleration-time curve will give the displacement-time curve. A graphical method for performing the integration process will also be discussed in this section.

Graphical Differentiation

In order to discuss the graphical differentiation procedure it would be well to consider an example. The curve shown in Fig. 21 represents a typical displacement-time curve. It is desired to obtain the velocity-time diagram for this displacement curve. The displacements were drawn with a scale of 1 inch = 8 inches, while the time scale chosen was 1 inch =

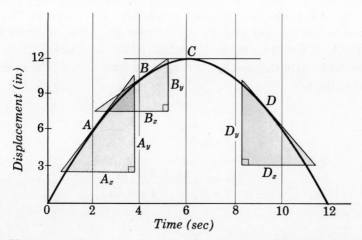

FIG. 21. Displacement-time curve. The curve shown is to be differentiated graphically. Tangents are drawn at points A, B, C, and D. The vertical distances divided by the horizontal distances for these tangents are the *slopes* of the curve at these points. The slopes represent the velocities; if the vertical distances are given their equivalent displacement values, and if the horizontal distances are given their equivalent time values, actual values of velocity result.

4 seconds. The displacement scale factor, K_d, and the time scale factor, K_t, are thus seen to be equal to the following:

$$K_d = 8 \ \frac{\text{in}}{\text{in}}, \quad \text{and} \quad K_t = 4 \frac{\text{sec}}{\text{in}}.$$

The scale factors are the constants which, when multiplied by the values read on the figure, give the actual values.

The next step is to draw tangents to various points on the curve. In Fig. 21, a tangent to the curve at point A is drawn. *The accuracy of the solution depends in great measure upon how accurately the tangent is drawn.* Very good accuracy can be obtained by using a reflecting bar to draw the tangent. However, for most applications, drawing the tangent by eye is sufficiently accurate. The horizontal line A_x and vertical line A_y are now drawn so that the tangent line becomes the hypotenuse of a right triangle having A_x and A_y for its legs. The lengths of lines A_x and A_y are arbitrary, but should be long enough to give reasonable accuracy in measuring.

The slope of the displacement at point A, is by definition equal to

Mechanism

A_y/A_x. Remembering our previous discussion, this slope is then proportional to the velocity at point A. By measuring the distances on the diagram, A_x is found to equal ¾ inches, while A_y equals 1 inch. Each of these values is multiplied by its respective scale factor. The velocity at point A is then

$$v_A = \frac{A_y K_d}{A_x K_t}$$

$$= \frac{1\text{ in} \times 8\text{ in/in}}{\text{¾ in} \times 4\text{ sec/in}}$$

$$= 2\tfrac{2}{3} \frac{\text{in}}{\text{sec}} .$$

The same procedure is followed for point B on the displacement curve. B_x is made equal to length A_x. It should be clear, that by making B_x equal to A_x, the velocities at A and B will be proportioned to A_y and B_y. Since A_y is larger than B_y, the velocity at A is greater than the velocity at B.

The tangent drawn to the curve at C, is a horizontal line. This simply means that the slope of the curve at that point is zero, and the velocity is therefore, zero.

The tangent drawn at point D slopes down, while the tangents drawn at A and B sloped up. If the slopes at A and B are considered positive, the usual case, the slope at D is considered to be negative. This means that while the velocities at A and B are positive, the velocity at D is negative.

The velocities, which have been determined, can be plotted to give the velocity-time diagram shown in Fig. 22. In this illustration, an arbitrary scale has been chosen for the velocity, while the same time scale used in the displacement diagram is used. The velocity scale factor chosen is

$$K_v = 2 \frac{\text{in/sec}}{\text{in}} .$$

The number of points that should be used is arbitrary. The more points

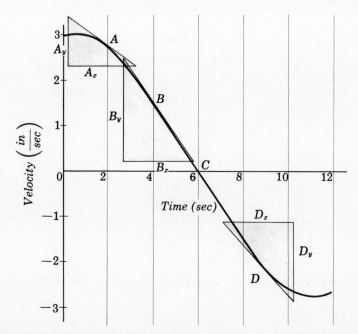

FIG. 22. Velocity-time diagram. The velocity-time diagram shown is differentiated by the same method used previously. The time scale must remain the same throughout the displacement, velocity, and acceleration diagrams to insure accuracy of final results.

used, however, the greater will be the accuracy. A good rule of thumb is to use many points where the curve is changing rapidly, and relatively few where the curve is changing slowly.

While the accuracy of the graphical differentiation method depends primarily upon how accurately the tangents can be drawn, the number of points chosen, as well as the scales used to draw the curves, are also contributing factors.

The velocity-time diagram may now be treated in a similar manner in order to obtain points with which to plot the acceleration-time diagram. Fig. 23 shows the diagram which results when the velocity curve is differentiated. The acceleration scale factor K_a was chosen as .50 in/sec²/in. It should be emphasized that the more times a curve is differentiated the greater is the chance that inaccuracies will occur.

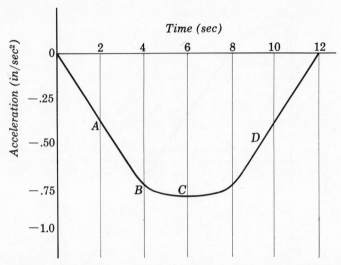

FIG. 23. Acceleration-time diagram. The diagram shown is the plot of the accelerations found in Fig. 22.

Graphical Integration

As was stated earlier, integration can be thought of as a process for obtaining the area underneath a curve. It is the reverse of the differentiation process. In other words, if an acceleration-time diagram is integrated, the velocity curve will result. Similarly, integrating the velocity-time diagram will give the displacement curve.

In order to help clarify the graphical integration procedure, consider the acceleration-time curve shown in Fig. 24A. Let us assume that the velocity at point A is known, and that it is desired to determine the velocity at point B. Remembering that *change in velocity* = *average acceleration* × *time*, it follows that the velocity at B is equal to the velocity at A plus the shaded area shown, since this area represents the difference in velocity between A and B.

Fig. 24B shows the method to be used in determining the magnitude of the shaded area. A vertical line, CD, is drawn midway between points 1 and 2. CD intersects the curve AB at D. A horizontal line drawn through D intersects the vertical lines through 1 and 2 at 1' and 2'. If area 1'AD is equal to area 2'BD, the entire area beneath the curve, 12BA, would be equal to the rectangular area 11'2'2. If the shaded areas

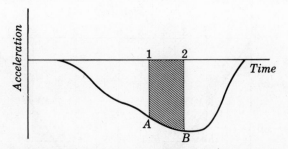

FIG. 24A. Since change in velocity equals average acceleration times time, the velocity at point B equals the velocity at A *plus* the area (height times width, or acceleration times time) of the shaded portion.

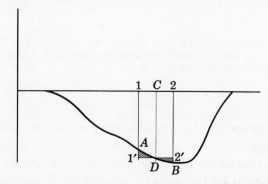

FIG. 24B. Shown is a method of approximating the area.

($1'AD$ and $2'BD$) are not approximately equal, a number of smaller intervals between 1 and 2 could be chosen so that the corresponding shaded areas are more nearly equal.

To further illustrate the procedure involved in graphical integration, let us consider the acceleration-time curve of Fig. 25, which repeats the curve of Fig. 23. The curve is first divided into an equal number of intervals. In this case, 12 intervals were chosen. Keep in mind that the time scales must be the same for all of the diagrams. The scale factors (K_s, K_v, K_a) will be given the same values they had for the differentiation procedure in order to bring us to the original starting point of our discussion of differentiation and integration, the displacement curve of Fig. 21. The difference between the velocities at points 0 and 2

Mechanism

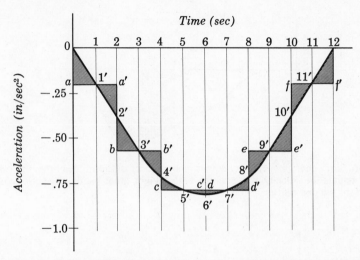

FIG. 25. Acceleration-time diagram. This diagram is a repeat of Fig. 23. The graphical integration method is used to obtain the velocity diagram. The area 022′ is approximately equal to the rectangular area 02a′a.

in Fig. 25 is represented by the area 022′, where the initial velocity is *given* as 3 in/sec.

There are several methods available for determining the area under a curve. One would be the use of a planimeter to determine the area. Another would be to draw the curve on fine-lined graph paper and to then estimate the area by counting the number of squares under the curve. The usual procedure is the method illustrated in Fig. 24, which is to draw horizontal lines through the points where a vertical line, drawn midway in the interval, intersects the curve. In other words, in order to determine area 022′ in Fig. 25, a vertical line 11′ is drawn midway between points 0 and 2. This vertical intersects the curve at 1′, through which the horizontal line aa′ is drawn. The required area 022′ is now approximately equal to the rectangular area 02a′a. The two areas would be exactly equal if area 01′a were equal to area 1′a′2′. As can be seen from the illustration, the two shaded areas, 01′a and 1′a′2′, will be exactly equal if the slope of the curve does not change in the first two seconds (from point 0 to 2′). The smaller the interval, the more likely is it that the slope will be constant. Thus, the desirability of making the intervals as small as possible is obvious.

248

Once the area 022′ has been determined, it is necessary to convert it to the proper velocity units. This is accomplished by multiplying the area, in square inches, by the time scale factor and the acceleration factor, or by measuring true velocity and time intervals:

$$\text{Change in velocity} = \text{area } (022') \times K_t \times K_a$$

$$= \text{area } (\text{in}^2) \times K_t \left(\frac{\text{sec}}{\text{in}} \right) \times K_a \left(\frac{\text{in/sec}^2}{\text{in}} \right)$$

$$= \frac{\text{in}}{\text{sec}} .$$

As can be seen from the illustration, the area, 022′, is negative. The velocity change is therefore negative. The velocity at point 2 is therefore equal to the velocity at point 0 minus the velocity change.

The same procedure is then followed to obtain the velocities of points 4, 6, 8, 10, and 12. The velocity diagram, shown in Fig. 26, can then be drawn.

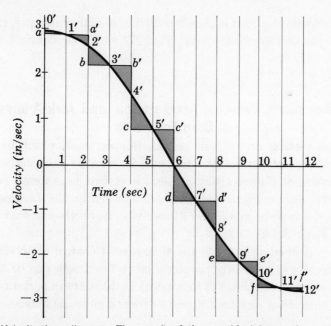

FIG. 26. Velocity-time diagram. The result of the graphical integration performed in Fig. 25 is the velocity diagram shown here. The graphical integration procedure is then repeated on this diagram.

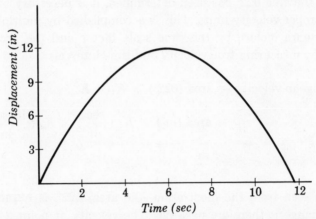

FIG. 27. Displacement diagram. The values used in plotting the displacement curve shown were obtained by the graphical integration of the velocity curve shown in Fig. 26. Note that by using the same acceleration and velocity scales to successively integrate the acceleration-time and velocity-time diagrams, we obtained the displacement diagram of Fig. 21.

The velocity diagram is then handled in a similar manner, in order to obtain the displacement curve, Fig. 27, which is identical to that in Fig. 21.

Displacement, Velocity, Acceleration, and Jerk Analysis of Cam Followers

In this section, an analysis of cam follower *motion* will be made. While the *displacement* of the follower for various motions was discussed previously, the velocities, accelerations, and jerks were not. Since the velocity, acceleration, and jerk are frequently the factors which determine the type of motion a follower is to have, they should be discussed in some detail.

Jerk is defined as equal to the time rate of change of acceleration. Since acceleration is directly proportional to force, jerk can be thought of as the time rate of change of force. Jerk is therefore important to cam designers because of its effect in terms of wear, noise, and stress.

Analysis of Uniform Motion

Uniform motion means that the follower is given a constant rate

250

of rise, in other words, the follower has constant velocity. This of course means that the acceleration is zero. The displacement equation is

$$s = s_i + Kt \tag{1}$$

where s is the total displacement at any time t, s_i is the initial displacement, and K is a constant.

The velocity equation can be obtained by differentiating the displacement equation. While the mathematical process of differentiation will be used in this section, the graphical method discussed in the previous section may be used with equally good results. Thus, for uniform motion:

$$v = \frac{ds}{dt} = K \ . \tag{2}$$

The derivative of the constant velocity is the acceleration

$$a = \frac{dv}{dt} = 0 \ . \tag{3}$$

The jerk is then found by taking the derivative of the acceleration

$$j = \frac{da}{dt} = 0 \ . \tag{4}$$

Fig. 28 shows the corresponding displacement, velocity, acceleration, and jerk diagrams for a follower undergoing uniform motion. The displacement diagram shows that the follower rise and return follow a straight line path. This type of motion is the simplest of the follower motions.

As can be seen from the velocity diagram, the velocity goes from zero to its maximum (constant) velocity in zero time. To accomplish this, the acceleration would have to be infinite. While the physical conditions in a cam system prevent infinite accelerations, the values for the acceleration are high. The jerk will also, theoretically, approach infinity. Conditions of high acceleration and jerk result in a large amount of shock. Uniform motion is therefore seldom, if ever, used in cam design.

Analysis of Modified Uniform Motion

It is possible to reduce the shock effects inherent in uniform motion cams by modifying the motion. The usual modification is to have the

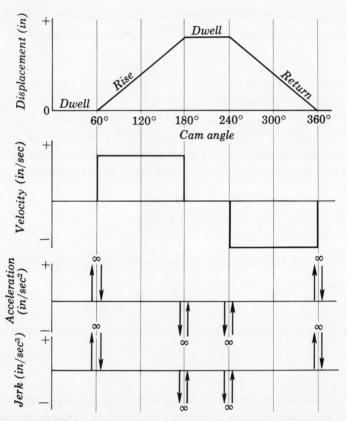

FIG. 28. Uniform motion. The displacement, velocity, acceleration, and jerk diagrams for uniform motion are shown. The follower dwells between 0° and 60°, rises with constant velocity between 60° and 180°, dwells from 180° to 240°, and returns with constant velocity from 240° to 360°. The abrupt motion changes inherent in this design result in high acceleration and jerk values which adversely affect follower (and linkage) life and smoothness of response.

follower undergoing uniform acceleration at the start of the constant velocity, and uniform deceleration at the end of the constant velocity interval.

Assume that the displacement diagram of Fig. 28 is to be modified to correspond to the sequence indicated above. From the diagram, it is evident that the follower rise occurs between 60° and 180°. The total rise takes place in 120° of cam rotation.

Before proceeding, it is important to first consider how the displacement will be affected by the constant acceleration and constant velocity intervals. During a constant acceleration, the velocity goes from a value of 0 to v. The average velocity for this interval is

$$v_{av} = \frac{v + 0}{2} = \frac{v}{2}.$$

The follower displacement during this interval is given by the expression

$$s_a = \frac{v}{2} t$$

where t is time and s_a is follower displacement during the interval. (The subscript a indicates that displacement s occurs during an interval of constant acceleration.) During an interval of *constant velocity* (or zero acceleration), the displacement is given by the expression

$$s_v = vt$$

where s_v is the follower displacement during a period of constant velocity. It can thus be seen that the follower will move twice the distance during an interval of constant velocity that it would move during an identical interval at constant acceleration (where the velocity during the constant acceleration interval goes from 0 to v, and the magnitude of v is the same as for the case of constant velocity). Another way of stating this is to say that, for a given displacement and a given maximum velocity, constant velocity motion will take half as long as constant acceleration.

In drawing the displacement diagram for modified uniform motion, Fig. 29, the constant acceleration occurs from 60° to 90°, and raises the follower through displacement $h/6$, where h is the total follower lift. The constant velocity occurs from 90° to 150°, and raises the follower another $4h/6$. Constant deceleration occurs from 150° to 180°, during which interval the follower is raised the final $h/6$ as the velocity gradually decreases to zero. Fig. 29 also shows the changes in the remaining motion diagrams for this modified uniform motion. As can be seen from the diagrams, the accelerations are no longer infinite. However, they may still be undesirably large. The jerk values are still, theoretically, infinite. This means that, while shock has been reduced somewhat, it still exists. As a result, this type modified uniform motion is used only for slow speed applications.

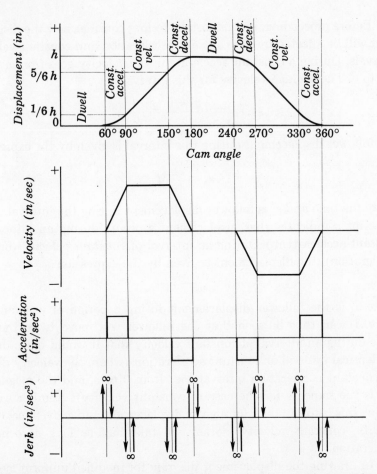

FIG. 29. The diagrams for displacement, velocity, acceleration, and jerk are shown for modified uniform motion. The follower dwells from 0° to 60°, rises with constant acceleration from 60° to 90°, continues to rise with constant velocity from 90° to 150°, and completes the rise with constant deceleration from 150° to 180°. After a dwell from 180° to 240°, the follower returns with constant deceleration from 240° to 270°, continues the return with constant velocity from 270° to 330°, and completes the return with constant acceleration from 330° to 360°. This modification results in manageable acceleration.

Analysis of Simple Harmonic Motion

The displacement equation for simple harmonic motion can be written in the form

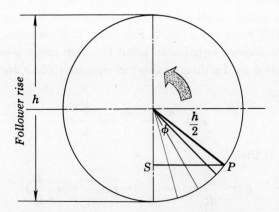

FIG 30. Harmonic motion. Point S, the projection of Point P, moves up and down the vertical diameter with harmonic motion as P rotates about a circle of radius h/2.

$$s = r \cos \phi \qquad (5A)$$

where r is the radius of the generating circle and ϕ is the angle turned through by the generating radius. See Fig. 30. In the case of a follower which is to be given a total lift h, the radius r in the equation becomes $h/2$. It would also be more convenient to have the equation in terms of the cam angle, rather than the generating circle angle. Let α be the angle the cam turns through while the generating circle is turning through 180°, or π radians. When the generating circle angle is some arbitrary angle ϕ, the cam angle is θ. The following equation, relating these angles, holds, where all angles are expressed in radians:

$$\frac{\phi}{\theta} = \frac{\pi}{\alpha} .$$

Therefore,

$$\phi = \frac{\pi}{\alpha} \theta.$$

The displacement equation (5A) can thus be rewritten as

$$s = \frac{h}{2} \cos \frac{\pi}{\alpha} \theta. \qquad (5B)$$

There is still a disadvantage to writing the equation in this form. The

255

motion starts at the middle of the rise when $\theta = 0$. In other words, when $\theta = 0$, $s = h/2$, since $\cos 0° = 1$. For cams, it is customary to have the follower displacement equal zero when the cam angle is zero. This can be accomplished by further modifying equation (5A) to the following form.

$$s = \frac{h}{2} - \frac{h}{2} \cos \frac{\pi}{\alpha} \theta. \qquad (5C)$$

The velocity is then

$$v = \frac{ds}{dt} = -\frac{h}{2} (-\sin \frac{\pi}{\alpha} \theta) (\frac{\pi d\theta}{\alpha dt}).$$

But $d\theta/dt = \omega$, where ω is the constant angular velocity of the cam. Therefore, the velocity equation becomes

$$v = \frac{h\pi}{2\alpha} \omega \sin \frac{\pi}{\alpha} \theta. \qquad (6)$$

The acceleration equation is then obtained by differentiating the velocity equation.

$$a = \frac{dv}{dt} = \frac{h\pi\omega}{2\alpha} (\cos \frac{\pi}{\alpha} \theta) (\frac{\pi d\theta}{\alpha dt})$$

$$= \frac{h\pi^2\omega^2}{2\alpha^2} \cos \frac{\pi}{\alpha} \theta. \qquad (7)$$

Differentiating the acceleration equation, gives the equation for jerk.

$$j = \frac{da}{dt} = \frac{h\pi^2\omega^2}{2\alpha^2} (-\sin \frac{\pi}{\alpha} \theta) (\frac{\pi d\theta}{\alpha dt})$$

$$= -\frac{h\pi^3\omega^3}{2\alpha^3} \sin \frac{\pi}{\alpha} \theta. \qquad (8)$$

The corresponding motion curves for simple harmonic motion are drawn in Fig. 31.

Simple harmonic motion cams are easy to manufacture, and hence are quite popular. However, as can be seen from Equation (7), the acceleration will be high if the required operating speed is high. There are also points in the motion for which the jerk is infinite (theoretically).

For these reasons, harmonic motion is not used for high speed applications, but rather, is limited to average speed applications.

Analysis of Cycloidal Motion

The drawing of the displacement diagram for cycloidal motion has been discussed previously. See Figs. 11 and 12. The curve is the path

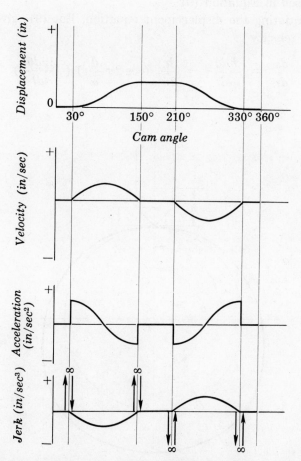

FIG. 31. The follower displacement, velocity, acceleration, and jerk diagrams for simple, harmonic motion are shown. The follower dwells from 0° to 30°, rises with simple, harmonic motion from 30° to 150°, dwells from 150° to 210°, returns with simple harmonic motion from 210° to 330°, and dwells from 330° to 360°. Note the effect on acceleration and jerk.

traced out by a point on a circle as the circle rolls on a straight line. The equation for the displacement can be written

$$s = h \frac{\theta}{\alpha} - \frac{h}{2\pi} \sin 2\pi \frac{\theta}{\alpha} \qquad (9)$$

where h is the total lift the follower is to be given, α is the angle the cam turns through while the follower receives its total lift, and θ is the cam angle during which the displacement s occurs. Fig. 32 illustrates the terms used in Equation (9).

Differentiating the displacement equation, Eq. (9), gives the expression for velocity

$$v = \frac{ds}{dt} = \frac{hd\theta}{\alpha dt} - \frac{h}{2\pi} (\cos 2\pi \frac{\theta}{\alpha}) (\frac{2\pi d\theta}{\alpha dt})$$

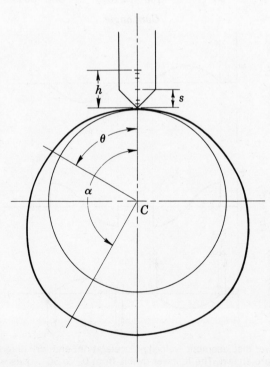

FIG. 32. The cam imparts a cycloidal motion to the follower. To impart the total displacement, h, the cam must rotate through an angle α. Displacement s at any time is a function of the cam rotation, Θ.

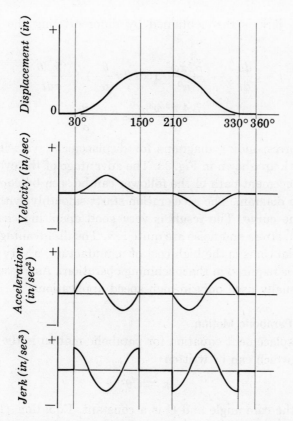

FIG. 33. The follower displacement, velocity, acceleration, and jerk diagrams for cycloidal motion are shown. The follower dwells from 0° to 30°, rises with cycloidal motion from 30° to 150°, dwells from 150° to 210°, returns with cycloidal motion from 210° to 330°, and then dwells from 330° to 360°.

but $d\theta/dt = \omega$, therefore

$$v = \frac{h\omega}{\alpha} - \frac{h\omega}{\alpha} \cos 2\pi \frac{\theta}{\alpha} \cdot \quad (10)$$

The acceleration is obtained by differentiating the velocity equation:

$$a = \frac{dv}{dt} = 0 - \frac{h\omega}{\alpha} \left(-\sin 2\pi \frac{\theta}{\alpha} \right) \left(\frac{2\pi d\theta}{\alpha dt} \right)$$

$$= h \frac{2\pi\omega^2}{\alpha^2} \sin 2\pi \frac{\theta}{\alpha} \cdot \quad (11)$$

259

Finally, the jerk is then obtained by differentiating the acceleration equation:

$$j = \frac{da}{dt} = \frac{h2\pi\omega^2}{\alpha^2}\ (\cos 2\pi\,\frac{\theta}{\alpha}\ )\ (\,\frac{2\pi d\theta}{\alpha dt}\ )$$

$$j = \frac{h\,4\,\pi^2\,\omega^3}{\alpha^3}\ \cos 2\,\pi\,\frac{\theta}{\alpha}\ . \tag{12}$$

The corresponding diagrams for displacement, velocity, acceleration, and jerk are shown in Fig. 33. The advantage of the cycloidal curve as the displacement path of the follower can be seen by considering the acceleration diagram. The acceleration starts smoothly, with no vertical jumps in the curve. The result is very good operating characteristics. Wear, shock, stress and noise are quite low. The disadvantage associated with cycloidal cams is the high cost of manufacture; a very high degree of precision is required in the machining operations. As a result, cycloidal cams are usually used only in high speed applications.

Analysis of Parabolic Motion

The displacement equation for parabolic motion is the equation of a parabola, which can be written

$$s = C\theta^2 \tag{13}$$

where θ is the cam angle and C is a constant. Equation (13) will give a constant acceleration. The equation is valid only between the initial point and the inflection point. Once the inflection point is passed, the follower is decelerating, rather than accelerating. The inflection point, or point where the acceleration changes to a deceleration, occurs midway during the follower rise. See Fig. 34. The following equations therefore apply only between the initial and halfway points.

Let α be the cam angle turned through while the follower is given a rise h. Thus, when the follower displacement is equal to $h/2$, the cam has turned through an angle $\alpha/2$. Therefore, from Equation (13)

$$\frac{h}{2}\ = C\ (\alpha/2)^2$$

$$C\ = \frac{h}{2}\ (2/\alpha)^2 = \frac{2h}{\alpha^2}\ .$$

We have thus arrived at the value of the constant C during that interval

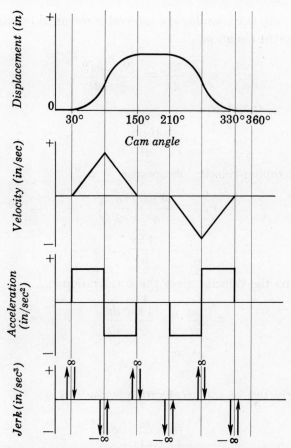

FIG. 34. The follower displacement, velocity, acceleration, and jerk diagrams for parabolic motion are shown. The follower dwells from 0° to 30°, rises with constant acceleration from 30° to 90°, continues to rise with constant deceleration from 90° to 150°, dwells from 150° to 210°, returns with constant deceleration from 210° to 270°, completes the return with constant acceleration from 270° to 330°, and then dwells from 330° to 360°.

of the parabolic curve which exhibits constant acceleration (from the initial point to the inflection point). The displacement equation can therefore be rewritten, replacing the constant C by an expression in terms of the maximum displacement h and the corresponding cam angle α:

$$s = \frac{2h}{\alpha^2}\,\theta^2 \,.$$

261

Mechanism

The velocity equation for the interval is obtained by differentiating the displacement equation.

$$v = \frac{ds}{dt} = \frac{2h}{\alpha^2} \frac{2\theta d\theta}{dt},$$

but $d\theta/dt = \omega$, therefore

$$v = \frac{4h\omega\theta}{\alpha^2}. \tag{14A}$$

Since the maximum velocity occurs at $\theta = \alpha/2$,

$$v_{max.} = \frac{4\,h\omega}{\alpha^2}\left(\frac{\alpha}{2}\right)$$

$$= \frac{2\,h\omega}{\alpha}. \tag{14B}$$

Differentiating the velocity gives the acceleration.

$$a = \frac{dv}{dt} = \frac{4\,h\omega}{\alpha^2} \frac{d\theta}{dt}$$

$$= \frac{4\,h\omega^2}{\alpha^2}. \tag{15}$$

The derivative of the acceleration is the jerk.

$$j = \frac{da}{dt} = 0, \tag{16}$$

except at changes in acceleration, where the jerk is infinite.

The set of equations for that part of the curve between the inflection point and the maximum displacement, can be written

$$s = C_1\theta^2 + C_2\theta + C_3, \tag{17A}$$

$$v = \frac{ds}{dt} = 2\,C_1\theta\omega + C_2\omega \tag{18A}$$

$$a = \frac{dv}{dt} = 2\,C_1\omega^2 \tag{19}$$

where the constants C_1, C_2, and C_3 are to be determined.

The following relationships between θ and the displacement and velocity exist.

1. $s = h$, when $\theta = \alpha$

2. $v_{max.} = \dfrac{2\,h\omega}{\alpha}$, when $\theta = \dfrac{\alpha}{2}$

3. $v = 0$, when $\theta = \alpha$

By substituting these three relationships into Equations (17A) and (18A), the displacement, velocity, and acceleration equations can be obtained. Values for the constants C_1, C_2, and C_3 can also be determined in terms of the (known) total displacement h and the corresponding (known) cam angle α.

When $\theta = \alpha$, Equation (17A) becomes:

$$h = C_1\alpha^2 + C_2\,\alpha + C_3. \qquad (17B)$$

When $\theta = \alpha/2$, Equation (18A) becomes:

$$\frac{2h\omega}{\alpha} = 2C_1\frac{\alpha\omega}{2} + C_2\omega. \qquad (18B)$$

When $\theta = \alpha$, Equation (18A) becomes instead:

$$0 = 2C_1\omega\alpha + C_2\omega. \qquad (18C)$$

We can now solve the above equations to determine the values of C_1, C_2, and C_3. Using Equation (18C) we obtain the following expression for C_2 in terms of C_1: $C_2 = -2C_1\alpha$. Substituting this expression for C_1 in Equation (18B) we obtain:

$$\frac{2h\omega}{\alpha} = C_1\alpha\omega - 2C_1\alpha\omega$$

$$= -C_1\alpha\omega.$$

Therefore

$$C_1 = \frac{2h\omega}{\alpha} \times \frac{1}{-\alpha\omega} = -\frac{2h}{\alpha^2}\,.$$

But $C_2 = -2C_1\alpha$, therefore

$$C_2 = -2\alpha\left(-\frac{2h}{\alpha^2}\right) = \frac{4h}{\alpha}\,.$$

263

Mechanism

Finally, substituting the expressions for C_1 and C_2 into Equation (17B), we can determine the value of C_3:

$$h = \left(-\frac{2h}{\alpha^2}\right)\alpha^2 + \left(\frac{4h}{\alpha}\right)\alpha + C_3$$

$$= -2h + 4h + C_3$$

$$C_3 = -h.$$

Having arrived at expressions for C_1, C_2, and C_3 in terms of the maximum follower rise, h, and the corresponding cam angle, α, we can substitute them back into the displacement equation for the second half of the parabolic motion (between the inflection point and the maximum displacement), Equation (17A) and differentiate to find velocity, acceleration and jerk.

$$s = C_1\theta^2 + C_2\theta + C_3$$

$$= \left(\frac{-2h}{\alpha^2}\right)\theta^2 + \left(\frac{4h}{\alpha}\right)\theta - h$$

$$= h\left(-\frac{2}{\alpha^2}\theta^2 + \frac{4}{\alpha}\theta - 1\right). \tag{20}$$

The velocity is then the derivative of the displacement

$$v = \frac{ds}{dt} = \frac{-2h}{\alpha^2}\ 2\theta\ \frac{d\theta}{dt} + \frac{4h}{\alpha}\ \frac{d\theta}{dt} - 0$$

$$= \frac{-4h\omega\theta}{\alpha^2} + \frac{4h\omega}{\alpha}$$

$$= \frac{4h\omega}{\alpha}\left(-\frac{\theta}{\alpha} + 1\right). \tag{21}$$

The acceleration is found by taking the derivative of the expression for the velocity, Eq. (21)

$$a = \frac{dv}{dt} = \frac{4h\omega}{\alpha}\left(-\frac{1}{\alpha}\ \frac{d\theta}{dt} + 0\right)$$

$$= \frac{-4h\omega^2}{\alpha^2}. \tag{22}$$

Finally, the jerk is given by

$$j = \frac{da}{dt} = 0 \tag{23}$$

except at changes in acceleration, where the jerk is infinite.

As can be seen from Equation (22), the acceleration for the second (latter) half of the rise is the same as that for the first half, except for the minus sign. This was to be expected, since the second half was a deceleration, while the first half was acceleration. The motion diagrams for parabolic motion are shown in Fig. 34.

The advantage of the parabolic cam is that the maximum acceleration needed to get the follower to a certain velocity is the smallest of all the curves discussed. However, as can be seen from the vertical jumps on the acceleration diagram, there are large, abrupt changes in acceleration at several points. This results in undesirable wear, stress, shock, and noise characteristics. The result is that parabolic cams are used only for low or medium speed applications.

While there are other types of motions (combination, elliptical, polynomial, etc.) the types just discussed are the ones most commonly used. In any event, the analysis would follow the same procedures discussed above.

In order to demonstrate the procedure used in solving typical cam problems, the following example is presented.

EXAMPLE—PROBLEM 1: A disk cam is to give its follower a rise of 2 inches, while rotating through 180°. The cam is rotating at a constant speed of 300 RPM. The required motion is a constant acceleration during the first part of the rise, and a constant deceleration, equal to ⅓ the acceleration, during the latter part of the rise. What is the value of the acceleration?

Solution: From the requirements for the acceleration of the follower we can construct an acceleration diagram for the 180° of cam rotation, indicating that position of cam rotation where the acceleration changes as the unknown angle θ. Since θ also indicates the point of maximum velocity on the follower velocity diagram, and the point of inflection on the displacement, we can draw the displacement, velocity, and acceleration diagrams shown in Fig. 35.

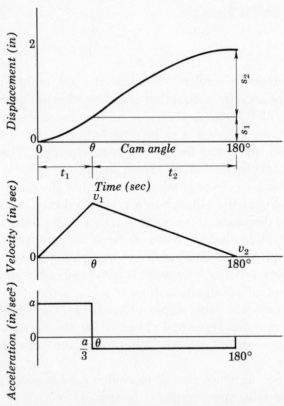

FIG. 35. The displacement, velocity, and acceleration diagrams shown are based on the data given in Example Problem 1. We know that at some time t_1 (or cam displacement θ) the acceleration will change as indicated. Displacement and velocity, functions of the acceleration, are drawn accordingly.

To be able to assign numerical values to our diagrams, it will be necessary to consider the motion from 0 to θ and from θ to 180°, and to determine the following unknown quantities:

cam angular displacement	follower velocity	follower acceleration	follower displacement
0 to θ	0 to v_1	a	s_1
θ to 180°	v_1 to v_2	$-a/3$	s_2

Clearly, to solve this problem, we will have to know more about the relationships between v_1 and v_2, t_1 and t_2, etc. The relationship between the two accelerations has been given as a condition of the follower motion, providing us with a starting point for the solution. Using the equation for velocity in terms of constant acceleration, we can arrive at the relationship between t_1 (interval of acceleration a) and t_2 (interval of deceleration $-a/3$).

$$v_1 = v_0 + at_1$$

but $v_0 = 0$, therefore

$$v_1 = at_1.$$

Similarly, for the second interval

$$v_2 = v_1 - \frac{a}{3} t_2$$

but $v_2 = 0$, or

$$0 = at_1 - \frac{a}{3} t_2$$

therefore

$$t_1 = \frac{t_2}{3} .$$

We now have the relationship between the time for the intervals. Since we already know the total amount of cam rotation ($180°$), let us obtain the angular velocity of the cam in degrees per second

$$\text{cam speed} = 300 \frac{\text{rev}}{\text{min}} \times \frac{1 \text{ min}}{60 \text{ sec}} \times \frac{360°}{1 \text{ rev}} = \frac{1800°}{\text{sec}} .$$

Relating the angular velocity of the cam to the cam angular displacement θ, we obtain the value for θ at t_1

$$t_1 = \frac{\theta}{1800°/\text{sec}} , \qquad t_2 = \frac{180° - \theta}{1800°/\text{sec}}$$

therefore

$$\frac{\theta}{1800°/\text{sec}} = \frac{180° - \theta}{1800°/\text{sec} \times 3}$$

$$3\theta = 180° - \theta$$

$$\theta = 45°.$$

Mechanism

Knowing now the value of θ, we can easily determine the values of the intervals t_1 and t_2

$$t_1 = \frac{\theta}{1800°/\text{sec}} = \frac{45°}{1800°/\text{sec}} = .025 \text{ sec.}$$

$$t_2 = \frac{180° - \theta}{1800°/\text{sec}} = \frac{180° - 45°}{1800°/\text{sec}} = .075 \text{ sec.}$$

Finally, using the formula for displacement in terms of acceleration, we can set up equations for s_1 and s_2, and solve for the acceleration.

$$s_1 = \frac{1}{2} a t^2{}_1 = \frac{1}{2} a \,(.025)^2 = .0003125 \, a$$

$$s_2 = \frac{1}{2} \frac{a}{3} t^2{}_2 = \frac{1}{2} \frac{a}{3} \,(.075)^2 = .0009375 \, a$$

Equating the sum of s_1 and s_2 to the total displacement, we have

$$s_1 + s_2 = 2 \text{ in}$$

or

$$.0003125 \, a + .0009375 \, a = 2$$

$$.00125 \, a = 2$$

$$a = 1600 \, \frac{\text{in}}{\text{sec}^2}.$$

Maximum and Minimum Values for Velocity and Acceleration

In designing a cam system, it is obviously important to be able to calculate the maximum values of follower velocity and acceleration. A function attains a value of relative maximum or relative minimum when its first derivative is equal to zero. Another way of stating this is to say that a particular curve will have relative maximums or minimums at those points where its slope is zero.

Applying this concept to cam analysis, it is clear that the maximum velocity and acceleration can be determined by considering the velocity and acceleration diagrams. The points on these curves where a tangent drawn to the curve is horizontal, in other words points where the slope is zero, are the maximum values. This method, of course, requires that the velocity and acceleration curves first be drawn.

268

A simpler procedure is to take the derivative of a given equation and set it equal to zero. The values obtained by solving this equation are the points at which the original function reaches its maximums. In order to obtain the maximum velocity its derivative, the acceleration, is set equal to zero. Similarly, the jerk is set equal to zero in order to obtain the maximum acceleration. The procedure just discussed is illustrated by the following example.

EXAMPLE—PROBLEM 2: A follower has a displacement given by the following equation:

$$s = t^4 - \frac{4}{3} t^3 - 10 t^2 + 5 t + 8.$$

Determine the maximum velocity and acceleration.
Solution: Given the equation for displacement, we can successively differentiate to find the equations for velocity, acceleration, and jerk:

$$v = \frac{ds}{dt} = 4 t^3 - 4 t^2 - 20 t + 5$$

$$a = \frac{dv}{dt} = 12 t^2 - 8 t - 20$$

$$j = \frac{da}{dt} = 24 t - 8.$$

To obtain the maximum velocity, the acceleration is set equal to zero:

$$12 t^2 - 8 t - 20 = 0$$

$$(4 t + 4) (3 t - 5) = 0$$

therefore

$$t = -1, \frac{5}{3}.$$

Since time is not negative, the maximum velocity occurs when $t = 5/3$. Substituting this value for t in the expression for velocity,

$$v_{max.} = 4 (\frac{5}{3})^3 - 4 (\frac{5}{3})^2 - 20 (\frac{5}{3}) + 5$$

$$= 4 \times 4.64 - 4 \times 2.78 - 33.3 + 5$$

$$= 18.6 - 11.1 - 33.3 + 5$$

$$= -20.8 \ \frac{in}{sec} \ .$$

The maximum acceleration occurs when the jerk is zero

$$j = 24\,t - 8 = 0$$

$$t = \frac{1}{3} \ .$$

Therefore, the maximum acceleration occurs at $t = 1/3$ and is:

$$a_{max.} = 12\ (\frac{1}{3})^2 - 8\ (\frac{1}{3}) - 20$$

$$= 12 \times \frac{1}{9} - \frac{8}{3} - 20$$

$$= -21.4 \ \frac{in}{sec^2} \ .$$

Positive Motion Cams

The cam types discussed up to this point depend on the force of gravity or a spring force to maintain contact between the cam and the follower during the return stroke. There are many applications for which it is necessary for the cam to exert positive control over the follower during the return, as well as during the rise. In this section, some of the more common types of positive motion cams are discussed.

Face Cam

One method of achieving positive motion is to cut a groove into the face of a cam. The roller follower then rides in this groove. During the rise, the inner surface of the groove (the side of the groove nearest the cam axis) causes the follower to move up, while on the return stroke, the outer surface of the groove, forces the follower down. This type of cam, known as a face cam, is shown in Fig. 36.

The face cam layout is very similar to that for the roller follower, discussed earlier. The pitch curve is obtained from the displacement diagram as before. Circles, having radii equal to the roller radius, are drawn at the appropriate points. The inner surface of the groove is obtained by drawing a smooth curve tangent to these circles. This is

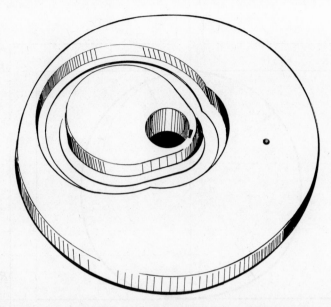

FIG. 36. Face cam. This type of cam imparts positive motion to the follower at all times. Since the follower is alternately driven by the inner and outer sides of the groove, a two-step layout is required to obtain the profile for both sides of the groove.

the exact procedure used to obtain the disk cam profile for the reciprocating roller follower discussed earlier.

The outer surface of the groove is obtained by drawing a smooth curve tangent to the *outside* of the circles on the pitch curve. A clearance between the follower and the groove surfaces is obviously necessary. Because of this clearance, a reversal of force occurs when the follower moves from contact on one surface of the groove to contact on the other surface. To reduce shock, the clearance should be kept as small as possible.

Constant-Breadth Cam

Another method for obtaining positive motion is the constant-breadth cam. This type of cam is shown in Fig. 37. As seen in the illustration, the cam surface is always in contact with the two parallel surfaces of the follower. The follower "boxes in" the cam. The distance between the parallel surfaces, d, is equal to the base circle diameter plus

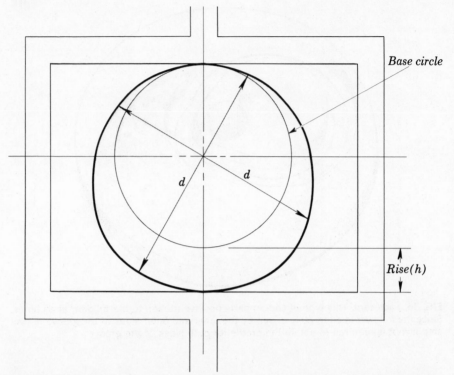

FIG. 37. Constant-breadth cam. While this type of cam provides positive motion, the disadvantage is that the motion from 180° to 360° of cam rotation must be the reverse of the motion from 0° to 180°.

the follower rise. Every point on the cam profile is a distance d from the point 180° from it. It is clear that the follower motion desired must occur between 0° and 180°. The cam profile between 180° and 360° must be such as to keep the distance d constant. In other words, the follower motion during the rise is the reverse of that during the return. This type of cam, obviously cannot be used for applications where the rise and return motions are different. Design methods for this type of cam are identical to those for cams with flat-face followers.

Conjugate Cams

Conjugate cams are a variation of constant-breadth cams. The system consists of two roller followers, 180° apart, and two cams mounted on the same shaft. See Fig. 38A. The first cam is designed to

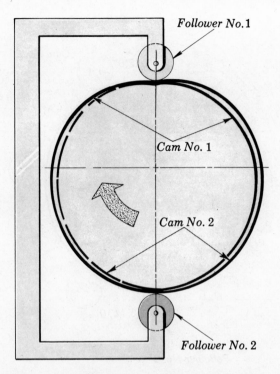

FIG. 38A. Conjugate cam. The conjugate cam system shown achieves continuous positive motion by making use of 2 cams and 2 followers. From 0° to 180°, cam 1 drives follower 1 to give the required motion. Between 180° and 360° cam 2 gives follower 2 the required motion. As can be seen from the figure, the cams will be driving their respective followers with positive motion at all times.

give the first follower the required motion between 0° and 180° of cam shaft rotation. You will recognize the design procedure as that for the on-center roller follower discussed earlier in this chapter. The second cam has a profile that is obtained by drawing circles whose centers are a fixed distance *d* from the follower No. 1 circles. In the interval from 180° to 360°, the first cam profile is obtained by drawing circles whose centers are a fixed distance *d* from the follower No. 2 circles. In this interval, however, the *second* cam gives its follower the required motion.

The layout for a conjugate cam system, Fig. 38B, is obtained in the following manner. The required displacement between 0° and 180° is indicated by the points 0-6 on the center line of follower No. 1.

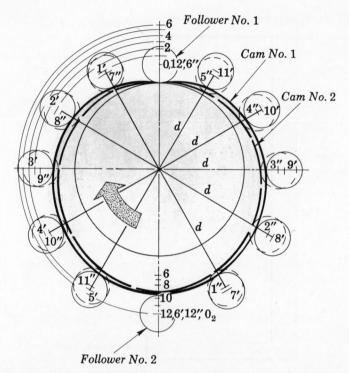

FIG 38B. The layout for the conjugate cam. The layout proceeds as for two separate disc cams, each with on-center roller followers. When laying out cam 2, however, the profile is obtained by shifting the construction lines 180°, since the cam rotates 180° before acting on follower 2.

Follower No. 1, driven by cam No. 1, provides this rise. The follower centers, 1'-6', are then obtained in the usual manner for roller followers. During the interval (0°-180°), follower No. 2 is a fixed distance d from follower No. 1. The distance between the followers is, of course, constant. Therefore points 1"-6" are established at a distance d from points 1'-6', respectively. The points 1"-6" are the centers of follower No. 2 during this interval. The primes (') will indicate follower No. 1, while the double primes (") will designate follower No. 2.

During the interval from 180°-360°, follower No. 2, driven by cam No. 2, provides the required motion. The points 6-12 on the center line of follower No. 2 are the required displacements. The points 6"-12" are obtained in the usual manner. There is one slight change, however. The usual procedure is to swing arcs from the displacement points on the follower center line to the corresponding adjacent radial lines (which was done to find points 1'-6'). However, since the cam rotates 180° before acting on follower No. 2, displacement points 6-12 will have to intersect *instead* the radial lines beginning with the line coincident with the center line of follower No. 1. Thus points 6''-12'' are determined. During this interval (180°-360°) follower No. 1 is the fixed distance from follower No. 2. Thus points 7'-12' are located. Follower No. 1 and cam profile No. 1 are drawn with solid lines, while follower No. 2 and cam No. 2 are drawn with dash lines.

The advantage of this type of positive motion cam over the constant-breadth cam is that wear is reduced because of the rolling action, and the force reversal is kept to a minimum because the clearance can be made extremely small. The biggest disadvantage is probably the fact that this type of cam is more expensive than other equally suitable cam designs.

There are other types of positive motion cams, but most are simply variations of the types discussed.

Cylindrical Cams

A cylindrical cam (see Fig. 1) is used to drive a reciprocating roller follower. A groove cut into the side of the cylinder provides the path for the follower. The follower may be cylindrical, but is usually conical because the wear is reduced for this type of follower. Cylindrical cams are positive motion cams, except for the type known as end cams. Another variation of the cylindrical cam is the barrel cam. This type of cam consists of a cylinder with a series of holes drilled into it. Plates of various shapes can be bolted to the outside of the cylinder. It is thus possible to get a wide variety of motions from a single cylindrical cam.

The layout for a cylindrical cam is quite simple. Fig. 39 shows such a layout. The diagram shows the developed, or "unwrapped," cylinder. The horizontal axis is equal to the circumference of the cam, while the vertical axis is equal to the length of the cam. The rise h is broken up into displacements 0-6. The centers for the roller circles 0'-6' are found in the usual manner. The location of the remaining centers also follows the previously used procedure. The smooth curves drawn tangent to the top and bottom of these circles represent the groove which is to be cut

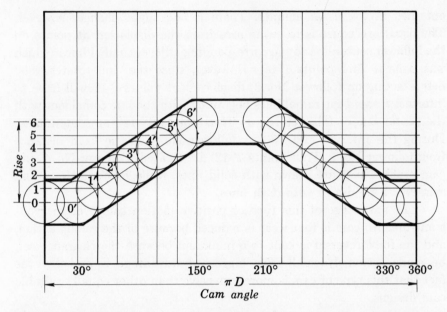

FIG. 39. Cylindrical cam layout. The groove shown in the "unwrapped" cylinder will give the roller follower the proper rise when cut into the actual cylinder.

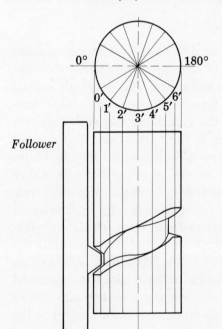

Follower

FIG. 40. Cylindrical cam. The groove, when cut into the cylinder, will give the follower shown the required rise and fall with positive motion.

276

into the cam. The developed groove can then be wrapped around the cam, and used to guide the cutting tool which is to cut the groove into the cam. Fig. 40 shows the cam in its actual shape with the groove cut into it.

Let us return to the question of the proper shape for the follower. The inside and outside of the groove will have different linear velocities. This fact can be verified by considering the top view of the cam follower, Fig. 41A. The velocity at the outside of the groove is

$$v_o = r_o \, \omega,$$

while at the inside of the groove the velocity is

$$v_i = r_i \, \omega.$$

Since r_o is greater than r_i, v_o is greater than v_i. Therefore, for a cylindrical follower, slipping must occur either at the top or the bottom of the groove. This condition can of course result in excessive wear of the

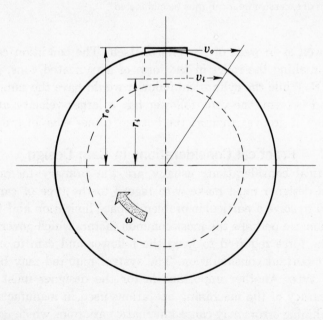

FIG. 41A. Cylindrical follower. Because of the difference in the velocities at the top and bottom of the groove, sliding at some point on the follower must occur. The result can be excessive wear of the groove as well as of the follower.

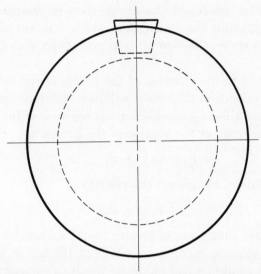

FIG. 41B. The truncated cone follower shown has a greater velocity at its top than at its bottom. However, the dimensions of the follower can be chosen so that at every point along the conical side the cone velocities conform to the corresponding groove velocities. The problem of excessive wear can thus be eliminated.

roller as well as in wear of the groove itself. The condition can be re-lieved by making the roller in the form of a truncated cone, as shown in Fig. 41B. While the cylindrical follower would have the same velocity at top and bottom, the cone follower has a larger velocity at the top (outer edge of groove) than at the bottom (inner edge of groove).

Practical Considerations in Cam Design

Practical considerations usually are the primary factors in the decision a designer must make with regard to the type of cam system to be used to solve a particular problem. Space limitation and the speed of operation are perhaps the most common factors which govern the de-cision. The force required to keep the follower and cam in contact is another important consideration. The system required may be gravity or spring type. Another important factor the designer must consider is the accuracy of the machining operations used in manufacturing the cam. Machining errors may cause kinematic variations which completely change the required operating conditions. For this reason, highly pre-cise machinery is required. See Fig. 42A and B.

FIG. 42A. Dimpling a cam master. (Parker-Hartford Corp.)

FIG. 42B. Production cam milling machine (Parker-Hartford Corp.)

With the need for high speed cams, the effect of vibrations on cam performance has also become more important. Unfortunately, a vibration investigation of a cam system requires information concerning the elasticity of the system. The determination of the elastic response of a cam system is an extremely difficult problem. The result is that not enough can be done in the design stage to give proper consideration to vibration effects. It is very often desirable to construct a prototype of the cam system. As a result of tests on the prototype, modifications can be made to ensure a satisfactory solution to the given problem.

Spur Gears:
Design and Analysis

Basic Considerations

There are a variety of machine elements available for transmitting power from one shaft to another. If the distance between the shafts is relatively small, a pair of friction wheels (rolling cylinders) may be used. In Fig. 1, which shows the cross-sectional view of such a pair, wheel No. 1 is the driver, while wheel No. 2 is the follower. Most phonographs make use of friction wheels to drive the turntable. However, the axes of the friction wheels are often at 90° to each other rather than parallel to each other as shown in Fig. 1.

The force that cylinder 1 can transmit to cylinder 2 depends on the friction that can be developed between the two cylinders. Assuming that the frictional resistance between the two wheels is sufficiently large to prevent slipping of one cylinder relative to the other, the following kinematic relationship holds:

$$v_P = r_1 \omega_1 = r_2 \omega_2$$

or

$$\frac{\omega_1}{\omega_2} = \frac{r_2}{r_1} \tag{1}$$

where v_P is instantaneous linear velocity of the point of contact in in/sec,

ω is angular velocity in rad/sec,

r is cylinder radius in in.

Equation 1 indicates that the angular speed ratio of the cylinders is inversely proportional to their radii. Another important fact to be observed from Fig. 1 is that the rotations of the cylinders are in oppo-

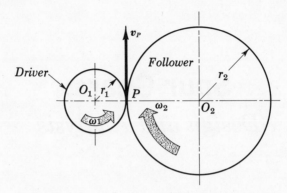

FIG. 1. Two friction wheels (external cylinders). As shown, cylinder 1 rotates counter-clockwise driving cylinder 2 in the clockwise direction. *If no slipping occurs,* the linear velocity of point P on cylinder 1 is equal to the linear velocity of point P on cylinder 2.

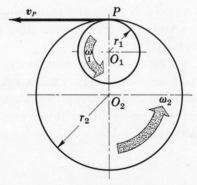

FIG. 2. Two friction wheels (internal contact). Both the driver (1) and the follower (2) rotate in the same direction. As before, the linear velocity of point P for both wheels is equal *if no slipping occurs.*

site directions (wheel No. 1 rotates counterclockwise, while wheel No. 2 rotates clockwise).

The cylinders shown in Fig. 1 are external to each other. Fig. 2 shows a similar situation, except that one of the cylinders is internal to the other. The only difference between the external and internal cylinder pairs is that the direction of rotation for both cylinders of the internal pair is the same. In other words, cylinder 1 and cylinder 2 are both rotating counterclockwise.

The big disadvantage of friction wheels is the possibility that slipping may occur between the cylinders. Therefore, when exact angular velocity ratios are required or a constant phase relationship must be

FIG. 3A. An external spur gear set. Spur gears are easily identified by their straight teeth which are parallel to the gear axis. (Boston Gear Works)

FIG. 3B. An internal spur gear. Internal gears permit a closer positioning of the gear shafts. (Automotive Gear Div., Eaton, Yale, & Towne)

FIG. 3C. A spur gear and rack set. This gear set permits precise translations and is frequently used as the drive train in manual controls. (Browning Mfg. Co.)

maintained between the driver and follower, a machine element known as a gear is commonly used.

A gear may be thought of as a friction wheel with teeth cut around the circumference. Thus, the transmission of motion from one shaft to another is independent of the frictional resistance between the wheels, and positive motion transmission can be achieved.

Gear Types

There are several types of gears in common use. Among the more important types are:

1. Spur gears (Fig. 3) and helical gears (Fig. 4)—used when the driver and follower shafts are parallel to each other.

2. Bevel gears (Fig. 5)—used when the shaft axes are intersecting.

3. Worm gears (Fig. 6) and crossed helical gears (Fig. 7)—used when the shaft axes are nonintersecting and nonparallel.

FIG. 4A. A single helical spur gear set. Helical spur gears provide less shock and smoother, quieter operation than straight spur gears. (Browning Mfg. Co.)

FIG. 4B. Herringbone gear, or double-helical gear. In some cases, the presence of end thrust inherent in helical gears is undesirable. Gears with opposing helices neutralize the end thrust of each helix. (Horsburgh & Scott Co.)

Fig. 5A. Straight bevel gears. Bevel gears are used in cases where the driver and driven shaft centerlines intersect. (Automotive Gear Div., Eaton, Yale, and Towne)

FIG. 5B. Spiral bevel gears. The spiral bevel gear is to the plain bevel gear what the helical gear is to the spur gear. However the spiral bevel gear has teeth with a circular rather than a helical curvature. (Automotive Gear Div., Eaton, Yale, and Towne)

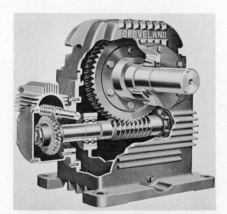

FIG. 6. The worm and worm gear set. The worm gear is a special helical gear, used where large speed reductions are to be transmitted. (Cleveland Worm & Gear Div., Eaton, Yale and Towne)

FIG. 7. Crossed helical gears are used with shafts which are non-parallel and non-intersecting. (Browning Mfg. Co.)

Spur Gear Terminology

A spur gear can be thought of as a cylinder which has teeth cut on its circumference parallel to the axis of the cylinder. Its design is the least complicated of gear designs. For this reason, the spur gear offers a convenient starting point for the study of gears, since the terms introduced will also apply to more complex gears discussed in the next chapter. Spur gears, which are used to transmit power between parallel shafts, are the most common type of gear in use. When two gears are in mesh, it is customary to refer to the smaller as the *pinion* and the larger as the *gear*.

Since it is necessary to a thorough study of gears to become completely familiar with gear terminology, the more important parts of gears are identified below and illustrated in Fig. 8.

Pitch Circle: the circle on a gear which corresponds to the contact surface of the friction wheel. Thus, for two gears in contact, the respective pitch circles can be imagined to roll on each other in the same

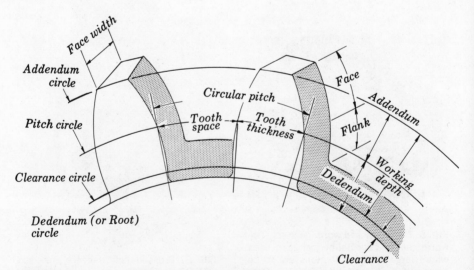

FIG. 8. Spur gear terminology. This figure illustrates some of the more important terms and dimensions associated with spur gears.

manner as the circles of two friction wheels in contact. A gear may be thought of as similar to a friction cylinder with the face width of the gear equal to the length of the cylinder, and the diameter of the pitch circle of the gear equal to the diameter of the cylinder.

Addendum: the radial distance from the pitch circle to the addendum circle.

Addendum Circle: the circle drawn through the top of the gear tooth. Its center is at the gear center.

Dedendum: the radial distance from the pitch circle to the root circle.

Root or Dedendum Circle: the circle drawn through the bottom of the gear tooth. Its center is at the gear center.

Clearance: the radial distance from the clearance circle to the root circle. Since the clearance is also equal to the distance between the top of the tooth and the root of the tooth of the mating gear, it can also be defined as the difference between the addendum of one gear and the dedendum of the mating gear.

Whole Depth: the radial distance between the addendum and dedendum circles.

Working Depth: the radial distance between the addendum and clearance circles. The working depth is also equal to the sum of the addendums of the two meshing gears.

Circular Pitch: the circular pitch, p, is the distance *measured along the pitch circle* from a point on one tooth to the corresponding point on the adjacent tooth of the gear. Therefore,

$$p = \frac{\pi d}{N} \tag{2}$$

where d is the diameter of the *pitch circle* in in., and N is the number of teeth of the gear. It is, therefore, equal to the circumference of the pitch circle divided by the number of teeth.

Diametral Pitch: The diametral pitch, P, is equal to the number of teeth of a gear divided by the diameter of the pitch circle. Thus,

$$P = \frac{N}{d} \, . \tag{3}$$

The circular and diametral pitches are extremely important in gear analysis. The pitch is an indication of the spacing and sizes of the gear

Mechanism

teeth. Additionally, in order for two gears to mesh, they must have the same pitch. There are other dimensions of gears which must be equal in order for two gears to mesh, but these will be discussed later.

A simple relationship exists between the circular and diametral pitches. Since

$$P = \frac{N}{d}, \qquad d = \frac{N}{P}$$

but $p = \pi d/N$, therefore

$$p = \frac{\pi}{N} \times \frac{N}{P}$$

or

$$Pp = \pi. \tag{4}$$

In other words, the product of the diametral pitch and the circular pitch is always equal to a constant, namely, π.

Fig. 9 shows a gauge which illustrates the comparative sizes of gear teeth for standard values of diametral pitch.

FIG. 9. The Morse gear gauge provides a basis for comparing the relative sizes of gear teeth for standard values of diametral pitch. (Morse Chain Co.)

EXAMPLE—PROBLEM 1: A spur gear, having 32 teeth and a diametral pitch of 4, is rotating at 400 RPM. Determine (A) its circular pitch and (B) its pitch line velocity.

Solution: (A) Since we know the diametral pitch, the circular pitch can be obtained directly from Eq. (4):

$$p = \frac{\pi}{P}.$$

Thus,

$$p = \frac{\pi}{4} = .7854 \text{ in.}$$

(B) To find pitch line velocity ($= r\omega$) we will first have to find the pitch diameter of the gear. From Eq. (3):

$$P = \frac{N}{d}.$$

Thus,

$$d = \frac{N}{P} = \frac{32}{4} = 8 \text{ in.}$$

Converting angular velocity of the gear from RPM to rad/sec,

$$\omega = 400 \ \frac{\text{rev}}{\text{min}} \times \frac{2 \text{ rad}}{1 \text{ rev}} \times \frac{1 \text{ min}}{60 \text{ sec}}$$

$$= 41.9 \ \frac{\text{rad}}{\text{sec}}.$$

Finally, the pitch line velocity is the product of the *pitch circle radius* and the angular velocity of the gear, Eq. (1)

$$v_p = r\omega = \frac{d\omega}{2}$$

$$= \frac{8}{2} \text{ in} \times 41.9 \ \frac{\text{rad}}{\text{sec}}$$

$$= 167.5 \ \frac{\text{in}}{\text{sec}}.$$

Backlash. If tooth spaces were made equal to tooth widths, it would be extremely difficult for the gears to mesh. Any inaccuracies in manu-

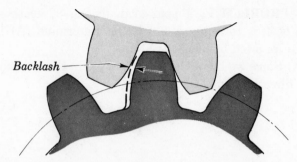

FIG. 10. Backlash between two meshing teeth is described as proportional to the angle the driving gear can be rotated through before contacting the mating face of the driven gear. (Pic Design Corp.)

facturing would cause the gears to jam. It is also very often necessary to lubricate gears. For these reasons, space must be provided between the meshing teeth. This is accomplished by making the tooth thickness less than the tooth space. The difference between tooth space and tooth width is known as *backlash*.

Backlash, which is measured on the pitch circle, is then equal to the distance between the nondriving side of a tooth and the side of the corresponding tooth of the meshing gear. If one of a pair of meshing gears is held stationary, the amount of backlash is then proportional to the angle the other gear can be rotated through. Fig. 10 shows the backlash between two gears.

The cutting tool used to manufacture gears can be set further into the gear blank, thus decreasing the tooth width and increasing the tooth space. This is the most common method of providing backlash for gears. Slight variations in backlash can also be obtained by changing the center distance of the gears.

It should be emphasized that, while some backlash is necessary, too much backlash can result in large shock loads. The backlash can become excessive, resulting in inaccurate gear motion.*

Fundamental Law of Gearing

As stated earlier, an important reason for the use of gears is to maintain a constant angular velocity ratio. The fundamental law of gearing states the condition which the gear tooth profiles must satisfy in

---

*In the June 9, 1966 issue of *Machine Design Magazine* an interesting discussion of the sources of backlash is presented.

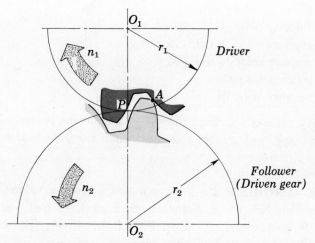

FIG. 11. Two gears are shown in mesh, with the pitch point at P. The meshing gear teeth are shown in contact at point A.

order to maintain a constant angular velocity ratio. The law may be stated as follows: *The shape (profile) of the teeth of a gear must be such that the common normal at the point of contact between two teeth must always pass through a fixed point on the line of centers.* The fixed point is called the *pitch point*. When the fundamental law is satisfied, the gears in mesh are said to produce *conjugate action*.

In Fig. 11, O_1 and O_2 are the centers of the two gears in mesh, r_1 and r_2 are the radii of the pitch circles, P is the pitch point, and A the point at which the gears are in contact.

The Velocity Ratio

Before proceeding with the discussion of conjugate action, it will be necessary to define the velocity ratio. The velocity ratio is equal to the angular speed (ω) of the *follower* (driven gear) divided by the angular speed of the driving gear. However, the ratio can also be defined in terms of RPM, pitch radii, and the number of gear teeth.

In the following equations the subscript 1 refers to the driver, while subscript 2 refers to the follower or driven gear :

$$r_v = \frac{\omega_2}{\omega_1} = \frac{n_2}{n_1} = \frac{r_1}{r_2} = \frac{N_1}{N_2} \qquad (5)$$

Mechanism

where

> $r_v =$ velocity ratio
> $\omega =$ angular velocity (rad/sec)
> $n =$ angular velocity in RPM
> $r =$ pitch circle radius
> $N =$ number of teeth.

The velocity ratio is less than one when the pinion is the driving gear (the usual case), and greater than one when the gear is the driver.

EXAMPLE—PROBLEM 2: Two spur gears have a velocity ratio of 1/4. The driven gear has a diametral pitch of 4, 96 teeth, and rotates at 500 RPM. Determine (A) the RPM of the driver, (B) the number of teeth of the driver, and (C) the pitch line velocity.

Solution: (A) The angular velocity (in RPM) is obtained directly from the velocity ratio, Eq. (5):

$$r_v = \frac{n_2}{n_1}.$$

Thus,

$$n_1 = \frac{n_2}{r_v} = \frac{500}{1/4} = 2000 \text{ RPM}.$$

(B) The number of teeth on the driver also follows directly from the velocity ratio:

$$r_v = \frac{N_1}{N_2}$$

$$N_1 = r_v N_2 = \frac{1}{4} \times 96 = 24 \text{ teeth}.$$

(C) Pitch line velocity is given by Eq. (1), the product of pitch circle radius and angular velocity, just as in Example Problem 1:

$$v_p = r_2 \omega_2, \qquad P = \frac{N_2}{d_2}.$$

Thus,

$$r_2 = \frac{d_2}{2} = \frac{N_2}{2P} = \frac{96}{2 \times 4} = 12 \text{ in.}$$

$$\omega_2 = N_2 \times \frac{2\pi}{60} = 500 \ \frac{\text{rev}}{\text{min}} \times \frac{2\pi \ \text{rad}}{1 \ \text{rev}} \times \frac{1 \ \text{min}}{60 \ \text{sec}} = 52.3 \ \frac{\text{rad}}{\text{sec}}$$

and

$$v_p = r_2\omega_2 = 12 \ \text{in} \times 52.3 \ \frac{\text{rad}}{\text{sec}} = 627.6 \ \frac{\text{in}}{\text{sec}} \ .$$

Check: Since v_p is also $= r_1\omega_1$,

$$r_v = \frac{r_1}{r_2} = \frac{\omega_2}{\omega_1} \ .$$

Therefore,

$$r_1 = \frac{1}{4} \times 12 \ \text{in} = 3 \ \text{in}.$$

$$\omega_1 = \frac{\omega_2}{r_v} = \frac{52.3}{1/4} = 209.2 \ \frac{\text{rad}}{\text{sec}}$$

and

$$v_p = r_1\omega_1 = 3 \ \text{in} \times 209.2 \ \frac{\text{rad}}{\text{sec}} = 627.6 \ \frac{\text{in}}{\text{sec}} \ .$$

Conjugate Action and the Involute Curve

Fig. 12 is a magnified view of the point of contact of two gears. Line tt is tangent to each of the two teeth at the point of contact, A. Line nn is perpendicular to tt, and is the common normal at the point

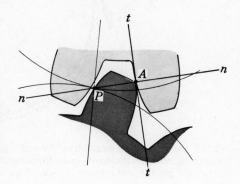

FIG. 12. Two gears in contact at point A. The tangent drawn to the contact point A is tt, while the normal, nn, to point A is drawn through the pitch point, P. In order for conjugate action to take place, the common normal to the point of contact must pass through the pitch point.

of contact A. In order for the fundamental law to be satisfied, nn must go through the fixed point P.

As the gears continue to rotate, other points on the teeth will come into contact. However, for each successive point of contact, the common normal to the contact point must continue to pass through the fixed point P in order for conjugate action to take place (to maintain constant angular velocity ratio).

When gear profiles are cut in such a way as to produce conjugate action, the curves are known as conjugate curves. Most gears are cut using the involute curve to obtain conjugate action. However, for certain specialized applications, gears are sometimes cut using a cycloidal curve as the tooth profile.

The Base Circle of an Involute. Consider a cylinder with a string wrapped around it. An involute curve is the curve traced out by a point on the string, as the string is unwrapped from the cylinder. In gear terminology the cylinder around which the string is wrapped is known as the *base circle*. In order to better understand what the involute curve looks like, consider Fig. 13. The base circle, of radius r_b, has a

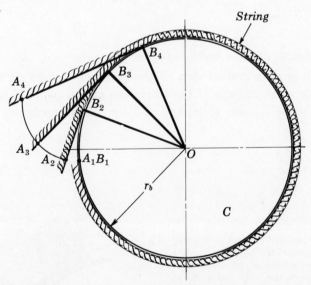

FIG. 13. Involute curve generation. As a string is unwrapped from a cylinder, the curve traced by a point on the string is an involute curve (A_1, A_2, A_3, A_4). The tangents to the base circle are the instantaneous radii of curvature of the involute.

string S wrapped around it. Point A is the point on the end of the string, while point B is the corresponding point on the circle at which the string leaves the circle.

Initially, while the string is still completely wrapped around the base circle, points A and B coincide. This condition is represented by points A_1 and B_1. As the string is unwrapped, point A moves to position A_2, while B_2 is the point at which the string leaves the base circle. As the string is further unwrapped, the positions A_3, B_3, A_4 and B_4 are likewise determined. The curve then drawn through points A_1, A_2, A_3 and A_4 is the involute curve.

Another important property possessed by the involute curve is that a normal drawn to it is tangent to the base circle. Referring again to Fig. 13, OB_1, OB_2, OB_3 and OB_4 are radii of the base circle, while A_2B_2, A_3B_3, and A_4B_4 are tangent to the base circle and perpendicular to the radii. The distance A_2B_2 is the radius of curvature of the involute at that instant, since point A_2 is rotating about point B_2 at that instant. Similar reasoning shows that A_3B_3, and A_4B_4 are also insantaneous radii of curvature. Therefore, it is clear that the radius of curvature of an involute curve is continuously varying. But, since at any given point on a curve the radius of curvature is normal to the curve, lines A_2B_2, A_3B_3, and A_4B_4 are normals drawn to the involute curve and are also tangent to the base circle. Thus, the earlier statement, that a normal to the involute curve is tangent to the base circle, is correct.

Involute Gear Tooth Relationships

It is now appropriate to consider the action that occurs when two gear teeth, cut with involute curve profiles, are in contact.

In Fig. 14, gear No. 1 is the driver and is rotating clockwise, while gear No. 2, the follower, rotates counterclockwise. The distance c in the diagram is called the *center distance*, and represents the spacing between the centers of the shafts upon which the gears are mounted. Eq. (6) may be used to determine the center distance

$$c = \frac{d_1 + d_2}{2} \tag{6}$$

where d_1 and d_2 are the diameters of the pitch circles. In practice, the center distance between two shafts and the speed ratio are usually

Mechanism

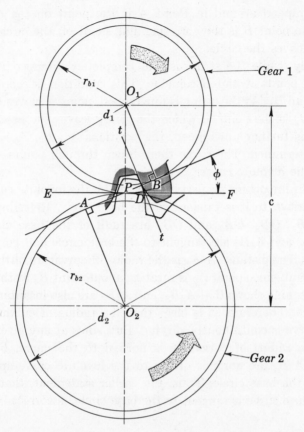

FIG. 14. Two gears in contact. The center distance, c, is equal to one-half the sum of the pitch diameters. As the gears continue to rotate, the other points of contact must have their common normal passing through the pitch point, P. Thus, all contact points must lie on line AB, called the *line of action*. Line AB is also called the *pressure line*, and ϕ is referred to as the *pressure angle*.

specified. With this information it is possible to determine the required pitch diameters.

EXAMPLE—PROBLEM 3: Determine the center distance for a pair of gears having a diametral pitch of 5, and 20 and 80 teeth respectively. **Solution:** Eq. (3) is used to find the pitch diameters for both gears:

$$P = \frac{N}{d}$$

$$d_1 = \frac{N_1}{P} = \frac{20}{5} = 4 \text{ in.}$$

$$d_2 = \frac{N_2}{P} = \frac{80}{5} = 16 \text{ in.}$$

Then, from Eq. (6),

$$c = \frac{d_1 + d_2}{2} = \frac{4 + 16}{2} = 10 \text{ in.}$$

The Line of Action

When two curves are in contact at a point, they must have the same tangent and normal at the point of contact (Fig. 12). In Fig. 14, point D is the point of contact between the two involute curves to which the teeth of gears 1 and 2 have been cut. The common tangent to the tooth surfaces is *tt*, while line AB, which is perpendicular to *tt* at the point of contact, is the common normal.

According to the fundamental law of gearing, this common normal must pass through a fixed point. In other words line AB must always pass through a fixed point, P. But, according to the properties of the involute curve discussed previously, the common normal is also the radius of curvature of the involute and is tangent to the generating, or base, circle. As the gears continue to rotate, other points will become contact points. The common normals for these points also must pass through the fixed point P, and also must be tangent to the base circles. The only way these conditions can be satisfied is for the points of contact always to lie on line AB.

The line AB is often called the *line of action* because the contact points of two gears in mesh must lie along it. The force that one gear tooth exerts on the tooth of the meshing gear acts along the common normal which is also line AB. Therefore, *pressure line* is another name commonly given to line AB.

The Pressure Angle

The angle ϕ, between the pressure line, AB, and the common tangent to the pitch circles, EF in Fig. 14, is known as the *pressure angle*. The pressure line is located by rotating the common tangent to the pitch circles, EF, through the angle ϕ in a direction opposite to the direction of rotation of the driver. Referring again to Fig. 14, since

Mechanism

gear No. 1, the driver, is rotating clockwise, the pressure line *AB* is located by rotating the common tangent *EF* counterclockwise through the angle ϕ.

While gears may be manufactured with a wide range of pressure angles, most gears are made with standard angles of 20° or 25°. Gears with 14½° pressure angles were once prevalent, but are now obsolete. Although gears with pressure angles of 14½° are still manufactured, they are mainly replacements for older gear trains still in use.

Varying the Pressure Angle

Although gears are designated by their pressure angle, it should be emphasized that the actual pressure angle between two gears in contact may differ from the designated value. Changes in center distance, c, will result in corresponding changes of the actual pressure angles. In other words, two nominally 20° gears actually may have a slightly larger pressure angle by increasing their center distance.

Example Problem 5, in the next section, will illustrate the difference between designated and actual pressure angles. However, at this point, a diagram can illustrate the effect of increasing the center distance. In Fig. 15A, gears 1 and 2 have their centers at O_1 and O_2. The pressure angle is 20°, and the base circle radii are r_{b1} and r_{b2}. The

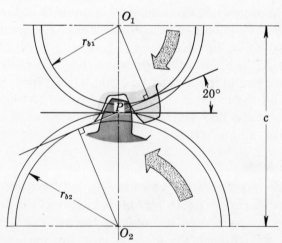

FIG. 15A. Two gears in mesh showing center distance, c, pressure angle of 20°, and the base circle radii, r_{b1} and r_{b2}.

298

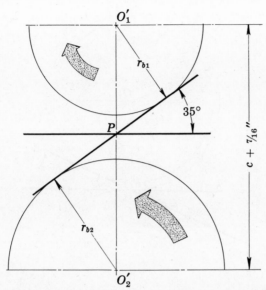

FIG. 15B. The center distance of the gears in Fig. 15A is shown increased by 7/16 in. The base radii remain unchanged; however, the pressure angle is now increased to 35°.

center distance is then increased so that the centers of the gears are at O_1' and O_2'. Fig. 15B shows the new situation with the increased center distance and unchanged base circle radii. As in Fig. 15A, the pressure line is drawn tangent to the base circles and through the pitch point. As can be seen from the illustration, the pressure angle is now increased to approximately 35°. The increase in the pressure angle has been made larger than would be the actual case for purposes of illustration.

Dimensional Relationships

In order to obtain a better understanding of gear tooth action, consider Fig. 16. Two gears, 1 and 2, are shown in mesh. The pitch radii r_1 and r_2, as well as the base circle radii r_{b1} and r_{b2}, are shown. The base circles were determined by drawing circles tangent to the pressure line AB. Therefore, the radii r_{b1} and r_{b2} are each pependicular to the pressure line at points D and C respectively.

By considering the right triangles O_1PD and O_2PC, a simple relationship between the pitch circle radius and the base circle radius is seen to exist:

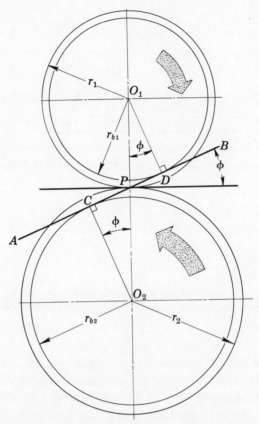

FIG. 16. This illustration shows the relationship between the base circle radii, the pressure angle, and the pitch circle radii: $r_b = r \cos \phi$.

$$\cos \phi = \frac{r_{b1}}{r_1} = \frac{r_{b2}}{r_2}, \quad \text{or} \quad r_b = r \cos \phi. \tag{7}$$

EXAMPLE—PROBLEM 4: Two meshing spur gears with diametral pitch of 4, pressure angle of 20°, and a velocity ratio of 1/4 have their centers 15 inches apart. Determine (A) the number of teeth of the driver (pinion), and (B) the base circle radius of the gear.

Solution: As usual, subscript 1 will refer to the pinion and subscript 2 will refer to the gear. (A) From the velocity ratio we know that

$$r_v = \frac{n_2}{n_1} = \frac{N_1}{N_2} = \frac{1}{4}$$

or

$$N_2 = 4N_1 .$$

Having conveniently established a relationship between N_1 and N_2, we can now set up a second equation in N_1 and N_2 (giving us two equations in two unknowns) and determine N_1 and N_2. Knowing the diametral pitch, P, and the distance between centers, c, we can substitute expressions for the pitch diameters d_1 and d_2 (which contain N_1 and N_2) into the equation for the center distance, Equation (6):

$$P = \frac{N}{d}, \quad \text{or} \quad d = \frac{N}{P} .$$

Therefore,

$$c = \frac{d_1 + d_2}{2} = \frac{1}{2} \frac{N_1 + N_2}{P}$$

$$= \frac{1}{2P} (N_1 + N_2).$$

Substituting the given values for c and P, we obtain the second equation in N_1 and N_2. Using the first relationship between N_1 and N_2, we arrive at the value of N_1:

$$15 = \frac{1}{2 \times 4} (N_1 + N_2) .$$

But $N_2 = 4N_1$, therefore

$$120 = N_1 + 4N_1 = 5N_1$$

$$N_1 = 24 \text{ teeth.}$$

(B) To solve for the base circle radius of the gear, we simply solve for r_1 and then use the velocity ratio and pressure angle formulas to find r_{b2}:

$$d_1 = \frac{N_1}{P} = \frac{24}{4} = 6 \text{ in.}$$

Therefore $r_1 = 3$ in., and

$$r_v = \frac{n_2}{n_1} = \frac{r_1}{r_2}$$

$$r_2 = \frac{r_1}{n_2/n_1} = \frac{3}{1/4} = 12 \text{ in.}$$

And from Equation (7), the base circle radius, r_{b2}, is given as

$$r_{b2} = r_2 \cos \phi$$

$$= 12 \cos 20° = 11.2 \text{ in.}$$

EXAMPLE—PROBLEM 5: Two 20° gears have a diametral pitch of 4. The pinion has 28 teeth while the gear has 56 teeth. (A) Determine the center distance for an actual pressure angle of 20°. (B) What is the actual pressure angle if the center distance is increased by .2 in?

Solution: (A) Using the data given, the center distance is found by using Eq. (3) to obtain the pitch circle diameters, and then using these values in Eq. (6):

$$P = \frac{N}{d}$$

$$d_1 = \frac{N_1}{P} = \frac{28}{4} = 7 \text{ in.}$$

$$d_2 = \frac{N_2}{P} = \frac{56}{4} = 14 \text{ in.}$$

Thus,

$$c = \frac{1}{2} (d_1 + d_2)$$

$$= \frac{1}{2} (7 + 14) = 10.5 \text{ in.}$$

(B) The base circle radius was determined when the gears were cut, and changing the center distance does not change the base circle radius. *However, increasing the center distance does increase the pitch radius, which in turn results in a larger pressure angle.* To find the actual pressure angle resulting from an increased center distance, we must first find the base circle radius and the new pitch radius. From Eq. (7):

$$r_{b1} = r_1 \cos \phi$$

$$= 3.5 \cos 20° = 3.29 \text{ in.}$$

The new center distance, c', is

$$10.5 + 0.2 = 10.7 \text{ in.}$$

The new pitch radii, r_1' and r_2', although changed numerically, will maintain the same proportion held by the original pitch radii. Thus, from Eq. 5:

$$r_v = \frac{N_1}{N_2} = \frac{r_1}{r_2} = \frac{r_1'}{r_2'} = \frac{1}{2}$$

or

$$r_2' = 2r_1'$$

but

$$c' = r_1' + r_2' = 10.7$$

therefore

$$r_1' + 2r_1' = 10.7$$
$$r_1' = 3.57 \text{ in.}$$

Since base circle radius doesn't change, we can now finally calculate the new pressure angle, using Eq. (7):

$$r_{b1} = r_1' \cos \phi$$

$$\cos \phi = \frac{r_{b1}}{r_1'} = \frac{3.29}{3.57} = .922$$

or,

$$\phi = 22.8°.$$

Contact Length. As was stated earlier, all the points of contact between two gear teeth must lie along the pressure line. The initial contact between two teeth will occur when the tip of the driven gear tooth is acted on by the flank of the driver tooth. The final point of contact will be at the flank of the driven gear tooth and the tip of the driver tooth. Another way of describing the interval of contact is to

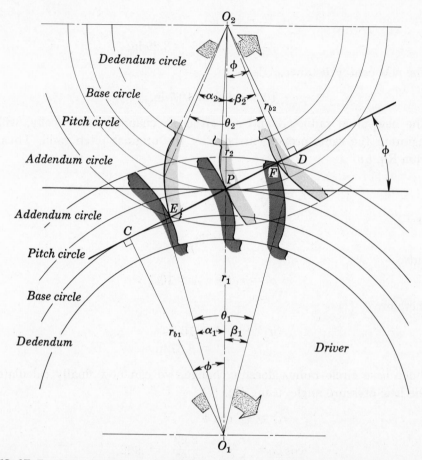

FIG. 17. For the contacting gear teeth shown, initial contact occurs at point *E* and final contact occurs at point *F*. Line *EF* is the length of the line of action. Angles θ_1 and θ_2 are the angles of action, α_1 and α_2 are the angles of approach, and B_1 and B_2 are the angles of recess. The angle of action is equal to the sum of the angle of approach and the angle of recess.

say that initial contact occurs where the addendum circle of the driven gear intersects the pressure line, and final contact occurs at the point where the addendum circle of the driver intersects the pressure line.

Fig. 17 illustrates the important points of the previous discussion. Initial contact occurs at point *E*, which is the intersection of the addendum circle of the driven gear and the pressure line. Point *F*, the intersection of the addendum circle of the driver and the pressure line, is the final contact point of the interval during which the teeth contact.

The distance between points E and F is known as the length of the line of action or the contact length.

The angles θ_1 and θ_2 shown in Fig. 17 are known as the angles of action. They are the angles turned through by the driver and follower gears respectively during the contact between a pair of gear teeth. The *arc of action* is the arc, measured on the pitch circle, turned through by a gear as a pair of meshing gear teeth go from initial to final contact. Note that θ_1 and θ_2 subtend the arcs of action.

Angles α_1 and α_2 are known as the angles of approach. The angle of approach is the angle turned through by a gear as measured from the initial contact point to the pitch point along the pitch circle.

The angle of recess is defined as the angle turned through by a gear while the contact between the teeth goes from the pitch point to the point of final contact. On Fig. 17, β_1 and β_2 are the angles of recess. It should be clear from the definitions as well as from the illustration that the angle of action is equal to the sum of the angle of approach and the angle of recess.

Contact Ratio. The circular pitch, as defined in an earlier section, is equal to the distance, measured on the pitch circle, between corresponding points of adjacent teeth. Let γ be the angle determined by the circular pitch, AB, as shown in Fig. 18. The angle γ is known as the *pitch angle.* We now define the *contact ratio* as *the angle of action divided by the pitch angle* or

$$\text{Contact Ratio} = \frac{\theta}{\gamma} = \frac{\alpha + \beta}{\gamma}. \tag{8A}$$

If the contact ratio were equal to one, Eq. (8A) would indicate that the angle of action is equal to the pitch angle. A contact ratio of one means that one pair of teeth are in contact at all times. If the contact ratio were less than one, there would be an interval during which *no* teeth would be in contact. Gears are usually designed with a contact ratio between 1.2 and 1.6. For a contact ratio of 1.2, one pair of teeth are always in contact, and 2 pair of teeth are in contact twenty percent of the time. Therefore, the contact ratio is also commonly defined as the average number of teeth in contact.

The contact ratio can be defined in still another way. However, in order to understand this definition, we must first define the base

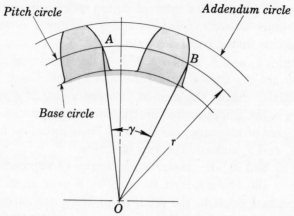

FIG. 18. The pitch angle, γ, is simply the angular equivalent of the circular pitch.

pitch. The *base pitch*, p_b, *is equal to the distance between corresponding points of adjacent teeth measured on the base circle.* Therefore,

$$p_b = \frac{\pi d_b}{N} \tag{9A}$$

where d_b is the diameter of the base circle, and N is the number of teeth. But, from Fig. 17, $r_b = r \cos \phi$, where ϕ is the angle between the pitch point and the point where the line of action is tangent to the base circle. Since $r_b = r \cos \phi$, it follows that $d_b = d \cos \phi$. Therefore,

$$p_b = \frac{\pi d \cos \phi}{N}.$$

But since $P = N/d$,

$$p_b = \frac{\pi \cos \phi}{P}$$

but $p = \pi/P$, therefore

$$p_b = p \cos \phi. \tag{9B}$$

The contact ratio can now also be defined as the ratio of the length of action divided by the base pitch. Referring again to Fig. 17, the line of action is equal to the distance between points E and F. This definition is valid since the length of action, *EF*, is the same distance the base circle rolls through as the involute is being generated. Therefore,

$$\text{Contact Ratio} = \frac{EF}{p_b} \cdot \tag{8B}$$

The length of action can be computed from the following formulas.

$$EF = EP + PF \qquad EP = ED - PD$$

To obtain *EF*, it will be necessary to determine component lengths *EP* + *PF*. In right triangle O_2DE, length O_2E is equal to the sum of the pitch radius and the addendum of driven gear 2:

$$O_2E = r_2 + a_2.$$

O_2D is the base radius of gear 2, and is given by

$$O_2D = r_{b2} = r_2 \cos \phi.$$

We can therefore determine length *ED* using the Pythagorean Theorem:

$$ED = \sqrt{(O_2E)^2 - (O_2D)^2}$$
$$= \sqrt{(r_2 + a_2)^2 - r_2{}^2 \cos^2 \phi} \ .$$

Also,

$$PD = r_2 \sin \phi.$$

Therefore

$$EP = ED - PD$$
$$= \sqrt{(r_2 + a_2)^2 - r_2{}^2 \cos^2 \phi} \qquad - r_2 \sin \phi.$$

The distance *PF* is found in a similar manner. Using triangle O_1CF, length O_1F equals the sum of the pitch radius and addendum of the driver:

$$O_1F = r_1 + a_1.$$

O_1C, the base radius of the driver, is given as

$$O_1C = r_{b1} = r_1 \cos \phi.$$

As for *ED*, *CF* is found using the Pythagorean Theorem

$$CF = \sqrt{(O_1F)^2 - (O_1C)^2}$$
$$= \sqrt{(r_1 + a_1)^2 - r_1{}^2 \cos^2 \phi} \ .$$

Also,

$$CP = r_1 \sin \phi$$

Therefore

$$PF = CF - CP$$
$$= \sqrt{(r_1 + a_1)^2 - r_1{}^2 \cos^2 \phi} - r_1 \sin \phi.$$

Finally, we obtain the length of the line of action solely in terms of the pitch radii, the addendums, and the common pressure angle

$$EF = EP + PF$$
$$= \sqrt{(r_2 + a_2)^2 - r_2{}^2 \cos^2 \phi} - r_2 \sin \phi$$
$$+ \sqrt{(r_1 + a_1)^2 - r_1{}^2 \cos^2 \phi} - r_1 \sin \phi.$$

Thus, the formula for the contact ratio, Eq. (8B), becomes

$$\text{Contact Ratio} = \frac{\sqrt{(r_2 + a_2)^2 - r_2{}^2 \cos^2 \phi} - r_2 \sin \phi}{p_b}$$
$$+ \frac{\sqrt{(r_1 + a_1)^2 - r_1{}^2 \cos^2 \phi} - r_1 \sin \phi}{p_b} \qquad (8C)$$

EXAMPLE—PROBLEM 6: Two 25° full-depth spur gears have a velocity ratio of 1/3. The diametral pitch is 5 and the pinion has 20 teeth. Determine the contact ratio (number of teeth in contact) for the gears. (The formula for the addendum of a 25° full-depth gear is given in Table 1 in the following section as $a = 1/P$.)

Solution: Before using Eq. (8C) to determine the contact ratio, we will first have to find the following values: r_1, r_2, a_1, a_2, P_b, $\sin \phi$ and $\cos \phi$. Thus, from Eq. (3), $P = N/d$,

$$d_1 = \frac{N_1}{P} = \frac{20}{5} = 4 \text{ in, \quad or \quad } r_1 = 2 \text{ in.}$$

And from the velocity ratio equation,

$$r_v = \frac{n_2}{n_1} = \frac{r_1}{r_2} = \frac{1}{3}, \quad \text{or} \quad r_2 = 6 \text{ in.}$$

The addendum is given by

$$a_1 = a_2 = \frac{1}{P} = \frac{1}{5} = 0.2 \text{ in.}$$

And

$$\cos \phi = \cos 25° = 0.906$$

$$\sin \phi = \sin 25° = 0.423.$$

The last of the unknowns is the base pitch. From Eq. (4), $Pp = \pi$,

$$p = \frac{\pi}{P} = \frac{\pi}{5} = 0.628,$$

and from Eq. (9B),

$$p_b = p \cos \phi$$

$$= 0.628 \times 0.906 = 0.57.$$

Thus the contact ratio formula, Eq. (8C), is solved with the values determined above:

$$\text{Contact Ratio} = \frac{\sqrt{(r_2 + a_2)^2 - r_2{}^2 \cos^2 \phi} - r_2 \sin \phi}{p_b}$$

$$+ \frac{\sqrt{(r_1 + a_1)^2 - r_1{}^2 \cos^2 \phi} - r_1 \sin \phi}{p_b}$$

$$= \frac{\sqrt{(6 + 0.2)^2 - 6^2 (0.906)^2} - 6(0.423)}{0.57}$$

$$+ \frac{\sqrt{(2 + 0.2)^2 - 2^2 (0.906)^2} - 2(0.423)}{0.57}$$

$$= \frac{\sqrt{38.60 - 29.50} - 2.54 + \sqrt{4.85 - 3.28} - 0.85}{0.57}$$

$$= \frac{.88}{.57} = 1.55 \ .$$

Standard Gears

It is economically desirable to standardize gears so that they are interchangeable. Gears with any number of teeth, but having the same pitch and pressure angle, are interchangeable if their tooth profiles have been cut to the same standard tooth system. Thus the standard tooth

TABLE 1. STANDARD GEAR PROFILES

System	Addendum	Dedendum	Clearance	Whole Depth
14½° Full-Depth Involute	$\dfrac{1}{P}$	$\dfrac{1.157}{P}$	$\dfrac{0.157}{P}$	$\dfrac{2.157}{P}$
14½° Composite	$\dfrac{1}{P}$	$\dfrac{1.157}{P}$	$\dfrac{0.157}{P}$	$\dfrac{2.157}{P}$
20° Full-Depth Involute	$\dfrac{1}{P}$	$\dfrac{1.25}{P}$	$\dfrac{0.25}{P}$	$\dfrac{2.25}{P}$
20° Stub-Tooth Involute	$\dfrac{0.8}{P}$	$\dfrac{1}{P}$	$\dfrac{0.2}{P}$	$\dfrac{1.8}{P}$
25° Full-Depth Involute	$\dfrac{1}{P}$	$\dfrac{1.25}{P}$	$\dfrac{0.25}{P}$	$\dfrac{2.25}{P}$

systems have specified values for addendum, dedendum, clearance, and tooth thickness.

Table 1 lists some of the most commonly used standard gear profile systems. The composite system has tooth profiles that are involute curves for a short distance and cycloidal for the remainder.

EXAMPLE—PROBLEM 7: A 20° full-depth spur gear has 35 teeth and a diametral pitch of 5. Determine (A) the addendum circle diameter, (B) the dedendum circle diameter, and (C) the working depth.

Solution: (A) The addendum and dedendum circle radii are found by adding the addendum to, and subtracting the dedendum from, the pitch circle radius respectively. Thus, we must find the pitch radius. (This problem requires the respective diameters, however.) Thus from Eq. (3), $P = N/d$, and the pitch circle diameter is

$$d = \frac{N}{P} = \frac{35}{5} = 7 \text{ in.}$$

From Table 1, we obtain the expression for the addendum of the gear system profile being considered

$$\text{addendum} = \frac{1}{P} = \frac{1}{5} = 0.2 \text{ in.}$$

The addendum circle diameter is

$$d_a = d + 2 \text{ (addendum)}$$

$$= 7 + 2 \text{ (0.2)} = 7.4 \text{ in.}$$

(B) Similarly, the dedendum is given by

$$\text{dedendum} = \frac{1.25}{P} = \frac{1.25}{5} = 0.25 \text{ in.}$$

and the dedendum circle diameter is

$$d_d = d - 2 \text{ (dedendum)}$$

$$= 7 - 2 \text{ (0.25)} = 6.5 \text{ in.}$$

(C) Working depth = whole depth − clearance. The clearance, from Table 1, is

$$\text{Clearance} = \frac{.25}{P} = \frac{.25}{5} = 0.05 \text{ in.}$$

Or, clearance = dedendum − addendum = 0.25 − 0.20 = 0.05 in.

Whole depth = addendum + dedendum = 0.20 + 0.25 = 0.45 in.

Finally

Working depth = whole depth − clearance = 0.45 − 0.05 = 0.40 in.

(Or, working depth = 2 × addendum = 2 × 0.2 = 0.4 in.)

Sliding Action of Gear Teeth

In the earlier discussion of friction wheels, the motion between the cylinders was pure rolling, except when the transmitted force was large enough to cause sliding. For gears, however, pure rolling motion occurs only when the contact point between gear teeth occurs at the pitch point (for spur gears, bevel gears, and helical gears on parallel shafts). Every other point of contact along the line of action results in sliding of one tooth on the other.

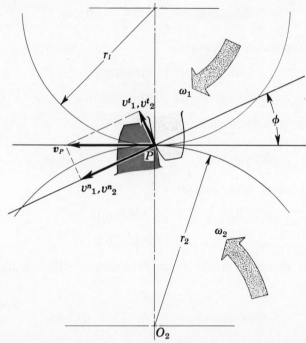

FIG. 19. The contact between the gears at the instant shown is at the pitch point. The pitch line velocity is identical for P_1 and P_2. Since normal and tangential velocity components are also identical, there can be no relative, or sliding, motion. The motion is pure rolling at this point.

Sliding Velocity

Fig. 19 shows two teeth in contact at the pitch point. The pitch line velocity, v_p, is given by

$$v_p = r_1\omega_1 = r_2\omega_2 \ .$$

Since the coincident contact points, P_1 and P_2, have the same velocity, it follows that the normal and tangential components of velocity will also be equal ($v^n_1 = v^n_2$, $v^t_1 = v^t_2$). The identical normal components represent the velocity of the gears along the line of action. As you will recall from Chapter Two, the difference in the tangential components of velocity of the two gears represents the *relative motion*, or the sliding. Since in this case the tangential components of velocity are equal, there is no relative motion, and therefore no sliding velocity. The motion is pure rolling at this instant.

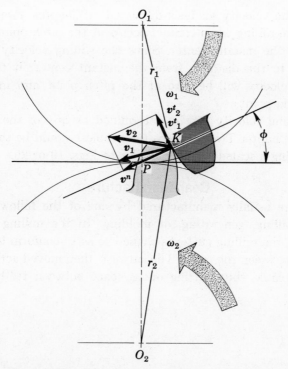

FIG. 20. Unlike the preceding illustration, the contact point K does not coincide with the pitch point, P. In this case, the tangential velocities are unequal, and sliding of one gear on the other must occur.

Fig. 20 shows two teeth in contact at a point K on the line of action, other than the pitch point. The velocities v_1 and v_2 are again given by $v_1 = r_1\omega_1$ and $v_2 = r_2\omega_2$, and in the directions shown. The components of velocities v_1 and v_2 acting along the line of action are equal, and are shown in the figure as v^n. Note that if the components along the line of action were unequal, the gear teeth would be separating. The velocities v^t_1 and v^t_2 are the components of v_1 and v_2 in the tangential direction. As can be seen from the Figure, v^t_1 and v^t_2 are unequal, and therefore one tooth must slide on the other.

The sliding velocity becomes greater as the point of contact between the teeth occurs further from the pitch point. The sliding velocity will therefore be a maximum at the points where the teeth first come into contact and where they leave contact. This can be shown by remembering the velocity analysis discussed in Chapter Two. Since the motion is pure rolling when contact occurs at the pitch point, the pitch point is also the instant center. Since the sliding velocity is directly proportional to the distance from the instant center, it follows that the sliding velocity will be zero at the pitch point and maximum at either extreme point.

The sliding velocity can be determined by any of the procedures discussed in Chapter Two. Perhaps the simplest would be the graphical approach, using a scaled drawing similar to Figs. 19 or 20.

Gear Manufacture

Gears are usually manufactured by one of the following general processes: milling, generating, or molding. In the milling method of manufacture, the milling cutter is shaped so as to conform to the shape of the space between the teeth. The cutter is then moved across the face of the gear blank, thus cutting out a space between teeth. The gear

FIG. 21. The milling cutter shown, like all milling cutters, is completely accurate only for a specific gear of fixed pitch and fixed number of teeth. (Horsburgh & Scott Co.)

blank is then automatically rotated until the next space to be cut lines up with the cutter. This process is continued until all the spaces have been cut out, thus completely forming the gear. Fig. 21 shows a typical milling cutter.

The disadvantage of the milling cutter is that a different cutter must be used, not only for different pitches, but also for different numbers of teeth. Gear manufacturers usually shape the milling cutters so that they are correct for the gear with the smallest number of teeth, in each of eight ranges of tooth numbers, for a given pitch. This means that when gears having a greater number of teeth are cut with this milling cutter, an error in the tooth profile results. The error increases toward the high end of each range of tooth numbers, but the error is usually acceptable for most applications.

It is extremely difficult to attain a high degree of accuracy in cutting teeth by the milling process. Gears to be used for high-speed, high-load applications are not cut accurately enough by the milling process. The generating method to be described next should be used whenever high accuracy is required.

Generating Gears

The generating process of gear cutting entails the use of either a hob, or a shaper. A hob, the cutting tool used in the hobbing process, is shown in Fig. 22. The cutting process is accomplished by moving the hob across the gear blank as both the gear blank and the hob are rotated.

Better accuracy results from this method because of the simultaneous rotation of both the cutter and the gear blank. In other words, the cutter acts in much the same manner to the gear being cut as will the eventual meshing gear. The generating method has the further advantage of not requiring a different cutter for gears of like pitch but different numbers of teeth.

A second method of generating gears is by the shaping process. The cutting tool used in the shaping method is either a rack cutter or a pinion cutter. The rack cutter, which has straight sides rather than an involute profile, has its addendum made equal to the dedendum of the gear being cut. The cutting process is started when the gear blank has been moved into the cutter until the pitch circle of the gear blank is tangent to the pitch line of the rack cutter. The cutter is then given

315

FIG. 22. Hobbing a gear. This method of gear production is more accurate than milling since a given hobbing cutter can cut with equal accuracy gears of various tooth numbers. (Horsburgh & Scott Co.)

a reciprocating motion, and after each cut, the gear blank is rolled through a small angle on the rack. The cutting and rolling action is continued until the end of the rack is reached. At this point the gear blank and the cutting rack are repositioned, and the rolling and cutting action continued until the gear has been completely cut.

The following discussion will be helpful in understanding how a rack cutter works. Fig. 23A shows one tooth profile on a rack cutter. In Fig. 23B a gear blank is shown. The gear blank and rack have been divided into several equal spaces (determined by the dimensions the gear is to have). The points 0 on the rack and 0 on the gear are made to coincide. The straight-sided tooth profile on the rack is then traced out (cut) on the gear blank. The numbered points in question are on the rack pitch line and on the gear pitch circle. The rack is rotated on the gear until the points 1 coincide. In the actual cutting operation,

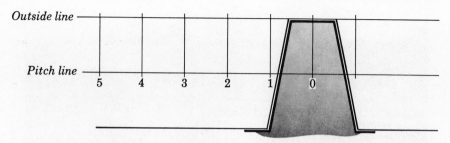

FIG. 23A. The profile of a single tooth on a rack cutter.

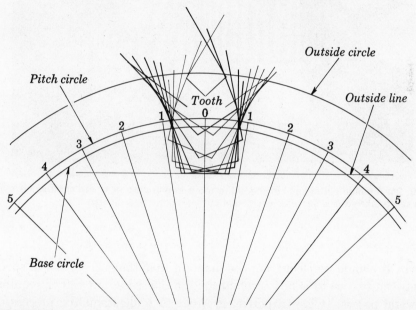

FIG. 23B. The pitch line of the rack is rotated on the pitch circle of the gear blank. At every point where the divisions 0-5 coincide (point 0 of pitch circle with point 0 of rack pitch line, point 1 with point 1, etc.) the tooth profile is traced out. The resulting profile is the side of one tooth, the intervening tooth space, and the side of the adjacent tooth.

the gear rotates while the rack translates, but the relative motion is the same as if the rack is rotated on the gear. The rack tooth profile is again traced out, as shown in Fig. 23B. The process is repeated until five tracings have been made. The five tracings on the other side of the pitch point are then made in a similar manner. As can be seen from Fig. 23B, the result of this procedure is the cutting of the side of one tooth, the intervening space, and the facing side of the next tooth on the

FIG. 24. A pinion cutter can cut the entire tooth in one pass or (more commonly) may be set to take several successively deeper cuts. (Fellows Gear Shaper Co.)

gear. It should be clear from the diagram that the cutting of the space between two teeth is not accomplished in one pass, but rather requires several passes. It is instructive, in order to understand the process of rack gear cutting, to actually perform the process outlined above.

The pinion cutter, as the name implies, is in the form of a gear rather than a rack. See Fig. 24. The cutting operation for the pinion cutter is basically the same as that for the rack cutter; both are shaper operations in which the cutting tool passes back and forth across the rotating gear blank. The pinion cutter is the tool used to cut internal gears.

There are two principal advantages to using generating cutters rather than milling cutters. The first is that a much higher degree of accuracy can be obtained in the cutting process. Secondly, a single cutter can be used to cut gears with any number of teeth of the same pitch.

Molding Gears

The third general method of manufacturing gears is molding. While the casting of gears was once a very common method, its present day application is limited to gears used at very low speeds. Injection molding and die casting are used when a large number of gears are required. Injection molding is used when the material is a plastic, while die casting is often the process used for metals such as brass and aluminum.

Gear Finishing Methods

If gears are to be used in applications involving high speeds and high loads, it is usually necessary to have a higher degree of accuracy than that obtained from the cutting process. One method of finishing is shaving. In this method the gear is run with a hard mating gear or a *shaving cutter*. This results in the removal of small amounts of the surface of the gear.

Another popular method used for finishing gears is grinding. In this method a form grinder or grinding wheel is used to obtain a high degree of accuracy. Of the two, the grinding method produces the most accurate finish.

Interference

Involute gear teeth have involute profiles between the base circle and the addendum circle. The portion of the tooth between the base circle and the dedendum circle is usually made a radial line. For this reason, if contact between two gears occurs below the base circle of one of the gears, interference will occur. The contact is then between two non-conjugate curves, and the fundamental law of gearing will be broken.

In other words, interference occurs whenever the addendum circle of a gear intersects the line of action beyond the *interference point*, which is the point where the line of action is tangent to the base circle.

In order to better understand interference, consider Fig. 25. Points A and B are the points of intersection of the addendum circles with the line of action. Points C and D are the points where the base circles are tangent to the line of action. Interference will occur for the gears shown since point B lies outside point D and point A lies outside point C. The interfering portion of the tooth is shown as the shaded area in Fig. 25.

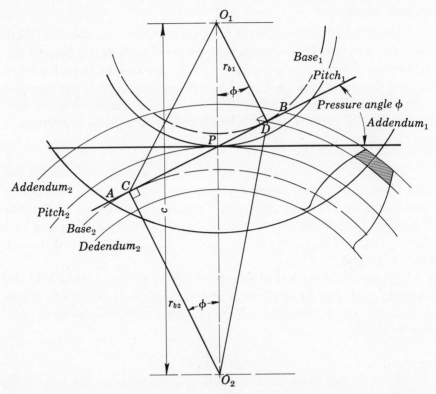

FIG. 25. Points A and B are referred to as *interference points*. The part of the tooth which would have to be removed in order to prevent interference is shown shaded.

Calculating for Interference

In order to prevent interference, the size of addendum circle diameter must be limited. Equations for determining the maximum allowable addendum circle radius without interference can be derived as follows. Referring again to Fig. 25, the maximum radii that the addendum circles may have to avoid interference are O_1C and O_2D respectively. From right triangle O_1CD, we observe the following relationships:

$$O_1C = r_{a1} \text{ (radius of addendum circle)} = \sqrt{(O_1D)^2 + (CD)^2}$$

$$O_1D = O_1P \cos \phi = r_1 \cos \phi = r_{b1}$$

$$PD = O_1P \sin \phi$$

$$CP = O_2P \sin \phi$$

$$CD = CP + PD = (O_1P + O_2P) \sin \phi .$$

Since $c =$ center distance between gear centers,

$$c = O_1P + O_2P$$

and the expression for CD becomes

$$CD = c \sin \phi.$$

The expression for the radius of the addendum circle of gear 1 then becomes

$$O_1C = \sqrt{r_1{}^2 \cos^2 \phi + c^2 \sin^2 \phi}$$

or

$$r_{a1}\ (max) = \sqrt{r_1{}^2 \cos^2 \phi + c^2 \sin^2 \phi}$$

$$= \sqrt{r_{b1}{}^2 + c^2 \sin^2 \phi}. \tag{10}$$

Similarly, for the other gear

$$r_{a2}\ (max) = \sqrt{r_2{}^2 \cos^2 \phi + c^2 \sin^2 \phi}$$

$$= \sqrt{r_{b2}{}^2 + c^2 \sin^2 \phi} .$$

If the addendum circle radius exceeds the value as calculated from the above equation, interference will occur. If it is equal to or less than the calculated value, no interference will occur.

EXAMPLE—PROBLEM 8: Two 20° full-depth gears have a diametral pitch of 3. The larger gear has 30 teeth while the pinion has 15 teeth. Will the gear be subjected to interference?

Solution: Eq. (10) will indicate the maximum permissible addendum circle radius for the gear in this problem. We must therefore calculate the base circle radius for the gear, r_{b2}, and the center distance, c, in order to use the formula. Thus, from Eq. (3), $P = N/d$,

$$d_2 = \frac{N_2}{P} = \frac{30}{3} = 10 \text{ in.}$$

$$d_1 = \frac{N_1}{P} = \frac{15}{3} = 5 \text{ in.}$$

therefore,

$$c = \frac{1}{2} (d_1 + d_2) = \frac{1}{2} (5 + 10) = 7 \frac{1}{2} \text{ in.}$$

Also, we will need the sine and cosine of the pressure angle:

$$\cos \phi = \cos 20° = .94$$
$$\sin \phi = \sin 20° = .342$$

The radius of the base circle of the gear is therefore

$$r_{b2} = r_2 \cos \phi$$
$$= \frac{10}{2} \cos 20° = 5 \times .95 = 4.70 \text{ in.}$$

Having determined the values for the base circle radius (r_{b1}), the center distance (c) and the sin of the pressure angle (ϕ), we can now use Eq. (10) to determine the maximum permissible addendum radius. By comparing the result to the actual value as determined from Table I, we finally find whether interference exists in this case.

$$r_{a2} \ (max) = \sqrt{r_{b2}{}^2 + c^2 \sin^2 \phi}$$
$$= \sqrt{(4.70)^2 + (7.5)^2 \ (.342)^2} = 5.35 \text{ in.}$$

From Table I, for the 20° full-depth gear,

$$a_2 = \frac{1}{P} = \frac{1}{3} = 0.333,$$

and the addendum circle radius is the sum of the pitch radius and the addendum, or

$$r_{a2} = r_2 + a_2 = 5 + 0.333$$
$$= 5.333 \text{ in.}$$

Finally, comparing the maximum permissible addendum radius to the actual value as determined by Table I, we find that there is no interference since the actual addendum circle radius is slightly less than the maximum allowable addendum circle radius. If r_{a2} had been greater than r_{a2} (max) interference would have occurred.

Methods of Preventing Interference

In the previous section, the generating gear cutters (rack and pinion) were discussed. During the cutting process, the cutter and gear blank act in a manner similar to two meshing gears. It is therefore possible for interference to occur. However, since one of the elements is a cutting tool, the portion of the gear which would be interfering is cut away. A gear which has had material removed in this manner is said to be *undercut*.

Fig. 26 shows undercut gear teeth with the undercut portion shaded. As can be seen, undercutting also removes a portion of the tooth profile *above* the base circle. This is a definite disadvantage, since the length of contact is reduced. Reducing the length of contact, of course, decreases the contact ratio and results in rougher and noisier gear action, since fewer teeth are in contact.

Since undercutting removes material from the base of the tooth, it also may seriously weaken the tooth. It should be emphasized that undercutting will not occur if the maximum allowable addendum circle radius, previously discussed, is not exceeded.

Methods other than undercutting are also available to reduce the amount of interference. Interference can also be eliminated if the height of the tooth is reduced by cutting off a portion of its tip. Interference occurs when the tip of one gear is in contact below the base circle of the mating gear. Removing a portion of the tooth tip will therefore prevent contact below the base circle. This type of gear is called a stub-tooth gear.

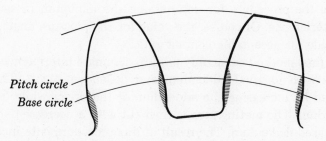

Pitch circle
Base circle

FIG. 26. When gears are undercut, the shaded portions of the teeth are removed. Since a part of the profile which lies above the base line is removed in the process, the result is a reduced length of contact.

Increasing the pressure angle will also decrease the problem of interference. A larger pressure angle decreases the diameter of the base circle and thus increases the involute portion of the tooth profile. The disadvantage of both of these procedures is that the active length of contact is reduced, which again leads to rougher, noisier gear operation.

An equation for determining the minimum pressure angle for which no interference will be present can be derived from Equation (10).

$$r_a \, (max) = \sqrt{r_b{}^2 + c^2 \sin^2 \phi}$$

$$r_a{}^2 \, (max) = r_b{}^2 + c^2 \sin^2 \phi,$$

and since $r_b = r \cos \phi$,

$$r_a{}^2 \, (max) = r^2 \cos^2 \phi + c^2 \sin^2 \phi \ .$$

But $\cos^2 \phi + \sin^2 \phi = 1$, therefore

$$r_a{}^2 \, (max) = r^2 \, (1-\sin^2 \phi) + c^2 \sin^2 \phi$$

$$= r^2 - r^2 \sin^2 \phi + c^2 \sin^2 \phi$$

$$= r^2 + (c^2 - r^2) \sin^2 \phi$$

therefore

$$\sin^2 \phi = \frac{r_a{}^2 \, (max) - r^2}{c^2 - r^2}$$

$$\sin \phi = \sqrt{\frac{r_a{}^2 \, (max) - r^2}{c^2 - r^2}} \ . \tag{11}$$

In using Eq. (11), the standard value for the addendum is to be used in determining $r_a \, (max)$. Example Problem 9, at the end of this section, illustrates the procedure for determining the minimum pressure angle for no interference. Of course, the value for the pressure angle, ϕ, must still provide an acceptable contact ratio.

The final method commonly used to eliminate interference is to cut the gears with unequal addendum and dedendum teeth. This is accomplished by increasing the addendum of the driver while decreasing its dedendum. The mating gear is then cut with a decreased addendum and increased dedendum. The result of this procedure is to increase the length of action for which involute action is obtainable. Gears of this type are usually called *long and short addendum teeth gears*.

324

The disadvantage of this procedure is an increase in the cost of the gear and the fact that gears cut in this manner are non-interchangeable. Gears of this type are also known as *non-standard gears*.

Finally, it should be clear from the previous discussion that the method used to eliminate interference depends upon the application for which the gear is to be used. The following, for example, will illustrate the procedure for eliminating interference by increasing the pressure angle.

EXAMPLE—PROBLEM 9: Two full-depth $14\frac{1}{2}°$ gears have a diametral pitch of 3. The pinion has 15 teeth, while the gear has 60 teeth. (A) Will there be interference on the gear? (B) If interference is present, to what value should the pressure angle be increased in order to eliminate the interference?

Solution: (A) The procedure is identical to that used in Example Problem 8 to determine interference. Thus, from Eq. (3), $P = N/d$,

$$d_1 = \frac{N_1}{P} = \frac{15}{3} = 5 \text{ in.}$$

$$d_2 = \frac{N_2}{P} = \frac{60}{3} = 20 \text{ in.}$$

From Eq. (6)

$$c = \frac{1}{2}(d_1 + d_2)$$

$$= \frac{1}{2}(5 + 20) = 12.5 \text{ in.}$$

And

$$\cos 14\frac{1}{2}° = 0.968$$

$$\sin 14\frac{1}{2}° = 0.251$$

The radius of the base circle of the gear is given by

$$r_{b2} = r_2 \cos \phi$$

$$= \frac{20}{2} \cos 14\frac{1}{2}° = 9.7 \text{ in.}$$

We can now use the formula which indicates the maximum permissible addendum radius without interference, Eq. (10), and compare the maximum permissible radius with the actual radius (per Table I) to determine whether interference exists.

$$r_{a2}\,(max) = \sqrt{(r_{b2})^2 + c^2\sin^2\phi}$$

$$= \sqrt{(9.7)^2 + (12.5)^2\,(0.251)^2} = 10.2 \text{ in.}$$

for $14\frac{1}{2}°$ full-depth gear. Now, from Table I

$$a_2 = \frac{1}{P} = \frac{1}{3} = 0.33 \text{ in.}$$

and

$$r_{a2} = r_2 + a_2 = 10 + 0.33 = 10.33 \text{ in.}$$

Since the actual addendum circle radius is greater than the maximum allowable addendum radius, interference exists.

(B) To determine the new pressure angle required to eliminate this interference, we substitute the known values of r, r_a, and c into Eq. (11).

$$\sin\phi = \sqrt{\frac{r_{a2}{}^2\,(max) - r_2{}^2}{c^2 - r_2{}^2}}$$

$$= \sqrt{\frac{(10.2)^2 - (10)^2}{(12.5)^2 - (10)^2}} = 0.268.$$

Therefore, the new pressure angle required to eliminate interference is
$$\phi = 15.5°.$$

In other words, if the pressure angle is increased to $15\frac{1}{2}°$, the interference will be eliminated.

Internal Gears

There are many applications, such as in epicyclic gear trains (to be discussed in a later chapter), for which the use of an internal gear is highly desirable. An internal gear has its teeth cut on the inside of the rim rather than on the outside.

Fig. 27 shows a typical internal gear in mesh with an external pinion. The important terms and dimensions associated with internal gears are shown. As can be seen from the illustration, the directions of

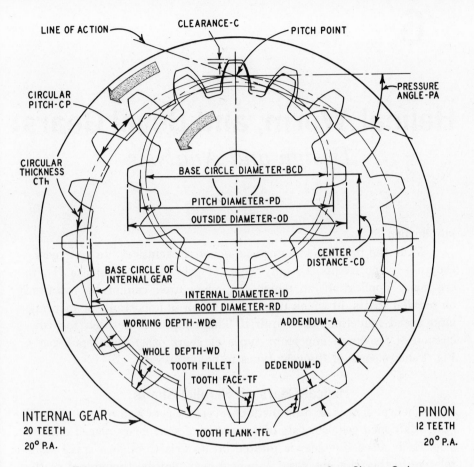

FIG. 27. Nomenclature for internal gears. (Fellows Gear Shaper Co.)

rotation for an internal and external gear in mesh are the same, whereas two external gears in contact have opposite directions of rotation.

Since the internal gear has a concave tooth profile, while the external gear's tooth profile is convex, the surface contact between the gears is increased, thus decreasing the contact stress. The center distance between the gears is less, thus making a more compact arrangement than for external gear sets. Internal-external gear sets have a greater number of teeth in contact, resulting in smoother and quieter operation.

Helical, Worm, and Bevel Gears:
Design and Analysis

Introduction

While the previous chapter was devoted exclusively to spur gears, they are by no means the only types of gears in common use. There are many applications in which the gears used cannot be mounted on parallel shafts, in which noise elimination is important, or in which large speed reductions are required. This chapter is devoted to a discussion of the more important types of gears other than spur gears. Fig. 1 shows some of the gear types to be discussed.

Helical Gears on Parallel Shafts

A helical gear is an outgrowth of a type of gear known as a stepped gear. A stepped gear consists of a number of spur gears placed side by side. Each successive gear is rotated on its axis through a small angle relative to the adjacent gear. A helical gear may be thought of as the limiting case of a stepped gear, with the width of each individual spur gear extremely thin and the angular rotations extremely small. The surface of a helical gear is thus a helix, rather than parallel to the axis as is the case for spur gears.

Hand

Helical gears are called right-hand or left-hand, depending on the direction in which the helix slopes away from the viewer. The line of sight is parallel to the axis of the gear. Thus, Fig. 2A illustrates a left-handed helical gear, while Fig. 2B shows a right-handed helical gear alongside a gear blank from which such a gear would be cut.

In order for two helical gears on parallel shafts to mesh, they must

FIG. 1A. A gear system consisting of helical gears (left foreground) and a worm gearset. (Horsburgh & Scott Co.)

FIG. 1B. A pair of crossed helical gears. (Boston Gear Works)

FIG. 1C. A pair of bevel gears. (Browning Mfg. Co.)

329

FIG. 2A. A left-hand helical gear. The teeth slope to the left (or counterclockwise) when viewed along the axis. (Horsburgh & Scott Co.)

FIG. 2B. A right-hand helical gear. The teeth slope to the right (or clockwise). (Barber-Colman Co.)

be of different hands. In other words if the driver is right-handed, the driven gear, or follower, must be left-handed.

Helical Gear Tooth Contact

Spur gears have an initial line contact, with the result that the impact (shock) that occurs when two teeth come into contact is much larger than for helical gears. The initial contact between two helical gears is a point. As the motion continues, the contact between the teeth becomes a line whose length gradually increases until the teeth are in full contact. To illustrate the contact that occurs between two meshing helical gears, consider Figs. 3A and B. The action that occurs as the gears mesh can be approximated by moving gear 1 toward gear 2. The first contact for teeth AA' and BB' occurs at the point where A and B touch. As the gears continue to rotate, or as gear 1 continues to move toward gear 2, more and more points come into contact. Fig. 3B, for example, shows the contact at a point C. Continued rotation brings more teeth into contact, until points A' and B' are touching. The tooth elements of each gear form an angle ψ with the axis of the gear, but the gears are of opposite hand.

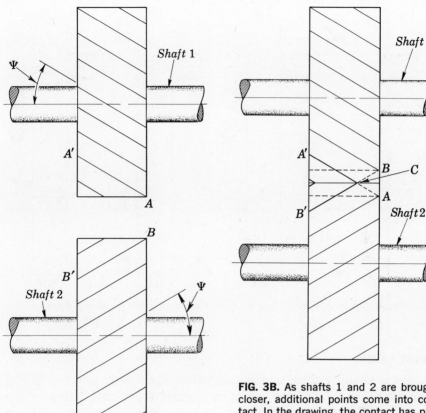

FIG. 3A. The contact between two helical gears can be approximated by considering the contact as the two shafts are brought together. As shafts 1 and 2 approach each other, the initial contact between teeth *AA′* and *BB′* occurs when points *A* and *B* coincide. Thus, initial contact is a point.

FIG. 3B. As shafts 1 and 2 are brought closer, additional points come into contact. In the drawing, the contact has progressed to point *C*. Finally, points *A′* and *B′* coincide and the teeth are fully in line contact. Of course, the shafts cannot be brought together as shown; this concept is merely a device to help visualize the progressing contact as both gears rotate in mesh.

The gradual engagement of helical gear teeth permits larger load transmission, smoother operation, and quieter transmission of power compared to spur gears of similar size. For these reasons, helical gears are preferred over spur gears for the applications mentioned previously, even though they are usually more expensive and difficult to manufacture.

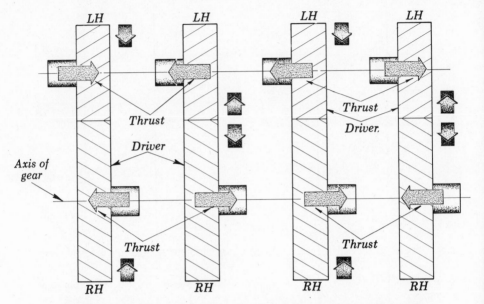

FIG. 4. Direction of thrust load for helical gears mounted on parallel shafts.

Thrust Load

As in all other direct contact mechanisms, the force that one helical gear exerts on its meshing gear acts normal (perpendicularly) to the line of contact. In the case of helical gears, this means that a thrust load, a force along the axis of the shaft, exists. The bearings supporting a gear shaft must therefore be able to resist this thrust load. Fig. 4 shows the direction of the thrust load for helical gears on parallel shafts. The direction of the thrust load is determined by the Right or Left Hand Rule (depending on the hand of the driver) applied to the driver: *Fingers point in the direction of rotation, then the thumb points in the direction of the thrust load.* The *driven* thrust load is then *opposite* to the direction of the thrust load on the driver. This thrust load can be eliminated by using double-helical or herringbone gears.

EXAMPLE—PROBLEM 1: Indicate the direction of the thrust loads for the helical gears shown in Fig. 5A.

Solution: The driver, gear *A*, on shaft number 1 is left-handed. Using

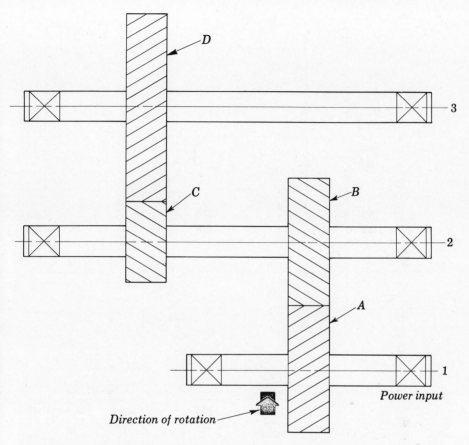

FIG. 5A. Two pairs of helical gears on parallel shafts are shown. Starting at the input, determine the thrust loads for each of the gears.

the Left-Hand Rule, the fingers of left hand are pointed in direction of rotation; the thumb then points in the direction of the thrust load. The thrust load for gear A, therefore, acts to the right. See Fig. 5B. The thrust load for gear B (the follower) must act in the opposite direction, and thus acts to the left.

Gear C on shaft 2 is the driver for the pair on the left. Applying the right hand rule, the thrust load acts to the right. The thrust load for gear D (the follower) must act in the opposite direction, and thus acts to the left. The thrust loads, F_t, are shown in Fig. 5B.

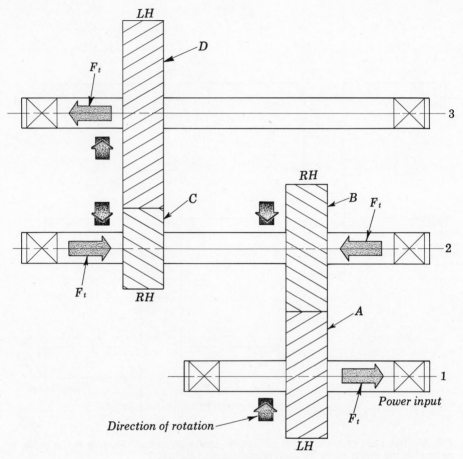

FIG. 5B. Solution to Problem 1.

Eliminating Thrust with Herringbone Gears. A herringbone gear can be thought of as a helical gear with half of its face cut right-handed and the other half cut left-handed. A space is usually cut between the two halves to permit easier manufacture. Thus, the thrust loads generated by the left-hand and right-hand teeth cancel each other. Fig. 6A shows a herringbone gear with no space provided between the right-hand and left-hand teeth, while Fig. 6B shows a double-helical or herringbone gear with a rather wide space between the two halves.

334

FIG. 6A. A herringbone (or double-helical) gear with no space between left-hand and right-hand teeth. (Horsburgh & Scott Co.)

FIG. 6B. A herringbone gear with a large space between the two halves. (Horsburgh & Scott Co.)

Helical Gear Terminology and Geometry

The terminology used for helical gears is very similar to that used for spur gears. In fact, most of the relationships developed for spur gears are equally applicable to helical gears on parallel shafts. Several additional terms are necessary, however.

Helix Angle. Fig. 7 shows a helical gear, with some of the more important terms expressed as symbols. The symbols are standardized, and are familiar to people engaged in gear design and production. As has been stated earlier, the teeth on a helical gear are not parallel to the axis of the shaft on which they are mounted. The angle the teeth make with the axis is known as the helix angle, ψ.

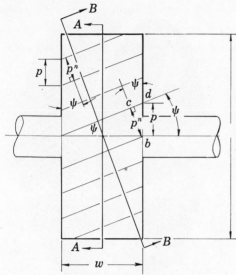

FIG. 7. Helical gear terms: the diagram shows the helix angle ψ, the pitch diameter d, the transverse circular pitch p, the *normal* circular pitch p^n, and the gear width w.

Normal Pitch. The circular pitch, p, is defined, as for spur gears, as the distance between corresponding points on adjacent teeth. However, the pitch of a helical gear can be measured in two different ways. Thus, the *transverse* circular pitch, p, is measured along the pitch circle just as for spur gears. The *normal* circular pitch, p^n, is measured normal to the helix of the gear, as shown in Fig. 7.

The diametral pitch, P, just as for spur gears, is given by the formula

$$P = \frac{N}{d}$$

where N is the number of teeth for the gear and d is the diameter of the pitch circle. The relationship between the normal diametral pitch and the normal circular pitch is identical to that between the diametral pitch and the circular pitch as given in the last chapter. Thus

$$P = \frac{\pi}{p} \quad \text{and} \quad P^n = \frac{\pi}{p^n} . \tag{1}$$

The normal pitch of a helical gear is an important dimension because it becomes the circular pitch of the hob cutter used to manufacture the gear. When the cutting is done, instead, by a gear shaper, the transverse circular pitch of the gear becomes the circular pitch of the cutter. It can thus be seen why both pitches are of importance. In the following section, we will derive the relationships between the transverse and normal pitches.

Face Width. The face width of the gear is w. As can be seen from Fig. 7, which shows a gear proportioned for the recommended minimum width,

$$\tan \psi = \frac{p}{w}, \quad \text{or} \quad w = \frac{p}{\tan \psi}.$$

While the above equation is the formula for the minimum gear width, the usual practice is to increase the width from 10-20%. It should be clear that when the face width exceeds the minimum width, the formula above no longer applies.

As seen from Fig. 7, the relationship between the transverse and normal circular pitch is

$$p^n = p \cos \psi. \tag{2}$$

Substituting the expression for the circular pitch employed in the last chapter ($p = \pi d/N$) we can also derive an expression for the pitch diameter in terms of the number of teeth, N, the *normal* circular pitch, p^n, and the helix angle, ψ:

$$d = \frac{pN}{\pi} = \frac{p^n N}{\pi \cos \psi}. \tag{3}$$

The following equations also hold:

$$pP = \pi$$

$$p^n P^n = \pi.$$

Therefore, we can express the *normal diametral pitch* in terms of the diametral pitch, P, and the helix angle:

$$P^n = \frac{\pi}{p^n} = \frac{\pi}{p \cos \psi} = \frac{P}{\cos \psi}. \tag{4}$$

Having derived the above three equations from Fig. 7, it is now possible to determine most of the important dimensions of the helical gear.

EXAMPLE—PROBLEM 2: A helical gear has 25 teeth, a helix angle of 25°, and a transverse circular pitch of $\pi/5$ in. Determine (A) the pitch diameter, (B) the diametral pitch, and (C) the normal circular and diametral pitches.

Solution: (A) The pitch diameter is directly obtained from Eq. (3):

$$d = \frac{pN}{\pi} = \frac{\pi/5 \times 25}{\pi} = 5 \text{ in.}$$

(B) The diametral pitch, P, is given by Eq. (1)

$$P = \frac{\pi}{p} = \frac{\pi}{\pi/5} = 5.$$

(C) The normal diametral pitch and the normal circular pitches are given by Eqs. (4) and (1) respectively. Thus, from Eq. (4):

$$P^n = \frac{P}{\cos \psi} = \frac{5}{\cos 25°} = 5.52$$

and the normal circular pitch is given by

$$p^n = \frac{\pi}{P^n} = \frac{\pi}{5.52} = 0.568 \text{ in.}$$

Pressure Angle. While spur gears were identified by means of one pressure angle, the geometry of helical gears requires the use of two pressure angles. Fig. 8A shows the tooth profile for section AA of the gear in Fig. 7, obtained by passing a plane perpendicular to the shaft axis. The pressure angle for this tooth profile is the transverse pressure angle, ϕ. Fig. 8B shows the tooth profile for section BB of Fig. 7, obtained by passing a plane normal to the tooth line. The pressure angle for this tooth profile is the *normal pressure angle*, ϕ^n.

In order to demonstrate that the angles ϕ and ϕ^n are pressure angles, consider Fig. 8C which depicts contact between two teeth on two racks. The pitch circles for gears become pitch *lines* for racks or stretched-out gears (line pp in Fig. 8C). Line FE is perpendicular to the tooth surfaces in contact and represents the line of action of the force between the teeth. The pressure angle was previously defined as the angle between the line of action between two teeth in contact and the tangent to the pitch circles at the pitch point. However, in Fig. 8C,

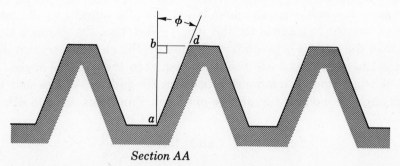

Section AA

FIG. 8A. This tooth profile is given by Section *AA* (perpendicular to the gear axis) of Fig. 7, showing the transverse pressure angle, ϕ.

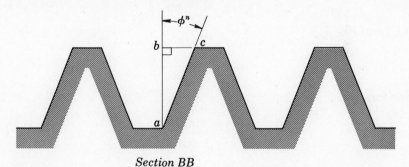

Section BB

FIG. 8B. Section *BB* (normal to the helix) of the gear of Fig. 7 illustrates the normal pressure angle ϕ^n.

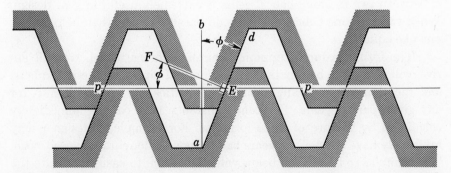

FIG. 8C. Note that the pressure angles *bad* and *bac* of Figs. 8A and 8B are consistent with the definition of the pressure angle given in the last chapter. The pressure angle, ϕ, for the rack teeth shown is the angle between the line of action, *FE*, and the tangent to the pitch line, *pp*. From the geometry of the diagram, ϕ and *bad* are equal, thus *bad* does indeed represent the pressure angle.

339

line *pp* is not only the pitch line, but is also the tangent to the pitch line (a tangent to a line is the line itself). Therefore, the pressure angle becomes the angle ϕ between lines *FE* and *pp*. Simple geometry can then be used to show that angle *bad* is also equal to the pressure angle.

A trigonometric relationship between the pressure angles and the helix angle of the gear can also be obtained. From Figs. 8A and 8B,

$$\tan \phi = \frac{bd}{ab} \quad \text{and} \quad \tan \phi^n = \frac{bc}{ab}.$$

Therefore,

$$\frac{\tan \phi^n}{\tan \phi} = \frac{bc}{bd}.$$

And, from Fig. 7,

$$\cos \psi = \frac{bc}{bd}.$$

Therefore,

$$\cos \psi = \frac{\tan \phi^n}{\tan \phi}. \tag{5}$$

It is clear from Equation (5) that the transverse pressure angle must always be larger than the normal pressure angle.

Center Distance. An equation for determining the center distance, *c*, between two meshing helical gears is extremely useful in gear design. When two meshing helical gears are on parallel shafts, their helix angles must be equal.

The formulas for determining center distance, which we will derive, will be seen to be functions of the normal pitch, the teeth numbers, and the common helix angle. These quantities are usually known for any given pair of gears. The center distance thus can be immediately calculated by the use of these formulas. For example, a designer may arbitrarily have chosen two gears based upon some required speed ratio. The formulas to be derived below will enable him to easily calculate the center distance to determine the space requirements (often a critical factor) for the particular gear set.

From the formulas for pitch diameter and center distance as derived in the last chapter, we obtain

$$d_1 = \frac{N_1 p}{\pi} \quad \text{and} \quad d_2 = \frac{N_2 p}{\pi}$$

and

$$c = \frac{d_1 + d_2}{2}$$

$$= \frac{p}{2\pi}(N_1 + N_2).$$

But $p^n = p \cos \psi$, therefore

$$c = \frac{p^n (N_1 + N_2)}{2 \pi \cos \psi}. \tag{6}$$

And since $p^n P^n = \pi$, another expression for the center distance is

$$c = \frac{N_1 + N_2}{2P^n \cos \psi}. \tag{7}$$

As an example, suppose the gears to be designed are to be mounted on shafts ten inches apart. The center distance is thus seen to be fixed. Since the normal pitch and helix angle are usually chosen first, the formulas may be used, instead of determining center distance, to determine the required value for the sum of N_1 and N_2. This value, together with the speed ratio, will enable the designer to determine the appropriate values for N_1 and N_2.

EXAMPLE—PROBLEM 3: A pair of meshing helical gears have a normal pressure angle of $20°$, a diametral pitch of 5, and a normal circular pitch of 0.55 in. The driver has 18 teeth and the follower has 36 teeth. Determine (A) the pressure angle, ϕ, and (B) the center distance, c.
Solution: (A) From Eq. (1) and the given data, the circular pitch is

$$p = \frac{\pi}{P} = \frac{\pi}{5} = 0.628 \text{ in.}$$

From Eq. (2), the helix angle is

$$p^n = p \cos \psi \quad \text{or} \quad \cos \psi = \frac{p^n}{p},$$

where

$$\cos \psi = \frac{0.55}{0.628} = 0.877$$

$$\psi = 28.8°.$$

Mechanism

From Eq. (5) we have the relationship between the helix and pressure angle:

$$\cos \psi = \frac{\tan \phi^n}{\tan \phi},$$

and the pressure angle is

$$\tan \phi = \frac{\tan \phi^n}{\cos \psi} = \frac{0.364}{0.877} = 0.418$$

$$\phi = 22.5°.$$

Finally, the center distance is found using Eq. (6):

$$c = \frac{p^n (N_1 + N_2)}{2 \pi \cos \psi}$$

$$= \frac{0.55 (18 + 36)}{2 \pi \times 0.877} = 5.4 \text{ in.}$$

Tredgold's Approximation for Helical Gears

A better understanding of helical gear geometry can be obtained by considering the tooth profiles in the transverse and normal planes. In Fig. 9A, if a vertical plane is passed perpendicular to the axis of the gear (section *AA*), the pitch circle shown in Fig. 9B results. The radius of curvature is equal to the radius of the transverse pitch circle. The tooth profile in this plane would be the same as that for the tooth profile of a spur gear having a pitch radius, r.

When a plane (section *BB* of Fig. 9A) is passed perpendicular to the helix at an angle ψ to the vertical plane an ellipse, shown in Fig. 9C, results. The radius of curvature of an ellipse is given by the formula:

$$r_c = \frac{r}{\cos^2 \psi}$$

where r is the pitch radius. The tooth profile in this plane is the same as that for the tooth of a spur gear having a pitch radius r_c. In other words, the properties of a helical gear are similar to those of an equivalent spur gear having a pitch radius equal to r_c.

The number of teeth on this equivalent spur gear are known as the equivalent, virtual, or formative number of teeth for the helical gear. The formative number of teeth, designated by the symbol N_f, is another

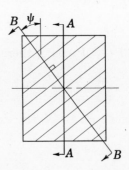

FIG. 9A. A helical gear, which is to be sectioned perpendicular to its axis and perpendicular to the helix angle of the teeth.

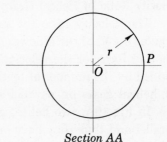

FIG. 9B. Section AA results in the pitch circle of the gear.

Section AA

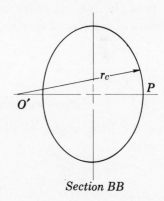

FIG. 9C. Section BB results in an ellipse. The radius of curvature, r_c, is the pitch radius of a spur gear which would approximate the characteristics of the helical gear shown in Fig. 9A.

Section BB

important parameter to the designer, and can be determined from the following equation:

$$N_f = P^n d_c.$$

But $d_c = 2r_c = 2r/\cos^2 \psi$, thus

$$N_f = P^n \frac{2r}{\cos^2 \psi} = \frac{P^n d}{\cos^2 \psi}.$$

But $P^n = P/\cos \psi$, therefore

$$N_f = \frac{Pd}{\cos^3 \psi}$$

or, since $Pd = N$, the expression becomes

$$N_f = \frac{N}{\cos^3 \psi} \qquad (8)$$

where N_f is the formative number of teeth for the imaginary spur gear, and N is the *actual* number of teeth for the helical gear.

Velocity Ratio of Helical Gears

The velocity ratio for spur gears was defined as the ratio of the angular speed of the follower divided by the angular speed of the driver. Another form for the velocity ratio is the number of teeth of the driver divided by the number of teeth of the follower. A similar situation holds for helical gears on parallel shafts.

In Fig 10A, two helical gears are shown in mesh. Their shafts are parallel and thus they have opposite hands and equal helix angles. The pitch line velocities are v_1 and v_2. From Fig. 10B, the normal components of the two velocities are given as v^n_1 and v^n_2. The normal components of velocity of any two meshing gears are equal. Thus,

$$v^n_1 = v^n_2.$$

From Fig. 10B

$$v^n_1 = v_1 \cos \psi_1 \quad \text{and} \quad v^n_2 = v_2 \cos \psi_2.$$

Since the helix angles of the two gears are equal, $\cos \psi_1 = \cos \psi_2$, therefore

$$v_1 = v_2.$$

And since

$$\omega_1 = \frac{v_1}{d_1/2} \quad \text{and} \quad \omega_2 = \frac{v_2}{d_2/2},$$

we obtain the velocity ratio of two helical gears as the ratio of their angular velocities:

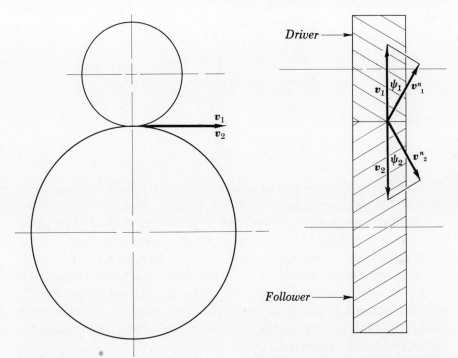

FIG. 10A. The pitch line velocities of meshing helical gears.

FIG. 10B. The normal components of the pitch line velocities are equal for any pair of meshing gears. The pitch line velocities have been rotated through 90° from their actual lines of action for purposes of illustration. The velocities shown are for contact at the pitch point.

$$r_v = \frac{\omega_2}{\omega_1}. \tag{9}$$

The velocity ratio for helical gears can also be stated as the ratio of the pitch diameters and as the ratio of the teeth of the two gears:

$$r_v = \frac{v_2/(d_2/2)}{v_1/(d_1/2)} = \frac{v_2\, d_1}{v_1\, d_2} = \frac{d_1}{d_2}. \tag{10}$$

Since

$$d_1 = \frac{N_1}{P_1} = \frac{N_1}{P^n{}_1 \cos \psi}$$

Mechanism

and

$$d_2 = \frac{N_2}{P_2} = \frac{N_2}{P^n_2 \cos \psi}$$

$$r_v = \frac{d_1}{d_2} = \frac{N_1 \, P^n_2 \cos \psi}{N_2 \, P^n_1 \cos \psi} = \frac{N_1 \, P^n_2}{N_2 \, P^n_1}.$$

And since $P^n_1 = P^n_2$,

$$r_v = \frac{N_1}{N_2}. \tag{11}$$

Thus, the velocity ratio can be determined simply from the number of teeth of the meshing gears.

Helical gears are rarely used interchangeably, so that there is no need for standardized tooth systems. However, some standardization is desirable in terms of the cutting tools required. The helix angle for most helical gears varies between 15°-30°, although some herringbone gears have helix angles as high as 45°. Since the thrust load varies directly with the tangent of the helix angle, the magnitude of the helix angle must be limited. In other words, if the helix angle becomes too large the thrust load will be excessive.

Helical gears are cut by the same general methods discussed in the previous chapter. Fig. 11A shows a helical gear being cut by a hobbing machine, while Fig. 11B shows the cutting of a herringbone gear by a gear generator.

Crossed Helical Gears

Helical gears can also be used when power is to be transmitted from one shaft to another non-parallel, non-intersecting shaft. These helical gears are referred to as *crossed helical gears*. Any helical gear can be used as a crossed helical gear; a helical gear becomes a crossed helical gear when it is meshed with another helical gear whose shaft is non-parallel and non-intersecting with the shaft of the first gear. A typical set of crossed helical gears is illustrated in Fig. 12.

Hand and Tooth Contact

While helical gears on parallel shafts must be of opposite hand, two crossed helical gears usually have the *same* hand. And while helical

FIG. 11A. Helical gear being cut by a hobbing machine. (Barber-Colman Co.)

FIG. 11B. Herringbone gear being cut on a Farrel gear generator. (Horsburgh & Scott Co.)

Mechanism

FIG. 12. A pair of crossed helical gears, used when the shafts are not parallel. Usually, crossed helical gears have the *same* hand. (Eaton Automotive Gear Div., Eaton, Yale, and Towne.)

gears on parallel shafts must have identical helix angles, the helix angles for crossed helical gears do *not* have to be equal.

Unlike helical gears on parallel shafts, crossed helical gears have point rather than line contact. However, after a wearing-in period, the point contact becomes line contact. While line contact does eventually occur, it is much poorer contact than that for the gear types previously discussed. Because of this poor contact, crossed helical gears are used only when small loads are to be transmitted.

An advantage of crossed helical gears is that the alignment of the gears does not have to be perfect in order to obtain smooth operation. For crossed helical gears, the normal pitch rather than the transverse pitch is usually referred to when specifying pitch. The reason for this is that while the normal pitches for helical gears are equal, the transverse pitches will be unequal if the helix angles are unequal.

Crossed Helical Gear Geometry

Some of the more important relationships involving crossed helical gears can be obtained by considering Fig. 13. The two helical gears shown have different helix angles, ψ_1 and ψ_2. Both gears are right-handed, and Σ is the angle between the shafts. For crossed helical gears,

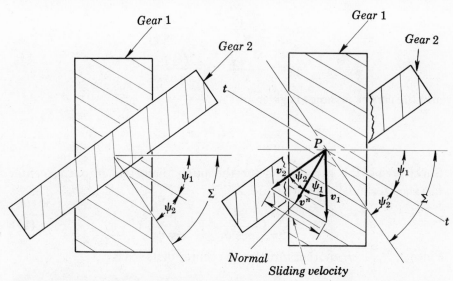

FIG. 13. The two crossed helical gears are of the same hand but have different helix angles. The shaft angle, Σ, is equal to the sum of the helix angles. The normal components of the pitch line velocities are equal, but a sliding velocity exists.

the angle between the shafts always equals the sum or difference of the helix angles of the two gears. As can be seen from Fig. 13,

$$\Sigma = \psi_1 + \psi_2 . \qquad (12A)$$

If the gears were of opposite hand, the shaft angle would be instead

$$\Sigma = \psi_1 - \psi_2 . \qquad (12B)$$

The pitch line velocities, v_1 and v_2, act as shown in the illustration. The normal components of v_1 and v_2 must be equal, are perpendicular to the axis t-t (the axis tangent to the teeth in contact), and are both labeled v^n. As seen from the illustration, a sliding velocity exists for crossed helical gears, even when they contact at the pitch point.

Center Distance. A procedure similar to that used to find the center distance for helical gears on parallel shafts, Equations (6) and (7), can be followed to obtain the formulas for the center distance between two crossed helical gears. Thus, the pitch diameters are again given by

$$d_1 = \frac{N_1\, p_1}{\pi} = \frac{N_1\, p^n}{\pi \cos \psi_1}$$

$$d_2 = \frac{N_2\, p_2}{\pi} = \frac{N_2\, p^n}{\pi \cos \psi_2}$$

and the center distance is given by

$$c = \frac{d_1 + d_2}{2}.$$

Substituting the expressions for the pitch diameters into the center distance formula, we obtain

$$c = \frac{p^n}{2\pi} \left(\frac{N_1}{\cos \psi_1} + \frac{N_2}{\cos \psi_2} \right). \tag{13}$$

Since $p_n P_n = \pi$, another form for the center distance is

$$c = \frac{1}{2\, P^n} \left(\frac{N_1}{\cos \psi_1} + \frac{N_2}{\cos \psi_2} \right). \tag{14}$$

Velocity Ratio of Crossed Helical Gears

The velocity ratio for crossed helical gears can be obtained by following the procedure used to obtain Equations (9)-(11). Thus, $v^n_1 = v^n_2$, and from Fig. 13,

$$v^n_1 = v_1 \cos \psi_1$$

$$v^n_2 = v_2 \cos \psi_2 .$$

Therefore,

$$v_1 \cos \psi_1 = v_2 \cos \psi_2 \quad \text{or} \quad v_1 = v_2 \frac{\cos \psi_2}{\cos \psi_1}.$$

We now have an expression for the pitch line velocities in terms of the separate helix angles of the crossed gears. We can use this relationship to obtain the velocity ratio of crossed helical gears in terms of their numbers of teeth. The angular velocity of the two gears are given by

$$\omega_1 = \frac{v_1}{d_1/2} \quad \text{and} \quad \omega_2 = \frac{v_2}{d_2/2}.$$

And since the velocity ratio, r_v, is the ratio of the angular velocities we obtain

$$r_v = \frac{\omega_2}{\omega_1} = \frac{v_2/(d_2/2)}{v_1/(d_1/2)} = \frac{v_2 d_1}{v_1 d_2}$$

or, since $v_1 = v_2 \cos \psi_2 / \cos \psi_1$,

$$r_v = \frac{d_1 \cos \psi_1}{d_2 \cos \psi_2}. \tag{15}$$

Since $d_1 = N_1/P_1$ and $d_2 = N_2/P_2$,

$$r_v = \frac{N_1 P_2 \cos \psi_1}{N_2 P_1 \cos \psi_2}.$$

But $P^n = P/\cos \psi$, therefore

$$r_v = \frac{N_1 P^n_2}{N_2 P^n_1}.$$

Since, as mentioned earlier, the normal diametral pitches of crossed helical gears must be equal ($P^n_1 = P^n_2$), we finally obtain

$$r_v = \frac{N_1}{N_2} \tag{16}$$

It can thus be seen that the velocity ratio defined *in terms of the number of teeth* is identical for both parallel helical gears and crossed helical gears. On the other hand, while parallel helical gears have a velocity ratio equal to the ratio of the pitch diameters, Equation (10), crossed helical gears in general have their velocity ratio not equal to the pitch diameter ratio. See Eq. (15). Fig. 14 shows the direction for the thrust loads for crossed helical gears.

EXAMPLE—PROBLEM 4: Two crossed helical gears have a normal circular pitch of 0.55 in. The driver has 20 teeth and a helix angle of 20°. The angle between the shafts of the driver and follower is 50°, and the velocity ratio is 1/2. The driver and the follower are both right-handed. Determine the center distance.

Solution: The helix angle of the follower is found using the known helix angle of the driver, the shaft angle, and Eq. (12A).

$$\Sigma = \psi_1 + \psi_2$$
$$\psi_2 = \Sigma - \psi_1 = 50° - 20° = 30°.$$

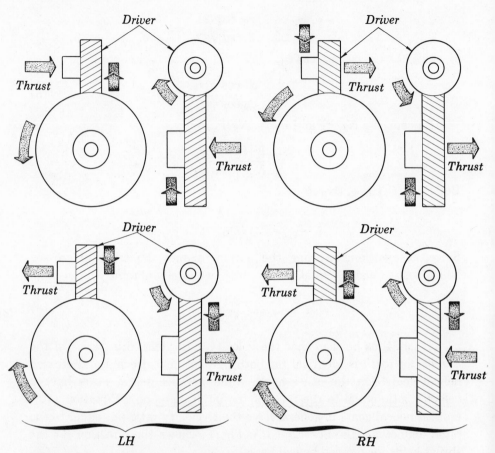

FIG. 14. Direction of thrust loads for crossed helical gears. A diagram of this type is convenient for quickly determining the direction in which thrust loads act for crossed helical gears. (Pic Design Corp., Benrus Watch Co.)

The number of teeth for the follower is found using the number of teeth of the driver and the velocity ratio formula, Eq. (16).

$$r_v = \frac{N_1}{N_2}$$

$$N_2 = \frac{N_1}{r_v} = \frac{20}{1/2} = 40 \text{ teeth.}$$

Finally, the center distance for a pair of crossed helical gears is found using Eq. (13)

$$c = \frac{p^n}{2\pi}\left(\frac{N_1}{\cos\psi_1} + \frac{N_2}{\cos\psi_2}\right)$$
$$= \frac{0.55}{2\pi}\left(\frac{20}{\cos 20°} + \frac{40}{\cos 30°}\right)$$
$$= 5.9 \text{ in.}$$

Worm Gears

If large speed reduction ratios are necessary between nonparallel shafts, crossed helical gears with a small driver and large follower are required. However, the magnitude of the load that can be transmitted by these gears is very limited. A better solution to the problem is the use of a worm and worm gear. However, it should be stated that worm gearsets can be considered a special case of crossed helical gears.

In Fig. 15 a typical worm gearset is shown. As can be seen from the figure, the worm is very similar to a screw. In fact, the teeth on a worm are often spoken of as threads. The worm gear, sometimes called a worm wheel, is a helical gear.

FIG. 15. A worm gearset with a hollow worm. This gearset is single-enveloping. (Horsburgh & Scott Co.)

If an ordinary cylindrical helical gear is used, the contact is a point. However, worm gears are cut with a concave rather than a straight width. See Fig. 15. This results in the worm gear partially enclosing the worm, and thus giving line contact. Such a set, which is called a single-enveloping worm gearset, can transmit much more power. If the worm is also manufactured with its length concave rather than straight, the worm teeth will partially enclose the gear teeth, as well as the gear teeth partially enclosing the worm teeth. Such a gearset, shown in Fig. 16, is known as a double-enveloping worm gearset, and will provide still more contact between gears, thus permitting even greater power transmission.

Proper alignment is extremely important for proper operation of worm gearsets. For single-enveloping sets, the worm gear must be accurately mounted, while for double-enveloping sets, both the worm and worm gear must be accurately mounted.

Worm gearsets are usually manufactured by using a hobbing tool to cut the worm gear teeth, and a milling cutter or a lathe to cut the worm. Fig. 17 shows a worm being manufactured, while Fig. 18 shows a worm gear being hobbed.

FIG. 16. A double-enveloping worm gearset. The worm length is concave so that the worm encloses; in addition to being enclosed by, the gear. (Excello Corp.)

FIG. 17. The manufacture of a concave worm on a thread generator cutter (Fellows Gear Shaper Co.)

FIG. 18. Hobbing a helical worm gear. Helical and worm gears can be cut from the same hob. The hob used to cut this worm gear could also be used to cut a spur gear. (Cleveland Worm and Gear Div., Eaton, Yale, and Towne)

Mechanism

Worm Gear Geometry and Terminology

A consideration of the geometry of worm gearsets would be informative at this point. The *axial pitch* of a worm is equal to the distance between corresponding points on adjacent threads measured along the axis of the worm. See Fig. 19A. The axial pitch of the worm and the circular pitch of the gear are equal in magnitude if the shaft axes are 90° apart, they also operate properly for shaft axes less than 90°.

Lead. The lead of a worm is equal to the apparent axial distance that a thread advances in one revolution of the worm. For a single-threaded worm, (a worm with one tooth) the lead is equal to the pitch,

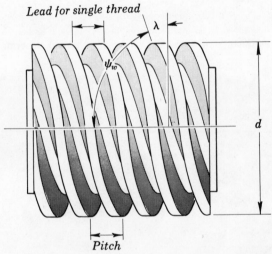

FIG. 19A. The relationship between the pitch and lead for a worm with a single thread.

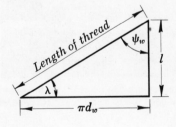

FIG. 19B. One tooth of a worm is shown unwrapped to illustrate the relationship between the lead, the lead angle, the pitch diameter and the helix angle. Note that the lead and helix angles are complimentary.

356

FIG. 20. A quadruple-threaded worm is used in this single-enveloping worm gearset. The start of each of the four threads is clearly visible at the right end of the worm. (Browning Mfg. Co.)

Fig. 19A. A double-threaded worm, a worm with 2 teeth, has a lead equal to twice the pitch. In a single-threaded worm, one thread is started in each revolution. For double-threaded worms, two threads are started in each revolution, etc. Fig. 20 shows a quadruple-threaded worm. Note the four threads started around the circumference.

The lead and the pitch of a worm are related by the following equation

$$l = p_w N_w \tag{17}$$

where

l is the lead,

p_w is the circular pitch of the worm, and

N_w is the number of teeth of the worm.

The triangle shown in Fig. 19B represents the unwrapping of one tooth of the worm shown in Fig. 19A. As seen from Fig. 19B,

$$\tan \lambda = \frac{l}{\pi d_w} \tag{18}$$

Mechanism

Since the lead angle, λ, and the helix angle, ψ, of the worm are complimentary to each other, Eq. (18) can be re-written as

$$\cot \psi = \frac{l}{\pi d_w}. \tag{19}$$

For shafts 90° apart, (the usual case for worm gearsets) the lead angle of the worm and the helix angle of the gear are equal.

Worm and Worm Gear Pitch Diameters. In designing worm gears, the worm pitch diameter may be assigned an arbitrary value. However, the following relationship, developed by the American Gear Manufacturers Association, has been used with optimum results:

$$d_w = \frac{(c)^{0.875}}{K} \tag{20}$$

where d_w is the pitch diameter of the worm, K is a constant between 1.7 and 3, and c is the center distance for the worm and worm gear. The usual value for K is taken as 2.2. If the proportions of the worm gearset satisfy Equation (20), good power capacity will result. It should be emphasized, however, that Eq. (20) merely indicates suggested proportions. It should also be clear that it is assumed the center distance between shafts is known when Eq. (20) is used in order to obtain a suitable value for d_w.

Once the worm pitch diameter has been determined, the gear pitch diameter can be found by using the equation for the center distance:

$$c = \frac{d_w + d_g}{2}. \tag{21}$$

Velocity Ratio of Worm Gearsets

The velocity ratio for worm gearsets is derived as was the velocity ratio for crossed helical gears. In the following derivations, the subscript w refers to the worm while the subscript g refers to the worm gear. Thus,

$$r_v = \frac{\omega \text{ (follower)}}{\omega \text{ (driver)}} = \frac{\omega_g}{\omega_w} = \frac{N_w}{N_g}. \tag{22}$$

From Eq. (17), the number of teeth on the worm is given by

$$N_w = \frac{l}{p_w} \ .$$

The number of teeth on the worm gear is given by

$$N_g = P_g \, d_g.$$

But $P_g = \pi/p_g$, therefore

$$N_g = \frac{\pi d_g}{p_g} \ .$$

Substituting the above values for N_w and N_g into the expression for the velocity ratio, we obtain

$$r_v = \frac{N_w}{N_g} = \frac{l p_g}{p_w \, \pi d_g} \ .$$

Since the axial pitch of the worm, p_w, and the circular pitch of the gear, p_g, are equal, the velocity ratio for the worm gearset becomes

$$r_v = \frac{l}{\pi d_g} \ . \tag{23}$$

In most worm gearsets, the worm is the driver. The set is, therefore, a speed reduction unit. It is possible for the gear to be the driver, thus making the set a speed increasing unit. Whether a given set is reversible or not depends on how much frictional force exists between the worm and gear. Almost all worm gearsets are irreversible because of the frictional force developed. Gearsets that are irreversible are usually referred to as self-locking. Small lead angles ($10°$ or less) and low speed operation usually result in irreversible gearsets.

In most applications, the most efficient transmission of power is desired. A self-locking gearset has a relatively high frictional force and, thus, a lower efficiency. The irreversible gearset would therefore be undesirable from the standpoint of efficient power transmission. However, there are some applications where the low efficiency of a self-locking gearset is a distinct advantage. For example, in a hoisting machine application, a self-locking gearset would be an advantage because of the braking action it provides. The designer, however, must be certain that the braking capacity of a gearset is sufficient to perform satisfactorily as a self-locking unit.

Mechanism

EXAMPLE—PROBLEM 5: A quadruple threaded worm has an axial pitch of 1 inch and a pitch diameter of 2 inches. The worm drives a gear having 42 teeth. Determine (A) the lead angle of the worm, and (B) the center distance between worm and gear.

Solution: (A) Since we know that the worm has four threads ($N_w = 4$) and that the axial pitch is 1 inch ($p_w = 1$) we can easily determine the lead of the worm from Eq. (17):

$$l = p_w N_w = 1 \times 4 = 4 \text{ in.}$$

Substituting this value into Eq. (18) we can determine the lead angle (λ) of the worm:

$$\tan \lambda = \frac{l}{\pi d_w} = \frac{4}{\pi \times 2} = 0.638,$$
$$\lambda = 32.5°.$$

(B) We can now determine the center distance. Since we must have the pitch diameters of the gear and worm in order to use the formula for the center distance, Eq. (21), we must first determine the pitch diameter of the gear. Eq. (23) gives us an expression containing this unknown. The value of the velocity ratio can be found using Eq. (22):

$$r_v = \frac{N_w}{N_g} = \frac{4}{42} = 0.095.$$

And from Eq. (23), $r_v = l_w/\pi d_g$, therefore

$$d_g = \frac{l_w}{\pi r_v} = \frac{4}{\pi \times 0.095} = 12.1 \text{ in.}$$

Finally, having found the pitch diameter of the gear, d_g, we can now use Eq. (21) to find the center distance:

$$c = \frac{d_w + d_g}{2} = \frac{2 + 12.1}{2} = 7.05 \text{ in.}$$

FIG. 21. A pair of bevel gears. The pitch surfaces for the two gears are rolling cones, which can be clearly visualized. (Browning Mfg. Co.)

Bevel Gears

When power is to be transmitted between two shafts that intersect, the type of gear usually used in this situation is a bevel gear. The pitch surfaces of two mating bevel gears are rolling cones, rather than the rolling cylinders that two mating spur gears have. Fig. 21 shows a typical pair of meshing bevel gears. While the shafts that bevel gears are mounted on are usually 90° apart, there are applications for which the shaft angle is greater or less than 90°.

Bevel Gear Terminology

Some of the more common terms used in bevel gearing are illustrated in Fig. 22 and are described below. As seen in the illustration, the tooth size decreases along the face width as the apex of the pitch cone is approached. The pressure angle for most straight bevel gears is 20°.

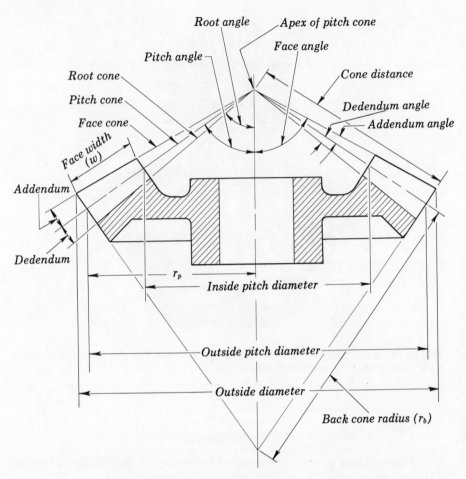

FIG. 22. Terminology associated with bevel gears.

Pitch Cone: The geometric shape of bevel gears needed to assure a rolling contact. The pitch cone is analogous to the pitch cylinders of spur gears.

Apex of Pitch Cone: The intersection of the elements making up the pitch cone.

Cone Distance: The cone distance is the slant height of the pitch cone. In other words, it is the length of a pitch cone element.

Face Cone: The cone formed by the elements passing through the top of the teeth and the apex.

Root Cone: The cone formed by the elements passing through the bottom of the teeth and the apex.

Face Angle: The angle between an element of the face cone and the axis of the gear.

Pitch Angle: The angle between an element of the pitch cone and the axis of the gear.

Root Angle: The angle between an element of the root cone and the axis of the gear.

Face Width: The width of a tooth.

Addendum: The distance from an element on pitch cone to an element on face cone, measured on the outside of the tooth.

Dedendum: The distance from an element on pitch cone to an element on the root cone, measured on the outside of the tooth.

Addendum Angle: The angle between an element on the pitch cone and an element on the face cone.

Dedendum Angle: The angle between an element on the pitch cone and an element on the root cone.

Inside Pitch Diameter: The pitch diameter measured on the inside of the tooth.

Outside Pitch Diameter: The pitch diameter measured on the outside of the tooth.

Back Cone: The cone formed by elements perpendicular to the pitch cone elements at the outside of the teeth.

Back Cone Radius: The length of a back cone element, r_b.

Since most bevel gears are mounted on intersecting shafts, at least one is usually mounted *outboard*. That is, one gear is mounted on the cantilevered end of the shaft. Fig. 23 shows a outboard-mounted bevel gear. Because of the outboard mounting, the deflection of the shaft where the gear is attached may be rather large. This would result in the

363

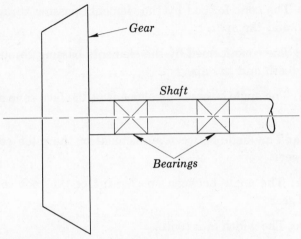

FIG. 23. An outboard-mounted bevel gear. The overhanging mounting of the gear can cause large deflections, which can seriously affect gear action.

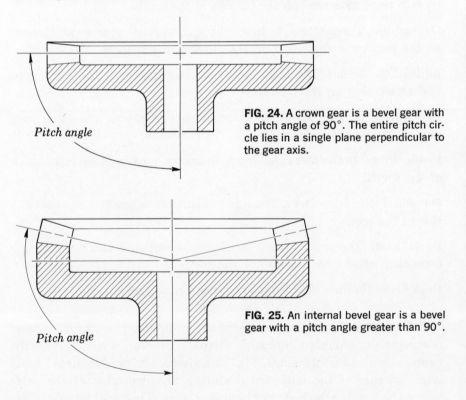

Pitch angle

FIG. 24. A crown gear is a bevel gear with a pitch angle of 90°. The entire pitch circle lies in a single plane perpendicular to the gear axis.

Pitch angle

FIG. 25. An internal bevel gear is a bevel gear with a pitch angle greater than 90°.

teeth at the small end moving out of mesh. The load would thus be unequally distributed, with the larger ends of the teeth taking most of the load. To reduce this effect, the tooth face width is usually made no greater than 1/3 of the cone distance.

Classifying Bevel Gears by Pitch Angle. Bevel gears are usually classified according to their pitch angle. A bevel gear having a pitch angle of 90° and a plane for its pitch surface is known as a *crown gear*. A crown gear is shown in Fig. 24.

When the pitch angle of a bevel gear exceeds 90°, it is called an *internal bevel gear*. Internal bevel gears, like that shown in Fig. 25, cannot have pitch angles very much greater than 90° because of the problems incurred in manufacturing such gears. In fact, these manufacturing difficulties are the main reason why internal bevel gears are rarely used.

Bevel gears with pitch angles less than 90° are the type most commonly used. Fig. 22 illustrates such an external bevel gear.

When two meshing bevel gears have a shaft angle of 90°, and have the same number of teeth, they are called *mitre gears*. In other words, mitre gears have a speed ratio of one. Each of the two gears has a 45° pitch angle. A mitre gearset is shown in Fig. 26.

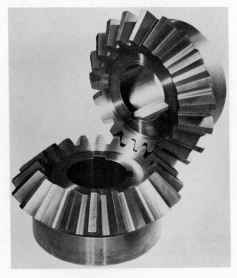

FIG. 26. A mitre gearset. A mitre gear is a bevel gear with a pitch angle of 45° and a speed ratio of one. The shaft angle for a mitre gearset is 90°. (Horsburgh & Scott Co.)

Tredgold's Approximation for Bevel Gears

The profile of bevel gear teeth on the back cone is very similar to the profile of a spur gear having a pitch radius, r_b. See Fig. 27. Using the properties of this equivalent spur gear of pitch radius r_b to approximate the properties of a bevel gear is known as Tredgold's approximation for bevel gears.

It is clear that the imaginary spur gear has more teeth than the bevel gear which it approximates. The number of teeth on the equivalent spur gear is known as the formative or virtual number of teeth.

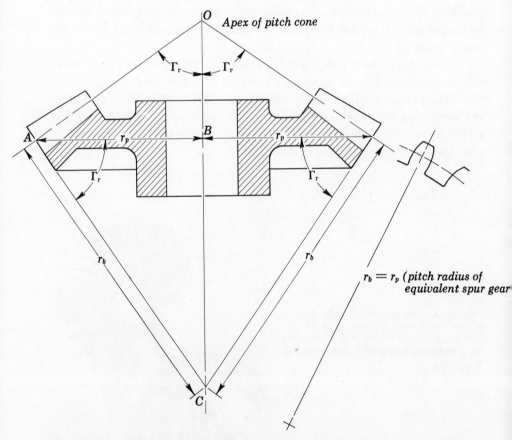

$$r_b = r_p \ (\textit{pitch radius of equivalent spur gear})$$

FIG. 27. The relationship (Tredgold's Approximation) between the actual number of teeth for the bevel gear, the pitch angle, and the formative number of teeth. The back cone radius, r_b, becomes the pitch radius for the equivalent spur gear.

The formative or virtual number of teeth (the number of teeth for the equivalent spur gear) is given by

$$N_f = d_b\,P = 2\,r_b\,P$$

where r_b is the back cone radius of the bevel gear, and P is the diametral pitch. From Fig. 27, it can be seen that

$$\cos \Gamma_r = \frac{r_p}{r_b} \quad \text{or} \quad r_b = \frac{r_p}{\cos \Gamma_r}$$

and since $N_f = 2\,r_b P$, the expression becomes

$$N_f = \frac{2r_p}{\cos \Gamma_r}\,P.$$

But $2\,r_p P = N$, therefore

$$N_f = \frac{N}{\cos \Gamma_r}\;. \qquad (24)$$

In other words, the virtual or formative number of teeth of the equivalent spur gear is equal to the actual number of teeth for the bevel gear divided by the cosine of the pitch angle of the bevel gear.

Velocity Ratio for Bevel Gears

The velocity ratio for bevel gears is given by the same expressions used to determine the velocity ratio for spur gears, where the subscripts 1 and 2 refer to the driver and follower:

$$r_v = \frac{\omega_2}{\omega_1} = \frac{r_1}{r_2} = \frac{N_1}{N_2} \qquad (9)\text{-}(11)$$

where r is the pitch circle radius and N is the number of teeth.

At this point it is desirable to derive some relationship between numbers of teeth and pitch angles for bevel gears. In Fig. 28, which shows two external bevel gears in mesh, Σ is the shaft angle, Γ and γ are the pitch angles, and r_p and r_g are the pitch radii for the pinion and gear respectively.

From Fig. 28,

$$\Sigma = \Gamma + \gamma$$

and

$$\sin \Gamma = \frac{r_g}{OP} \quad \text{and} \quad \sin \gamma = \frac{r_p}{OP}$$

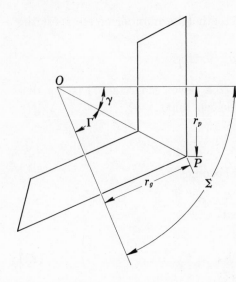

FIG. 28. Two meshing external bevel gears, illustrating the relationship between the shaft angle, the pitch angles, and the pitch radii.

$$OP = \frac{r_g}{\sin \Gamma} = \frac{r_p}{\sin \gamma}$$

$$\sin \Gamma = \frac{r_g}{r_p} \sin \gamma = \frac{r_g}{r_p} \sin (\Sigma - \Gamma)$$

$$= \frac{r_g}{r_p} (\sin \Sigma \cos \Gamma - \cos \Sigma \sin \Gamma).$$

Dividing this expression for $\sin \Gamma$ by $\cos \Gamma$, we obtain

$$\frac{\sin \Gamma}{\cos \Gamma} = \tan \Gamma = \frac{r_g}{r_p} (\sin \Sigma - \cos \Sigma \tan \Gamma)$$

$$\tan \Gamma + \frac{r_g}{r_p} \cos \Sigma \tan \Gamma = \frac{r_g}{r_p} \sin \Sigma$$

$$\tan \Gamma = \frac{(r_g/r_p) \sin \Sigma}{1 + (r_g/r_p) \cos \Sigma} = \frac{\sin \Sigma}{(r_p/r_g) + \cos \Sigma}.$$

At this point, we can utilize our original velocity ratio formula to arrive at the desired formula involving both the pitch angles and the numbers of teeth for both bevel gears. From Equations (9)-(11),

$$\frac{r_p}{r_g} = \frac{N_p}{N_g}.$$

Therefore,

$$\tan \Gamma = \frac{\sin \Sigma}{(N_p/N_g) + \cos \Sigma} . \tag{25}$$

Similarly,

$$\tan \gamma = \frac{\sin \Sigma}{(N_g/N_p) + \cos \Sigma} . \tag{26}$$

Finally, for shaft angle $\Sigma = 90°$ (which is usually the case) we obtain

$$\tan \Gamma = \frac{1}{(N_p/N_g) + 0} = \frac{N_g}{N_p} \tag{27}$$

and

$$\tan \gamma = \frac{1}{(N_g/N_p) + 0} = \frac{N_p}{N_g} . \tag{28}$$

The formulas just derived are quite useful to the designer. The shaft angle, or angle at which one shaft intersects the other, and the required speed ratio are usually known to the designer. Since the speed ratio is also equal to the ratio of the number of teeth, it should be obvious that the formulas can thus be used to calculate the pitch angle required for each gear.

EXAMPLE—PROBLEM 6: A pair of straight-tooth bevel gears are mounted on shafts which intersect each other at an angle of 70°. The average pitch diameter of the pinion is 6 in., and the velocity ratio of the gears is ½. Determine the pitch angles of the gears.

Solution: Since $r_v = r_1/r_2$,

$$r_2 = \frac{r_1}{r_v} = \frac{3}{½} = 6 \text{ in.}$$

Knowing the velocity ratio, we can use Eq. (25) and (26) to find the pitch angles for bevel gears with a shaft angle other than 90°. Thus,

$$\tan \Gamma = \frac{\sin \Sigma}{(N_p/N_g) + \cos \Sigma}$$

and since $N_p/N_g = r_p/r_g = ½$,

$$\tan \Gamma = \frac{\sin 70°}{½ + \cos 70°}$$

$$= \frac{0.94}{0.842} = 1.12$$
$$\Gamma = 48.2°.$$

Similarly,

$$\tan \gamma = \frac{\sin \Sigma}{(N_g/N_p) + \cos \Sigma}$$
$$= \frac{0.94}{2.342} = 0.401$$
$$\gamma = 21.8°.$$

Other Types of Bevel Gears

There are a number of other types of bevel gears in addition to straight-toothed gears. Spiral bevel gears, Fig. 29, are used when high speed, high load applications occur. For these gears, the transmission of power is much smoother than for straight bevel gears, since there is

FIG. 29. Spiral bevel gears feature a spiral rather than a helical tooth design. However, to simplify the manufacture of spiral bevel gears, the tooth is usually made circular instead of spiral. (Arrow Gear Co.)

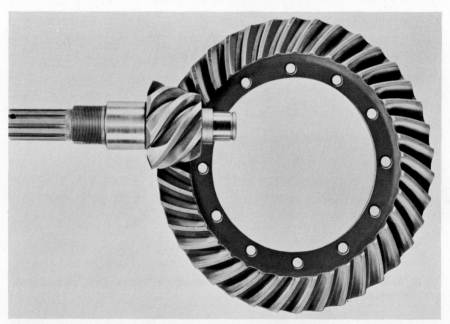

FIG. 30. Hypoid gears are spiral bevel gears designed to operate on *non-intersecting* shafts. (Eaton Automotive Gear Div., Eaton, Yale, and Towne)

gradual tooth contact in addition to more teeth being in contact at any instant.

While a wide variety of spiral angles are used, the 35° spiral angle is most common. It is helpful, in understanding spiral bevel gears, to compare them to straight bevel gears in the same manner that helical gears are compared to spur gears.

For shafts that are non-intersecting, hypoid gears (Fig. 30) are used. While hypoid gears are similar to spiral bevel gears, they are stronger and quieter in operation. Since the shafts on which they are mounted are non-intersecting, they may be placed between bearing supports. Gears used on automobile axles are usually hypoid gears because they allow the drive shaft to be placed closer to ground level, and also permit large speed reduction ratios in a relatively compact space.

Zerol bevel gears, shown in Fig. 31, are the same as spiral gears, except that the spiral angle is zero. Zerol gears are used when it is

FIG. 31. Zerol bevel gears are spiral bevel gears with a zero spiral angle. (Eaton Automotive Gear Div., Eaton, Yale, and Towne)

desired to reduce the thrust loads that occur when spiral bevel gears are used.

While there are other types of bevel gears, those which have been discussed are the types most often used. It is suggested that the various gear manufacturers' catalogs be consulted when information about other specialized gears is desired.

Chapter

7

Drive Trains:
Design and Analysis

Introduction

Most electric motors, internal combustion engines and turbines operate efficiently at high rotating speeds—speeds much higher than the optimum speeds for operating machinery. For this reason, gear trains and other speed reducers are used with almost every industrial and domestic engine. In this chapter the various drive trains will be examined in terms of their operation, i.e., the manner in which they effect a speed reduction.

In addition to speed reduction, some gear trains permit us to change output speed even though the input speed remains constant. A pair of gears may be removed from the train and replaced by a pair having a different speed ratio. When the speed ratio change is required only occasionally, a design of this type is satisfactory. For rapid or frequent speed ratio changes, pairs of gears having different ratios are engaged by shifting the location of the gears themselves, and by employing bands and clutches within the transmission.

Velocity Ratios for Spur and Helical Gear Trains

Spur Gear Trains

We know from the preceding chapter that, for *any* pair of gears with fixed centers, the angular velocity ratio is given by

$$\left| \frac{n_2}{n_1} \right| = \frac{N_1}{N_2} \tag{1}$$

where $\left| n_2/n_1 \right|$ is the absolute value of the ratio of speeds of rotation, and N_1 and N_2 represent the number of teeth in each gear. Since the diametral pitch, P (the number of teeth per inch of pitch diameter), must also be equal in the case of meshing gears, pitch diameters d_1 and d_2 must be proportional respectively to N_1 and N_2:

$$P = \frac{N_1}{d_1} = \frac{N_2}{d_2} \quad \text{and} \quad \frac{N_1}{N_2} = \frac{d_1}{d_2}.$$

Thus, for straight spur gears, the above equation (1) may be written as

$$\frac{n_2}{n_1} = -\frac{N_1}{N_2} = -\frac{d_1}{d_2}. \tag{2}$$

The minus sign refers to the fact that the rotation direction changes for any pair of external gears. If one of the gears in the pair is a ring gear (an internal gear), then

$$\frac{n_2}{n_1} = \frac{N_1}{N_2} = \frac{d_1}{d_2} \tag{3}$$

and there is no change in the direction of rotation.

Helical Gear Trains

Helical gears are often used in place of spur gears to reduce vibration and noise levels. A pair of helical gears *on parallel shafts* will have the *same* helix angle, but one will be right hand and the other left-hand. The hand is defined as it is for screw threads. As in the case of spur gears, the speed ratio for helical gears on parallel shafts is $n_2/n_1 = -N_1/N_2 = -d_1/d_2$, where N is again the number of teeth and d the pitch diameter.

In the case of *crossed* helical gears (gears on non-parallel shafts) the velocity ratio is still equal to the inverse ratio of the number of teeth: $|n_2/n_1| = N_1/N_2$. While helical gears on parallel shafts must have equal helix angles, *crossed* helical gears usually have *unequal* helix angles. This means that the velocity ratio for crossed helical gears is, in general, *not* equal to the ratio of the pitch diameters. When the helix angles are unequal (as is frequently the case), the velocity ratio is instead given by

$$\left| \frac{n_2}{n_1} \right| = \frac{d_1 \cos \psi_1}{d_2 \cos \psi_2} \tag{4}$$

where d_1 and d_2 are the pitch diameters and ψ_1 and ψ_2 are the respective helix angles. See the section on Crossed Helical Gears in Chapter Six.

A worm drive is a special case of a pair of helical gears on crossed shafts. In the more general case, a pair of non-parallel shafts may be at any angle to one another but may not intersect. Ordinarily, both gears have the same hand. Equations (1) and (4) give the speed ratio for a worm gearset but, as is the case for crossed helical gears, Equations (2) and (3) do not apply. Rotation direction should be shown on each gear in the train to insure an accurate solution.

Idlers

An idler may be described as a gear placed between, and meshing with, the input and output gears. Its purpose is to reverse the direction of the output. Thus, an idler gear affects the sign of the angular velocity ratio. For the gear train of Fig. 1,

$$\frac{n_2}{n_1} = -\frac{N_1}{N_2} \quad \text{and} \quad \frac{n_3}{n_2} = -\frac{N_2}{N_3}.$$

Multiplying the first equation by the second, we obtain

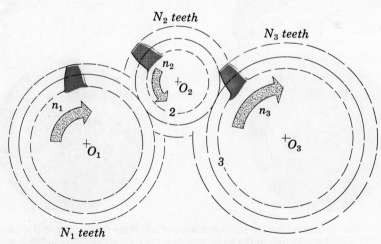

FIG. 1. Gear train with idler. The idler affects the direction of rotation, but not the numerical value of the speed ratio.

$$\left(\frac{n_3}{n_2}\right)\left(\frac{n_2}{n_1}\right) = \left(-\frac{N_2}{N_3}\right)\left(-\frac{N_1}{N_2}\right)$$

which reduces to

$$\frac{n_3}{n_1} = \frac{N_1}{N_3}. \qquad (5A)$$

The number of teeth in gear 2, the idler, does not affect the velocity ratio of the train. However, the idler does affect the direction of rotation of the output gear and, of course, takes up space. Since gear 2 meshes with both gears 1 and 3, all three gears must have the same diametral pitch. Thus, for spur gears, we may also write

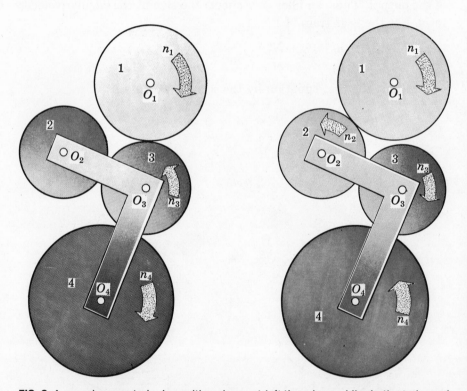

FIG. 2. A reversing gear train. In position shown at *left* there is one idler in the train, and input and output shafts turn in the same direction. There are two idlers in the train when the arm is moved to the position shown at *right*, and the output shaft direction is reversed.

$$\frac{n_3}{n_1} = \frac{d_1}{d_3} \tag{5B}$$

since $P = N_1/d_1 = N_3/d_3$.

Occasionally, several idlers are used to transmit power between shafts which are too far apart for the use of a single pair of gears. With an odd number of idlers, the driver and driven shafts rotate in the same direction. With an even number of idlers, one shaft turns clockwise and the other counterclockwise. The reversing gear train of Fig. 2 illustrates the effects of one and two idlers.

Double Reductions

The minimum number of teeth which a spur gear may have is limited by considerations of contact ratio and interference. While there is no theoretical *maximum* number of teeth, practical considerations like cost and overall size may prevent the designer from specifying a gear with more than, say, one hundred teeth. A speed reduction of the order of one hundred to one can be accomplished instead in two to four steps with a transmission requiring as many pairs of spur gears and considerable space. A double or triple reduction is thus used in preference to a single pair of gears in cases where the required speed reduction is so great that the output gear of a single pair of spur gears would have to be unreasonably large.

The double reduction of Fig. 3 is called a *reverted* gear train because the output shaft is in line with the input shaft. Examining this gear train, we see that gears 2 and 3 are keyed to the same shaft and have the same angular velocity:

$$n_3 = n_2 = -n_1 \frac{N_1}{N_2},$$

and that

$$n_4 = -n_3 \frac{N_3}{N_4},$$

from which the ratio of output speed to input speed becomes:

$$\frac{n_4}{n_1} = \frac{N_1 N_3}{N_2 N_4}. \tag{6A}$$

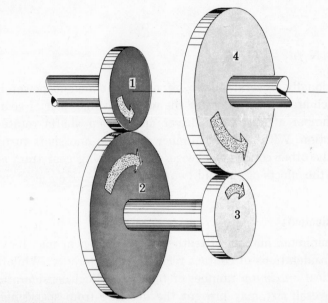

FIG. 3. A reverted gear train. The input and output shafts have the same centerline. The speed ratio equals the product of the tooth numbers of the driving gears divided by the product of the tooth numbers of the driven gears.

Since gears 1 and 2 must have the same diametral pitch, and since gears 3 and 4 must also have the same diametral pitch, Equation (6A) may be re-written:

$$\frac{n_4}{n_1} = \frac{d_1 d_3}{d_2 d_4}.$$ (6B)

Note that gear 1 drives gear 2, and that gear 3 drives gear 4. By adding more pairs of gears and examining the results, we find the general relationship to be

$$\left| \frac{n_{output}}{n_{input}} \right| = \frac{\text{Product of driving gear teeth}}{\text{Product of driven gear teeth}}$$ (7)

which applies to all gear trains in which the shaft centers are fixed in space. The torque-arm speed reducer shown in Fig. 4 is a practical example of such a double reduction.

FIG. 4. Torque-arm speed reducer. This double reduction is available with 1:15 and 1:25 output to input speed ratios. The helical involute teeth have an elliptoid form, slightly narrower at the ends for more even load distribution. (Dodge Mfg. Co.)

Reversing Direction

It is seen in the above work that the introduction of an idler in a spur gear train changes the velocity direction of the output. Both the driver and the driven gear rotate in the same direction with one idler in a simple train. When two idlers are inserted in the train, the driver and driven gear rotate in opposite directions. In Fig. 2, gears 1 and 4 have fixed centers O_1 and O_4, while gears 2 and 3 rotate in bearings which are held in an arm. Reversing trains of this type have been used in lathes. The velocity ratio when the arm is fixed in the position shown in Fig. 2, *left*, is given by

$$\frac{n_4}{n_1} = \frac{N_1}{N_4},$$

where n refers to rotation speed and N refers to number of teeth.

Mechanism

When the arm is rotated about O_4 to the position shown in Fig. 2, *right*, the velocity ratio becomes

$$\frac{n_4}{n_1} = - \frac{N_1}{N_4}.$$

This type of train is satisfactory for infrequent direction changing, but unsatisfactory for frequent direction changes because the gears do not always correctly engage when shifted. In some cases the gears must be manipulated by hand before they will fully mesh.

Speed Ratio Change

Idlers may also be used to permit the changing of speed ratios. An arm holds idler gear 2 to drive gear 1 in Fig. 5. Gear 1 is keyed or splined to the input shaft and turns with it. The arm, A, does not rotate with the input shaft and gear 1, but is connected to gear 1 by a sleeve. The arm is moved axially along the input shaft with gear 1 when a new speed ratio is required. The speed ratios available are

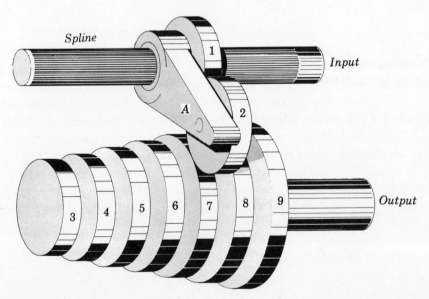

FIG. 5. Speed changer employing an idler. Gear 1 turns with the input shaft. Arm A keeps idler gear 2 in contact with gear 1 and one of the gears on the output shaft. Arm A is fixed in space except when changing gears.

$$\frac{n_{output}}{n_{input}} = \frac{N_1}{N_3}, \frac{N_1}{N_4}, \frac{N_1}{N_5}, \text{etc.}$$

A typical industrial lathe may have a "cone" of as many as twelve gears on the output shaft of a train similar to Fig. 5. This train is partly responsible for the wide variation of feeds which are available. (Feed refers to the movement of the cutting tool along or into the workpiece.) With two other speed selectors, the total number of feeds available and therefore the number of different pitches of screw threads which can be cut would be 48. Since thread cutting requires a high degree of accuracy, a gear drive, which provides precise speed ratios, is ideal for this application.

The operator of a lathe or other machine tool may find it quite satisfactory to stop what he is doing in order to change speed ratio. Practical, efficient, and safe vehicle operation, however, requires a smooth, quick transition from one speed ratio to another without completely stopping the machine; different types of transmissions are therefore necessary.

Transmissions with Axial Shifting

Automotive transmissions in common use include gear trains with axial shifting, fluid drive units, planetary gear trains and combinations of the above. The transmission shown in Fig. 6A is called a three speed transmission even though it offers a reverse speed ratio in addition to three forward speed ratios and a neutral position. The axial distance between gears in the sketch has been exaggerated for clarity; a typical transmission (like the one shown in Fig. 6B) would be more compact.

In Fig. 6A, shafts A, B, and D and the shaft of idler gear 6 turn in bearings mounted in the transmission housing, but bearings and parts of the shafts have been omitted from the sketch. Gear 1 is an integral part of input shaft A. Output shaft D is not directly connected to the input, but power may be transmitted to it through clutch C or through gears on the countershaft B. In the position shown, no torque is transmitted between input and output shafts because gear 7 is not rigidly connected to output shaft D, but turns freely on it. This position is called *neutral*.

Clutch C and gear 1 have cone shaped internal and external mating faces respectively. Clutch C and the end of the output shaft

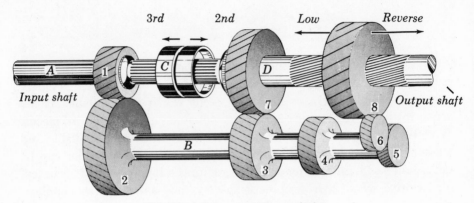

FIG. 6A. A three speed transmission.

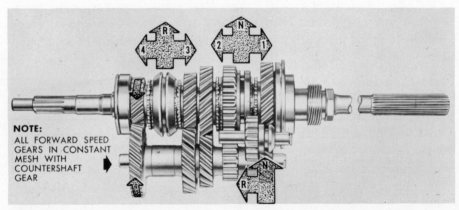

FIG. 6B. A four-speed transmission. The shifting pattern for four forward speed ratios, neutral and reverse is shown by arrows on the gears. (Ford Motor Co.)

on which it rides are splined so that the two turn together, even though *C* may be moved axially on the shaft. When *C* is made to contact the conical face of gear 1, the two begin to move at the same speed. In addition to the conical friction faces, *C* and gear 1 have internal and external mating "teeth" which insure a positive drive after the initial contact synchronizes the input and output shaft speeds. The resulting direct drive, or one-to-one speed ratio, is called *high* or *third gear* in the three speed transmission.

TABLE 1. POSITION, PATH, AND SPEED RATIOS FOR A THREE-SPEED
TRANSMISSION, FIG. 6A

Gear	Position of Synchro-mesh Clutch, C	Position of Gear 8	Path of Transmitted Power	Output to Input Speed Ratio n_D/n_A
Neutral	center	center	—	—
3rd (High)	left	center	A-1-C-D	$+\ 1$
2nd	right	center	A-1-2-3-7-C-D	$+\ \dfrac{N_1 N_3}{N_2 N_7}$
1st (Low)	center	left	A-1-2-4-8-D	$+\ \dfrac{N_1 N_4}{N_2 N_8}$
Reverse	center	right	A-1-2-5-6-8-D	$-\ \dfrac{N_1 N_5}{N_2 N_8}$

The engine is not directly connected to the input shaft, but a disc clutch (not shown) is installed between the two. Synchronizing of the input and output shafts is essentially independent of the engine speed when the disc clutch is disengaged. The word *clutch* above ordinarily refers to the disc clutch, while clutch C is called a *synchromesh clutch*. The synchromesh clutch is shifted by a fork which rides in an annular groove.

We see in Fig. 6A that gears 1 and 2, gears 3 and 7 and gears 5 and 6 mesh at all times. Gears 2, 3, 4, and 5 are integral parts of counter-shaft B. Therefore, all gears except gear 8 turn at all times when the input shaft is in motion. One face of gear 7, like gear 1, mates with clutch C. Since output shaft D and the internal surface of gear 7 are smooth where they contact, clutch C must engage the clutch face of gear 7 when power is transmitted through that gear. The effect is a reverted gear train of gears 1, 2, 3, and 7, or symbolically, the path of power transmission from input to output is A-1-2-3-7-C-D. Output to input speed ratio is given by

$$\frac{n_D}{n_A} = \frac{N_1 N_3}{N_2 N_7}$$

where N_1 is the number of teeth in gear 1, etc. Ratios N_1/N_2 and

Mechanism

N_3/N_7 are both less than one and there is a speed reduction. This position is called *second gear*. The disc clutch is disengaged when shifting so that the speed of gear 7 can be synchronized with the output shaft speed.

Gear 4 is made smaller than gear 3 so that engaging gear 8 with gear 4 produces an even lower speed ratio called *low* or *first gear*, symbolically noted as *A*-1-2-4-8-*D*. The speed ratio is given by

$$\frac{n_D}{n_A} = \frac{N_1 N_4}{N_2 N_8}.$$

Of course, the shifting mechanism must be designed so that clutch *C* is first disengaged from gear 7 or we would have simultaneously two different speed ratios. (Actually, the result would be a locked gear train or a broken transmission.) If there is no synchromesh in first gear, it is best to shift when the output and input shafts are stationary. This is the case when the vehicle is stationary and the disc clutch has been disengaged a few moments before shifting. Shifting of gear 8 along the splined portion of the output shaft is accomplished by a fork which rides in a grooved ring (not shown). The ends of the teeth of gears 4, 6, and 8 are rounded to facilitate engagement.

Gear 5 is made slightly smaller than gear 4 so that gear 8 cannot mesh with it, but may be shifted to mesh with idler gear 6. For first, second, and third gears examined above, the ratios were positive; the output shaft turned in the same direction as the input shaft. But, when engaged with gear 5, idler gear 6 causes an odd number of direction changes, and the output to input speed ratio is given by

$$\frac{n_D}{n_A} = -\frac{N_1 N_5}{N_2 N_8}.$$

This arrangement is the *reverse gear*, symbolically given by *A*-1-2-5-6-8-*D*. When shifting to reverse, as when shifting to first gear, the disc clutch is disengaged, and both input and output shafts are stationary. Except for reverse and first gear ratios, gear 8 must turn freely, engaging neither gear 4 nor gear 6.

Helical gears are often selected for transmissions because of their greater strength and smoother, quieter operation. Meshing helical gears on parallel shafts are of opposite hand, where a right-hand helical gear resembles a right-hand screw. If gear 1 of Fig. 6A is left-hand, then gear

384

2 must be right-hand. If gear 1 turns counterclockwise (as seen from the right), creating a thrust to the left, there is a thrust to the right on the countershaft at gear 2. When in second gear, gear 3 will have a balancing thrust (to the left) if it is a right-hand helix. Gear 4 is also a right-hand helix so that countershaft thrust is balanced in first gear. Since gear 8 meshes with both gears 4 and 6, gear 6 must be right-hand, making gear 5 left-hand. Thus, thrust is not balanced when in reverse. Finally, all speed ratios and paths of power transmission for the transmission of Fig. 6A are summarized in Table 1.

Automotive transmissions with four or more forward speed ratios are available, some including synchromesh in all forward gears. See Fig. 6B. While there are many innovations among manufacturers, the basic principles differ but slightly from the above example. Although the above discussion centers around speed reduction, in a few instances it is desirable to increase speed. Kinematically, the equations apply to speed increases as well as reductions. Friction losses, however, make large increases in speed impossible.

Designing for a Particular Speed Ratio

For many applications, it is necessary to have a specific relationship between output and input speed. When the required relationship is a ratio of small whole numbers, say one-half or five-sevenths, etc., we have a wide selection of satisfactory pairs of gears to choose from. However, some speed ratios are impossible to obtain exactly and others may be impractical to obtain exactly. An example of a speed ratio which cannot be obtained with gears is the square root of two, an irrational number. An example of a speed ratio difficult to obtain exactly (from a practical standpoint) is 503/2003, the ratio of two prime numbers.

In the first case, we cannot express the desired ratio as a fraction made up of whole numbers, and thus cannot select a corresponding set of gear tooth numbers. The second example involves a pair of numbers, neither of which can be factored. An exact solution involving a pair of gears with 503 and 2003 teeth might be prohibitively expensive. Either problem, however, may be solved if a small variation from the desired ratio is permitted.

One convenient way of making rough approximations of ratios is by using a slide rule. One of the C-scale index numbers is set over the desired ratio on the D-scale. Integers which line up closely are possible candidates for gear tooth numbers. Let us select a pair of gears to approximate a speed ratio of the square root of two to one (approximately 1.414214 to 1). Setting the left-hand C-index over 1.414 on the D-Scale, we scan the C and D scales for integers which line up. For practical reasons (cost and space requirements), gears with over 50 teeth will not be considered. Possible choices are 17 and 12; 24 and 17; 34 and 24; 41 and 29; 48 and 34. Depending on the tooth system selected, it may be necessary to eliminate gears of less than 15 or 20 teeth for considerations of contact ratio and interference. The remaining ratios are then calculated "longhand" or by using a desk calculator, and the one closest to the desired value is selected. If none of the ratios are close enough, we might consider using gears of up to 100 teeth, or using two or more pairs of gears or a planetary train.

In some instances, a table of factors may be used to advantage. Suppose, for example, we needed the exact speed ratio: $n_o/n_i = 1501/1500$, where n_o and n_i represent the output and input speeds. For a gear train similar to Fig. 3, $n_4/n_1 = + N_1N_3/N_2N_4$, leading us to try $N_1N_3 = 1501$ and $N_2N_4 = 1500$. Fortunately, both numbers are factorable; $1501 = 19 \times 79$ and $1500 = 2^2 \times 3 \times 5^3$. Letting $N_1 = 19$, $N_3 = 79$, $N_2 = 2^2 \times 5 = 20$ and $N_4 = 3 \times 5^2 = 75$, we have the desired ratio exactly. When the desired ratio consists of a pair of large numbers which cannot be factored to give reasonable gear sizes, we may then be forced to a more complicated and expensive solution or to an approximate solution.

Planetary Gear Trains

Gearsets of the type shown in Fig. 7 are called *epicyclic* or *planetary* gear trains. In planetary trains, one or more gears are carried on a rotating planet carrier rather than on a shaft which rotates on a fixed axis. Several types of gear trains may be shifted manually to obtain greater or lesser values of speed reduction. The shifting process, however, is difficult to accomplish automatically with gears which rotate about fixed centers. On the other hand, planetary gear trains are readily adapted to automatic control. Some planetary gear trains are designed to change ratios simply by using electrically or hydraulically operated band brakes to keep one or more of the gears stationary. Other planetary trains operating with fixed gear ratios are selected for their compact design and high efficiency.

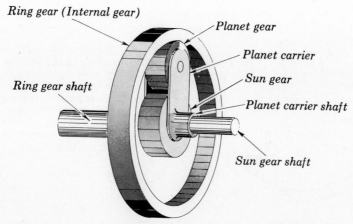

Ring gear (Internal gear)

Planet gear

Planet carrier

Sun gear

Ring gear shaft

Planet carrier shaft

Sun gear shaft

FIG. 7. A planetary gear train. The versatility of this type of gear train stems from the fact that the axis of the planet gear is not fixed in space. The planet gear carrier is pinned to the planet gear, but is independent of the sun gear shaft. This permits several variations of relative rotation.

Tabular Analysis of Simple Planetary Trains (Superposition)

The simple planetary gear train sketched in Fig. 7 consists of a sun gear in the center, a planet gear, a planet carrier or arm, and an internal, or ring, gear. The sun gear, ring gear, and planet carrier all rotate about the same axis. The planet gear is mounted on a shaft which turns in a bearing in the planet carrier; the planet gear meshes with both the sun gear and the ring gear. Since the planet gear does not rotate about a fixed center, some of the rules developed for gears rotating about fixed centers must be re-examined.

The rotation of the planet carrier complicates the problem of determining gear speeds in a planetary train. However, by the simple device of calculating rotation *relative to the carrier* and combining it with the rotation of the entire train turning as a unit we can find velocities in two simple steps. If the planet carrier is kept stationary so that the centers of all gears are fixed, gear speed ratios equal the inverse of the ratios of tooth numbers.

The direction of rotation changes when two external gears mesh, but does not change when an external gear meshes with an internal

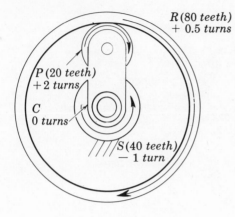

R(80 *teeth*)
+ 0.5 *turns*

P(20 *teeth*)
+2 *turns*

C
0 *turns*

S(40 *teeth*)
− 1 *turn*

FIG. 8A. Planetary train with sun gear fixed. When solving the velocity ratio of a planetary train by the superposition method, the fixed gear is *assumed* to rotate so that the entire locked train turns through one revolution. To maintain a net sun gear motion of zero, the planet carrier is fixed while the sun gear is rotated *back* through one revolution.

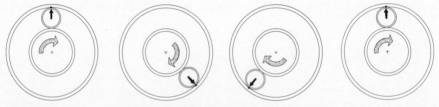

FIG. 8B. The locked planetary train is given one clockwise rotation. It is seen, by observing the arrow marked on the planet, that the planet makes one clockwise rotation (in addition to the motion of the planet center).

gear. If the sun or ring gear is actually fixed, the constraint is (theoretically) temporarily relaxed and that gear is given one turn. The effect on the entire train is calculated. Of course, since the net rotation of the fixed sun or ring gear must be zero, a compensating rotation must take place to correct its position. That compensating motion is one rotation of the entire locked train *in the opposite direction.*

As an example, consider the planetary train of Fig. 8A where the sun, planet, and ring gears have, respectively, 40, 20 and 80 teeth, with the sun gear fixed. Let the entire train be locked together and given one clockwise rotation. The sun and ring gears and the planet carrier will each have turned through one clockwise rotation about their common center of rotation. By examining Fig. 8B, it is seen that the planet also turns through one clockwise rotation relative to its center while its center describes a circle.

388

Since the above motion has violated the requirement that the sun gear be fixed, the sun gear will be given one counterclockwise rotation, yielding a net sun gear motion of zero. While the sun gear is rotated counterclockwise, the arm will be fixed so that all gears rotate on fixed centers. The results up to this point are conveniently tabulated by denoting clockwise rotations as positive ($+$) and counterclockwise rotations as negative ($-$). Thus we are able to construct the following table:

TABLE 2A. STEP 1 OF SUPERPOSITION METHOD FOR SOLVING PLANETARY TRAIN SPEED RATIOS, FIG. 8A

Gear	Sun	Planet	Ring	Planet Carrier
No. of teeth	40	20	80	
Step I. Rotations with train locked	$+1$	$+1$	$+1$	$+1$
Step II. Rotations with planet carrier fixed	-1			

TABLE 2B. STEP 2 OF SUPERPOSITION METHOD FOR SOLVING PLANETARY TRAIN SPEED RATIOS, FIG. 8A

Gear	Sun	Planet	Ring	Planet Carrier
No. of teeth	40	20	80	
Step I. Rotations with Train Locked	$+1$	$+1$	$+1$	$+1$
Step II. Rotations with planet carrier fixed	-1	$+2$	$+0.5$	0
Total rotations	0	$+3$	$+1.5$	$+1$

As noted above, the planet carrier will be fixed as we complete the problem. One counterclockwise rotation of the sun gear results in

$$n_P = n_S \left(-\frac{N_S}{N_P}\right) = -1\left(-\frac{40}{20}\right) = +2$$

rotations of the planet and

$$n_R = n_P \left(\frac{N_P}{N_R}\right) = +2\left(+\frac{20}{80}\right) = +0.5$$

rotations of the ring as shown in Fig. 8A. The planet carrier is given zero rotations. Including these values in the table 2A and adding each column, we obtain Table 2B.

Inspecting the last row of figures in Table 2B, we see that the ring gear makes 1.5 turns for each turn of the planet carrier. Hence, if the ring gear is on the input shaft and the planet carrier on the output shaft, the ratio of output to input is given by $n_o/n_i = 1/1.5 = + 2/3$. The reader will observe that, in the second step of the calculations, the planet acts as an idler and affects only the sign of the speed ratio. Thus, it is not necessary to compute rotations of the planet; the figures for the planet are included only for purposes of illustration.

As a second example, let the ring gear in Fig. 8A be held stationary while the planet carrier, sun, and planet gears are permitted to rotate. In order that the results be more general, the number of teeth in the sun, planet, and ring gears will be represented respectively by N_S, N_P, and N_R. In tabulating the solution, Table 3, the first step is identical with the previous example. In this case, however, the net rotation of the ring gear must be zero. To accomplish this, the ring gear is given one counterclockwise rotation in the second step of Table 3 while the planet carrier remains fixed. Noting that the planet gear acts as an idler in the second step, we obtain $+ N_R/N_S$ rotations of the sun gear for -1 rotations of the ring gear. Tabulating these values and adding as before, we obtain the total rotations.

TABLE 3. SPEED RATIOS FOR A PLANETARY TRAIN WITH THE RING
FIXED, FIG. 8A

Gear	Sun	Planet	Ring	Planet Carrier
No. of Teeth	N_S	N_P	N_R	C
Step I. Rotations with train locked	$+ 1$	$+ 1$	$+ 1$	$+ 1$
Step II. Rotations with planet carrier fixed	$+ \dfrac{N_R}{N_S}$		-1	0
Total Rotations	$1 + \dfrac{N_R}{N_S}$		0	$+ 1$

The last line of the Table 3 indicates that, with the ring gear fixed, the ratio of sun gear speed to planet carrier speed is

$$\frac{n_S}{n_C} = 1 + \frac{N_R}{N_S}. \tag{8}$$

Repeating the first example, using symbols to represent the actual numbers of teeth, the ratio of ring gear speed to planet carrier speed becomes

$$\frac{n_R}{n_C} = 1 + \frac{N_S}{N_R}. \tag{9}$$

If the gear train operates instead with the planet carrier stationary, it no longer acts as a planetary train. Then, the ratio of sun gear speed to ring gear speed becomes $-N_R/N_S$ to 1 by inspection.

Compound Planetary Trains

A gear train which may be designed for extremely low ratios of output to input speed employs *two* planet gears and *two* ring gears. The reducer of Fig. 9 is made up of a sun gear, S, two ring gears, R_1 and R_2, and two planets gears, P_1 and P_2, which rotate at the same speed. The planets are held in the common planet carrier, C, which is free to rotate. The input is the sun gear and the ring gear R_2 is the output. Ring gear R_1 is fixed.

As in the previous examples, we begin by rotating the entire train one turn clockwise (Step I, Table 4). In the second step, the planet carrier is fixed, while ring gear R_1 is returned to its original position by one counterclockwise turn. The number of rotations of each gear is entered in Table 4, noting that both planets turn at the same speed. From the sum of the motions of Steps I and II, it is seen that the ratio of output to input speed is given by

$$\frac{n_{R2}}{n_S} = \frac{1 - (N_{R1}N_{P2}/N_{P1}N_{R2})}{1 + (N_{R1}/N_S)}. \tag{10}$$

If the gears are chosen so that the value of the term $N_{R1}N_{P2}/N_{P1}N_{R2}$ is very near to unity, the output speed will be very low making a very high output *torque* available. Of course, if the term equals one (exactly), the reducer will be useless since the output shaft will not turn.

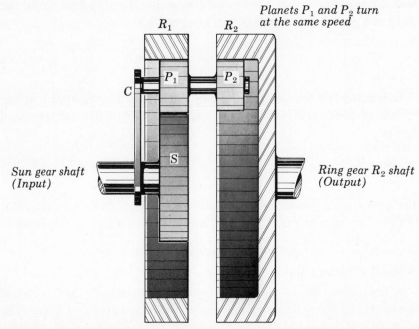

FIG. 9. Planetary speed reducer. This planetary train employs two planets and two ring gears.

TABLE 4. SPEED RATIOS FOR A COMPOUND PLANETARY SPEED REDUCER
WITH RING GEAR R_1 FIXED, FIG. 9

Gear	S	P_1	P_2	R_1	R_2	C
No. of Teeth	N_S	N_{P1}	N_{P2}	N_{R1}	N_{R2}	
Step I. Rotations with Train Locked	$+1$	$+1$	$+1$	$+1$	$+1$	$+1$
Step II. Rotations with Planet Carrier Fixed	$+\dfrac{N_{R1}}{N_S}$	$-\dfrac{N_{R1}}{N_{P1}}$	$-\dfrac{N_{R1}}{N_{P1}}$	-1	$-\dfrac{N_{R1}}{N_{P1}}\dfrac{N_{P2}}{N_{R2}}$	0
Total Rotations	$1+\dfrac{N_{R1}}{N_S}$			0	$1-\dfrac{N_{R1}}{N_{P1}}\dfrac{N_{P2}}{N_{R2}}$	

Balanced Planetary Trains

In the above examples, only one planet gear was shown meshing with the ring gear. Kinematically, this is sufficient, but better balancing of gear tooth loads and inertia forces will result if two or more planets mesh with each ring gear. See Figs. 10 and 11. The planetary gear train of Fig. 8A, for example, can be redesigned with four planets. The planet shafts are mounted in bearings in a planet carrier similar to the one shown in Fig. 10. Kinematically, the gear train of Fig. 10 is identical to the train shown in Fig. 8A, and Equations (8) and (9) are fully applicable to both gear trains.

For a simple train of the type shown in Figs. 8A and 10, the pitch diameter of the ring gear is obviously equal to the sum of the pitch diameter of the sun gear plus twice the planet gear pitch diameter. Since the diametral pitch must be the same on all of the gears in order that they mesh, tooth numbers are related by the following equation:

$$N_R = N_S + 2N_P \tag{11}$$

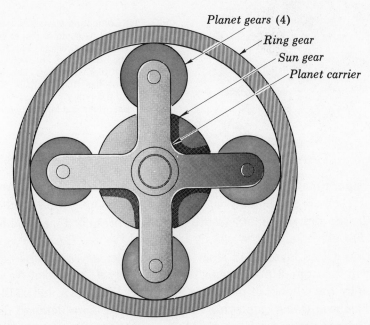

FIG. 10. Planetary train with four planets. Forces are more readily balanced in a planetary train with three or four planets. Kinematically, there is no difference; speed ratio remains the same whether one or several planets are used.

FIG. 11A. Simple planetary train. A train typical of the wheel planetaries used in drive axles of loaders and scrapers. Although this drive with three planets is kinematically equivalent to a drive with only one planet, this configuration balances the loading and has greater capacity. The planet carrier is not shown. (Fairfield Mfg. Co., Inc.)

FIG. 11B. Compound planetary train. This assembly with two sets of planet gears is used in a motorized wheel. The sun gear is driven by the shaft of an electric motor rated at 400 horsepower. The outside diameter of the ring gear is over 39 inches and the unit is designed for heavy duty service. (Fairfield Mfg. Co., Inc.)

where subscripts R, S, and P refer to the ring, sun, and planet respectively. When several equally spaced planet gears are to be used as in Fig. 10, the designer must insure that it is possible to assemble the train. For example, if $N_S = 25$, $N_P = 20$, $N_R = 65$, Eq. (11) is satisfied. However, a layout will show that four planets cannot be equally spaced in the train. Equal spacing is possible only if the sum of $N_S + N_R$ divided by the number of planets is an integer. Figs. 11A and 11B illustrate balanced trains employing three planets. A more detailed discussion of planet spacing is given by Mabie and Ocvirk.[9]

9. H. H. Mabie and F. W. Ocvirk, *Mechanisms and Dynamics of Machinery* (2nd ed.; New York: John Wiley & Sons, Inc., 1963), pp. 178-82.

Planetary Differential Drives

An alternate method of obtaining low ratios of output to input speed employs two sun gears and two planet gears as shown in Fig. 12. The planet carrier, C, is keyed to the input shaft which goes through the center of sun gear S_1. Sun gear S_1 is fixed, and sun gear S_2 is keyed to

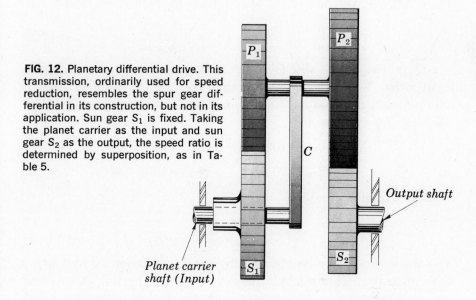

FIG. 12. Planetary differential drive. This transmission, ordinarily used for speed reduction, resembles the spur gear differential in its construction, but not in its application. Sun gear S_1 is fixed. Taking the planet carrier as the input and sun gear S_2 as the output, the speed ratio is determined by superposition, as in Table 5.

TABLE 5. SPEED RATIOS FOR A PLANETARY DIFFERENTIAL DRIVE WITH SUN GEAR S_1 FIXED, FIG. 12

Gear	S_1	P_1	P_2	S_2	C
No. of Teeth	N_{S1}	N_{P1}	N_{P2}	N_{S2}	
Step I. Rotations with Train Locked	$+1$	$+1$	$+1$	$+1$	$+1$
Step II. Rotations with Planet Carrier Fixed	-1	$+\dfrac{N_{S1}}{N_{P1}}$	$+\dfrac{N_{S1}}{N_{P1}}$	$-\dfrac{N_{S1}N_{P2}}{N_{P1}N_{S2}}$	0
Total Rotations	0			$1-\dfrac{N_{S1}N_{P2}}{N_{P1}N_{S2}}$	1

the output shaft. Planet gears P_1 and P_2 are both keyed to the same shaft which turns freely in the planet carrier. Ring gears are not used in this speed reducer.

Speed ratios are again found by rotating the entire locked gear train and then correcting the position of sun gear S_1 while the planet carrier remains stationary. Thus, we obtain Table 5.

The result, as given in Table 5, is an output to input speed ratio:

$$\frac{n_o}{n_i} = \frac{n_{S2}}{n_C} = 1 - \frac{N_{S1}N_{P2}}{N_{P1}N_{S2}}. \tag{12}$$

Gear sizes can be specified to produce a wide variety of output to input ratios. By selecting gears so that the fraction $N_{S1}N_{P2}/N_{P1}N_{S2}$ is approximately one (but not exactly one), we obtain very great speed reductions. For example, let

$$N_{S1} = 102 \qquad N_{P2} = 49$$
$$N_{P1} = 50 \qquad N_{S2} = 100$$

Then, from Equation (12),

$$\frac{n_o}{n_i} = 1 - \frac{4998}{5000} = + \frac{1}{2500}.$$

The above result may be obtained by hand calculation or by using a desk calculator. This example illustrates one of the few cases where slide rule accuracy is not sufficient since the answer represents a very small difference between two numbers.

In considering the above example the reader may come to an extraordinary conclusion. According to the calculations, if the shaft of S_2 is given one turn, the planet carrier C will make 2500 revolutions. In an actual gear train possessing this speed ratio, however, friction would prevent gear S_2 from driving the train, since a small friction torque on the planet carrier shaft would be so greatly magnified. As is also the case with most worm drives, this particular gear train may only be used to reduce speed. Commercially available planetary trains of this type may be used to *step up* speed by using sun gear S_2 for the input, and the planet carrier C for the output. Ordinarily, though, n_o/n_i may not exceed 20.

A planetary speed reducer of the type sketched in Fig. 12 is very flexible; most output-to-input ratios may be approximated simply by selecting the appropriate gear sizes. Exact ratios, however, are not always obtainable. Suppose, for example, that a speed ratio $n_o/n_i = 1/2000$ is called for where n_o is the speed of S_2, the output, and n_i is the speed of C, the input. Instead of using a trial and error method to select a suitable combination of gears, we will examine Equation (12). If the term

$$\frac{N_{S1}N_{P2}}{N_{P1}N_{S2}} = \frac{1999}{2000}, \qquad \text{then } \frac{n_o}{n_i} = \frac{1}{2000} \text{ (exactly)}.$$

Let us, therefore, try to specify the gear sizes so that $N_{S1} \times N_{P2} = 1999$, and $N_{P1} \times N_{S2} = 2000$. Referring to a table of factors and primes such as that given by Selby, Weast, Shankland and Hodgman,[10] we see that $2000 = 2^4 \times 5^3 = 2 \times 2 \times 2 \times 2 \times 5 \times 5 \times 5$, which suggests $N_{P1} = 5 \times 5 = 25$ and $N_{S2} = 2 \times 2 \times 2 \times 2 \times 5 = 80$. Unfortunately, 1999 has no factors except 1 and 1999; it is a prime number.

Since we cannot manufacture a pair of gears with 1 and 1999 teeth for this application, we refer again to the table of factors and primes. Noting that $2001 = 3 \times 23 \times 29$, we may specify $N_{S1} = 3 \times 23 = 69$ and $N_{P2} = 29$, so that $N_{S1} \times N_{P2} = 2001$. Then, from Equation (12), $n_o/n_i = 1 - 2001/2000 = -1/2000$. The minus sign indicates that the output and input shafts rotate in opposite directions. If this is objectionable, an additional gear may be added to the train to change the output direction.

Alternately, the desired speed ratio of $1/2000$ may be approximated by using the same factors, except that in this case

$$N_{P1} = 29 \qquad N_{P2} = 25$$
$$N_{S2} = 69 \qquad N_{S1} = 80.$$

Using Eq. (12), the result is

$$\frac{n_o}{n_i} = 1 - \frac{80 \times 25}{29 \times 69} = + \frac{1}{2001},$$

a value which in most cases would be close enough to be acceptable.

Manufacturing difficulties are sometimes encountered with reverted gear trains. For the gear train of Fig. 12, the distance between centers of gears S_1 and P_1 is the same as for S_2 and P_2 since S_1 and S_2 turn

10. S. M. Selby and R. C. Weast (eds.), Table of Factors and Primes in *Handbook of Chemistry and Physics* (47th ed.; Cleveland: Chemical Rubber Publishing Co., 1967), pp. A167-76.

about the same axis. Therefore pitch diameters are related by the equation

$$d_{S1} + d_{P1} = d_{S2} + d_{P2}\ .$$

(Recall that gears which mesh must have the same diametral pitch.) If the loading is such that a diametral pitch of ten teeth per inch of diameter is satisfactory for gears S_2 and P_2 in the last example, then

$$d_{S1} + d_{P1} = d_{S2} + d_{P2} = \frac{25}{10} + \frac{69}{10} = 9.4 \text{ in.}$$

The diametral pitch of gears S_1 and P_1 will be

$$P = \frac{N_{S1} + N_{P1}}{d_{S1} + d_{P1}} = \frac{80 + 29}{9.4} = 11\frac{56}{94} \text{ teeth per in. diam.}$$

Since 11-56/94 is not a standard diametral pitch, special cutters must be manufactured, increasing the cost of this gear train. On the other hand, the use of only standard gears severely limits the number of different speed ratios which may be obtained. The planetary differential drive shown in Fig. 13 offers a wide range of speed ratios due to a broad selection of available component gears.

FIG. 13A. Planetary differential drive. Mounted within the driven pulley and directly on the shaft of the driven equipment, this speed reducer requires little additional space. A wide range of speed ratios and output torque capacities result from changes in tooth number. The available output to input speed ratios range from 1:1.79 to 1:482, with output direction opposite input in some cases. (Airborne Accessories Corp.)

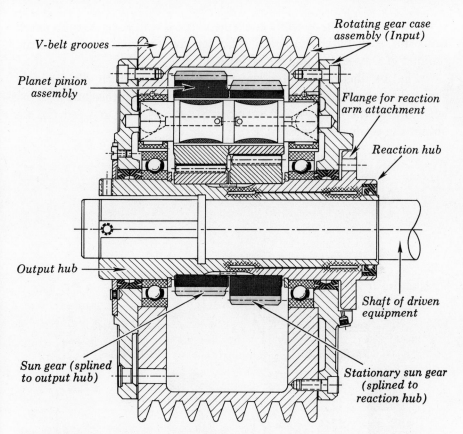

V-belt grooves

Rotating gear case assembly (Input)

Planet pinion assembly

Flange for reaction arm attachment

Reaction hub

Output hub

Shaft of driven equipment

Sun gear (splined to output hub)

Stationary sun gear (splined to reaction hub)

FIG. 13B. Section view of Planetary differential drive. The driven pulley of a V-belt drive forms the rotating gear case of the compound planetary drive. The gear case carries the planet assemblies, each consisting of two helical planet gears splined to the same shaft. Power is transmitted to a helical sun gear on the output shaft through differential action between the planets and a fixed helical sun gear.

Tandem Planetary Trains

For most planetary trains, there is no loss in generality when speed ratios are analyzed by giving the entire train one rotation and then superimposing a correcting rotation with the planet carrier fixed. When the gear train has more than one planet carrier this procedure, if applied to the train as a whole, would arbitrarily restrict the planet carriers to the same speed—a result which may contradict the actual problem constraints. A convenient method of solving tandem planetary trains

399

is to divide the train at some convenient point and solve for the speed ratios for each half. The speed ratio for the entire train is then the product of the separate speed ratios.

Fig. 14 illustrates a tandem planetary train which divides conveniently between R_2 and R_3. Following the usual procedure for the left hand of the train, which includes S_1, P_1, P_2, R_1, R_2 and C_1, we obtain the equivalent of Eq. (10):

$$\frac{n_{R2}}{n_{S1}} = \frac{1 - (N_{P2}N_{R1}/N_{P1}N_{R2})}{1 + (N_{R1}/N_{S1})}.$$

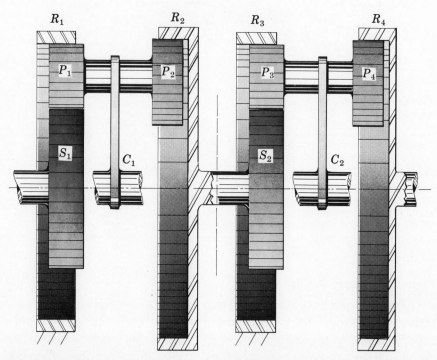

FIG. 14. Train with two planet carriers. With two independent planet carriers in a train, the reader should assume that they do *not* rotate at the same speed. To solve for the overall speed ratio, the reader can solve for the speed ratio of each half of this train separately, thus correctly using the superposition method. The speed ratio for the entire train is then the *product* of the ratios of the two halves.

Similarly, for the last half of the train, we obtain:

$$\frac{n_{R4}}{n_{S2}} = \frac{1 - (N_{R3}N_{P4}/N_{P3}N_{R4})}{1 + (N_{R3}/N_{S2})}.$$

Since $n_{R2} = n_{S2}$, the output to input ratio for the entire train is the product of the above ratios:

$$\frac{n_o}{n_i} = \frac{n_{R2}}{n_{S1}} \cdot \frac{n_{R4}}{n_{S2}}.$$

Using a table of factors and primes as in a previous example, we may demonstrate the flexibility and the extreme speed reductions available with this type of gear train. For example, letting

$$N_{R1} = N_{R3} = 87 \text{ teeth}$$

$$N_{P1} = N_{P3} = 20 \text{ teeth}$$

$$N_{S1} = N_{S2} = 47 \text{ teeth}$$

$$N_{P2} = N_{P4} = 23 \text{ teeth}$$

$$N_{R2} = N_{R4} = 100 \text{ teeth}$$

the speed ratio of each part of the gear train separately is

$$\frac{n_{R4}}{n_{S2}} = \frac{n_{R2}}{n_{S1}} = -\frac{47}{268,000}.$$

The product of the two ratios is the output to input speed ratio:

$$\frac{n_o}{n_i} = +\frac{1}{32,500,000} \text{ (approx.)}$$

The above set of values is only an illustration of the planetary train's potential for speed reduction. We might never need such extreme ratios in actual practice, but trains of this type are commonly used for speed reductions of one to several thousand.

Speed Changing in Planetary Transmissions

When smooth and rapid changing of speed ratios is required, planetary transmissions are often selected. Automotive requirements, for example, may call for a gear train with two positive (forward) speed ratios and one negative (reverse) speed ratio. These speed changes can be accomplished by clutches and brakes in a planetary transmission.

401

Mechanism

Fig. 15 illustrates, schematically, such a transmission. With the gears as shown, there is no output since both sun gear S_2 and the ring gear R are free to turn. Gear P_1 meshes only with S_1 and P_2. Thus, the carrier C could remain stationary even though the input shaft was turning.

If sun gear S_2 is locked to the input shaft by engaging a clutch (not shown), a direct drive is obtained. Since the two sun gears rotate at the same speed (and in the same direction), the planet gears are, in effect, locked to the sun gears. The planets are also locked to each other since the sun gears tend to rotate the meshed planets in the same direction (preventing any relative motion). Any motion of planets P_1 and P_2 relative to the sun gears would be incompatible with the fact

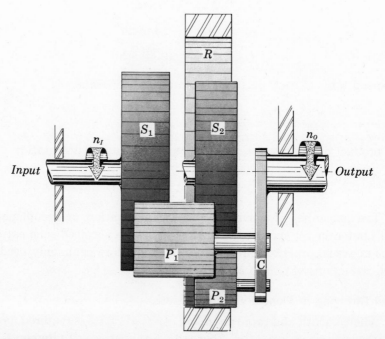

FIG. 15. Planetary transmission. Planets P_1 and P_2 are carried by the *common* planet carrier. P_1 meshes only with S_1 and P_2. When both S_2 and R are free to turn, there is no output; the transmission is in neutral. S_2 may be locked to the input shaft by engaging a clutch, giving a one-to-one ratio of output to input. See Tables 6 and 7. (Note: Gear positions in an actual transmission do not correspond with this schematic.)

that both planets are held in the same planet carrier. Thus, when S_2 is locked to the input shaft, all gears lock together and turn as a unit. The ratio of output to input speed becomes $n_o/n_i = 1$.

In order to fix either the ring gear or sun gear S_2 to the frame, band brakes may be used. The brakes would engage the outer surface of the ring gear or a drum attached to sun gear S_2. Both bands and drums are omitted from Fig. 15 so that we may examine the kinematics of the problem without additional complications. The effect of locking sun gear S_2 to the frame is given by Table 6. In the first step, the entire train is given one clockwise rotation, just as in each of the previous examples. In the second step the carrier is fixed while the sun gear S_2 is given one counterclockwise rotation, so that it has zero net motion.

TABLE 6. SPEED RATIOS FOR THE PLANETARY TRANSMISSION OF FIG. 15
WITH SUN GEAR S_2 FIXED

Gear	S_1	P_1	P_2	S_2	R	C
No. of Teeth	N_{S1}	N_{P1}	N_{P2}	N_{S2}	N_R	
Step I. Rotations with Train Locked	$+1$	$+1$	$+1$	$+1$	$+1$	$+1$
Step II. Rotations with Planet Carrier Fixed	$+\dfrac{N_{S2}}{N_{S1}}$			-1		0
Total Rotations	$1 + \dfrac{N_{S2}}{N_{S1}}$			0		$+1$

By adding steps I and II in Table 6, we obtain an output to input speed reduction of

$$\frac{n_o}{n_i} = \frac{1}{1 + (N_{S2}/N_{S1})} \tag{13}$$

when gear S_2 is fixed.

When the ring gear is free to rotate, Fig. 15, it serves no purpose in the transmission. When the ring is fixed and gear S_2 is free to turn, however, a negative or reverse ratio is obtained. The results are given in Table 7, which is obtained by proceeding as in Table 6 except that in this case the ring gear R is given the zero net rotation.

TABLE 7. SPEED RATIOS FOR THE PLANETARY TRANSMISSION OF FIG. 15
WITH THE RING GEAR R FIXED

Gear	S_1	P_1	P_2	S_2	R	C
No. of Teeth	N_{S1}	N_{P1}	N_{P2}	N_{S2}	N_R	
Step I. Rotations with Train Locked	$+1$	$+1$	$+1$	$+1$	$+1$	$+1$
Step II. Rotations with Planet Carrier Fixed	$-\dfrac{N_R}{N_{S1}}$				-1	0
Total Rotations	$1 - \dfrac{N_R}{N_{S1}}$				0	1

In this case, sun gear S_2 turns freely and serves no useful purpose. The output to input speed ratio is

$$\frac{n_o}{n_i} = \frac{1}{1 - (N_R/N_{S1})} \tag{14}$$

with the ring fixed. Since N_R must be greater than N_{S1}, this ratio is always negative, indicating that the output direction of rotation is opposite the input.

Planetary Trains with More than One Input

In some planetary gear train applications, *none* of the gears are fixed. As an example, it might be necessary to find the angular velocity n_C of the planet carrier of Fig. 8A being given n_S and n_R, the velocities of the sun and ring respectively. The data already calculated in Tables 2 and 3 enables us to solve this problem by superposition.

Let the sun have 40 teeth and the ring 80 teeth. Given speeds will be $n_S = +900$ RPM and $n_R = +1500$ RPM (both clockwise). The last line of Table 2B gives gear speeds when the sun is fixed. Since these speeds are only relative, the entire last line of Table 2B may be multiplied by 1000 to give the correct ring speed. We have, then, the following speeds (in RPM) from Table 2B, adjusted to give the correct speed for n_R:

$$n_S = 0$$
$$n_R = 1.5 \times 1000 = 1500$$
$$n_C = 1 \times 1000 = 1000 .$$

Next, the values of N_S and N_R are substituted into the last line of Table 3 and it is multiplied by 300 to give the correct sun gear speed when the ring is fixed. The result is

$$n_S = 3 \times 300 = 900$$

$$n_R = 0$$

$$n_C = 1 \times 300 = 300.$$

Adding the values for the case where the sun gear is fixed to the values for the case where the ring is fixed, we obtain:

$$n_S = 0 + 900 = +900$$

$$n_R = 1500 + 0 = +1500$$

$$n_C = 1000 + 300 = +1300.$$

A superior method which avoids making use of previous results is the following. We begin the problem by rotating the entire train $+v$ revolutions (where the value of v is to be found later), instead of $+1$ revolutions as done previously. Thus, we have step I of Table 8. In step II, the sun gear, S, is given $+w$ rotations with the carrier fixed (w is also unknown at this time). Noting the gear ratio, we obtain $(-N_S/N_R) \times w$ rotations of the ring gear in step II. The last line of Table 8 is the sum of steps I and II, from which

$$n_S = v + w$$

$$n_R = v - \frac{N_S}{N_R} w$$

$$n_C = v.$$

Substituting the value for w from the first equation into the second equation, we obtain

$$n_R = n_C - \frac{N_S}{N_R} (n_S - n_C) \qquad (15)$$

from which,

$$n_C = \frac{n_R + n_S (N_S/N_R)}{1 + (N_S/N_R)} \qquad (16)$$

405

and

$$n_S = n_C + \frac{N_R}{N_S}(n_C - n_R). \tag{17}$$

These three equations describe the motion of a planetary train, like those shown in Figs. 7 and 8A, *for any input or output given in terms of angular velocity*. When the data of the above problem is substituted into the equation for n_C, we again obtain $n_C = 1300$ RPM clockwise.

TABLE 8. SPEED RATIOS FOR THE PLANETARY TRAIN OF FIG. 7
WITH NO FIXED GEARS

Gear	Sun	Planet	Ring	Carrier
No. of Teeth	40	20	80	
Step I. Rotations with Train Locked	$+v$	$+v$	$+v$	$+v$
Step II. Rotations with Carrier Fixed	$+w$	$-\dfrac{N_S}{N_P}w$	$-\dfrac{N_S}{N_R}w$	0
Total Rotations	$v+w$	$v-\dfrac{N_S}{N_P}w$	$v-\dfrac{N_S}{N_R}w$	v

Differentials

While engineering problem solving often suggests the use of electronic analog and digital computers, there are many specialized applications for mechanical computing devices. Automatic control of a certain process may depend on the addition of two input functions. An aircraft or a missile in flight may be guided by mechanically-computed products and sums of signals from sensing devices. We can see by inspection of Fig. 16 that a simple mechanical linkage can average two functions. If the paths of the upper and lower sliders are equidistant from the center slider

$$v = \frac{x+y}{2} \tag{18}$$

where x and y are the velocities of the upper and lower sliders. Of course, the range of this linkage is very limited. If the displacements of the upper and lower sliders differ appreciably, the linkage will not operate.

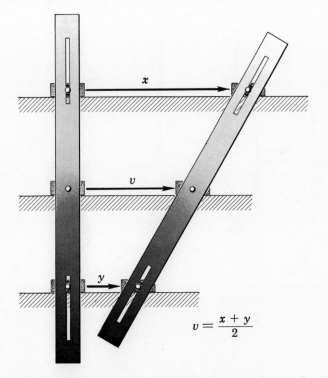

$$v = \frac{x + y}{2}$$

FIG. 16. A mechanical averaging linkage. Given two input speeds, x and y, the velocity at v will represent the average of the inputs. The mechanism is useful where values of x and y are close.

A more practical averaging device can be developed from the above principle (averaging two functions). The straight link in the averager of Fig. 16 is replaced by a planetary bevel gear, P, in Fig. 17. Input velocities to the planet are x and y, the pitch line velocities of gears S_1 and S_2 respectively in Fig. 17A. From the geometry of the system, it is seen that the velocity of the planet center is

$$v = \frac{x + y}{2}$$

where v lies in the plane of x and y.

Alternately, the tabular method may be employed with a modifica-

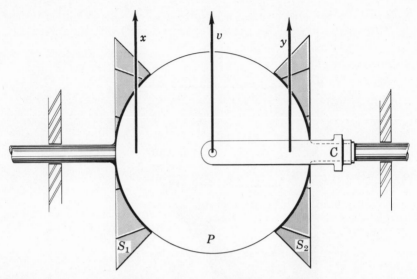

FIG. 17A. When x and y are given as pitch line velocities, v is in the plane of x and y and, as in the preceding illustration, $v = (x + y)/2$.

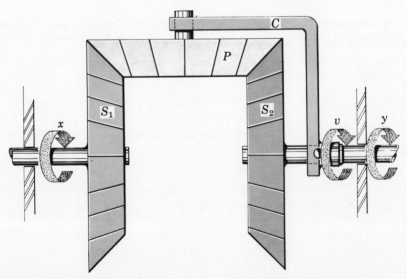

FIG. 17B. When x and y are given as *angular* velocities of S_1 and S_2 respectively, v is the angular velocity of the planet carrier and $v = (x + y)/2$. Table 9 illustrates how this result may be obtained using a variation of the superposition method.

tion to incorporate two *angular* inputs, Fig. 17B. In the first step (Table 9), the entire locked train is given $+v$ rotations. In the second step, the planet carrier is fixed while gear S_1 is given $+w$ rotations. If S_1 and S_2 have the same number of teeth, then S_2 makes $-w$ rotations. The results are given in Table 9, where x and y represent the actual total rotations of S_1 and S_2 respectively.

TABLE 9. SPEED RATIO FOR THE BEVEL GEAR DIFFERENTIAL OF FIG. 17 WITH TWO INPUTS

Gear	S_1	S_2	C
Step I. Rotations with Train Locked	v	v	v
Step II. Rotations with Planet Carrier Fixed	$+w$	$-w$	0
Total Rotations	$x = v + w$	$y = v - w$	v

On adding the values of x and y, it is seen that $x + y = 2v$, or

$$v = \frac{x + y}{2}.$$

In this mechanism x, y, and v may represent angular displacement, angular velocity or angular acceleration. Fig. 18A illustrates a miniature bevel gear differential. The range of this mechanism is unlimited; there are no physical stops such as are present in the linkage sketched in Fig. 16.

If the sum of the two inputs, x and y, is required it is only necessary to double the output (the rotation of the planet carrier shaft). This may be accomplished simply by a scale change or by using gears to effect a two to one speed increase. The function $v = (x-y)/2$ is obtained by using a pair of equal gears to turn the shaft of S_2 opposite to the direction of y. The value of the function $v = Ax + By$, where A and B are constants, is obtained by additional pairs of gears driving the input shafts. See Fig. 18B. Since rotation direction changes with each meshing pair of external spur gears, idlers may be used to obtain the correct sign.

Multiplication is also practical for special applications. The product $s = t\,u$ may be found by taking the anti-logarithm of $v = x + y$,

FIG. 18A. The large bevel gears which act as sun gears are mounted on bearings. Each of the sun gears may be directly attached to a spur gear through which input motion is transmitted. The planet bevel gear, bearing mounted on a cross arm, drives the junction block which is rigidly connected to the shaft through the sun gears. (PIC Design Corp.)

FIG. 18B. When this mechanism is used to *add or subtract*, the shafts at the right and left foreground act as inputs (to the pair of gears driving the bevel sun gears) and the planetary bevel gear cross arm drives the output shaft. When used as a *phase shifter*, the shafts at the right and left foreground become the input and output respectively. Rotation of the junction block changes the relative position (phase) between input and output. (PIC Design Corp.)

where $x = \log t$ and $y = \log u$. Likewise $s = t^A u^B$ is obtained by letting $x = A \log t$ and $y = B \log u$. The logarithm and anti-logarithm functions are obtained by using cams and the constants A and B from fixed gear ratios. Since the logarithm cams must be cut for a certain range of values, a mechanism of this type has limited range.

When an automobile is making a turn, the wheels on the outside of the turn travel farther than the wheels on the inside. A differential allows the rear wheels to rotate at different velocities so that the tires are not required to drag along the road during a turn. A typical automotive differential is similar to the sketch in Fig. 17, except that *several* bevel planet gears are carried on the same planet carrier which is driven by a pair of hypoid gears (Fig. 19). Kinematically, there is no difference in the differential itself. The input to the planet carrier (C of Fig. 17) is transmitted through the planet P to the rear axles represented by the shafts of S_1 and S_2. The sum of the axle speeds is equal to twice the planet carrier speed: $x + y = 2v$. On a straight, dry road $x = y = v$. When turning, x does not equal y; however, the average of x and y is v. If there is no provision for positive traction, the torque delivered to both axles is equal. Then, with one wheel on ice and the other on

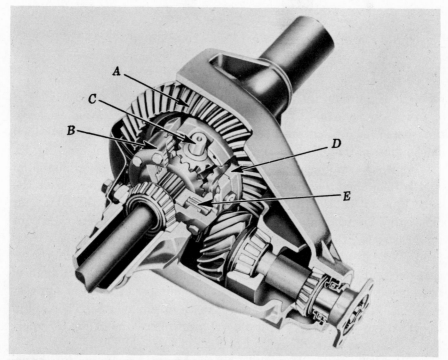

FIG. 19. Limited slip automotive differential. Engine power is transmitted to the large hypoid gear (A), which drives the differential case (planet carrier B). The driving force moves cross pins (C) up cam surfaces (D) engaging disc clutches (E). This type differential *applies the greatest amount of torque to the wheel with the most traction* to prevent the other wheel from spinning on ice or snow. (Dana Corp.)

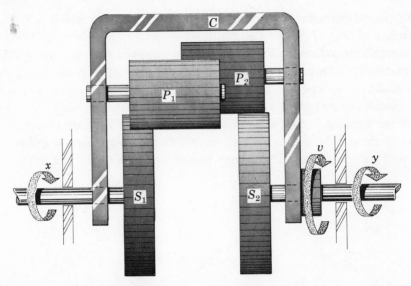

FIG. 20. Spur gear differential. When $N_{S1} = N_{S2}$, the carrier velocity is $v = (x + y)/2$.

concrete, the tire on the ice may turn freely at a speed of $2v$ while the other tire does not turn at all. This is the price we pay to avoid excessive tire wear. This obvious disadvantage can be remedied by devices which deliver most of the torque to the wheel which is *not* slipping. See Fig. 19.

A mechanism kinematically equivalent to the bevel gear differential may be manufactured using spur gears. See Fig. 20. Referring at the same time to Table 8, it is seen that the sun gears of the spur gear differential are to rotate at the same velocity but in opposite directions (one clockwise, the other counterclockwise) when the planet carrier is fixed. While one planet gear is sufficient to obtain this motion in a bevel gear differential, the spur gear differential of Fig. 20 requires a train of two planets held in the planet carrier. The number of teeth in sun gear S_1 in Fig. 20 will equal the number of teeth in sun gear S_2. Then, all of the equations which apply to the bevel gear differential of Fig. 17 apply also to the spur gear differential of Fig. 20.

Fig. 21 illustrates the use of a different type of spur gear differential in an actual final drive assembly. The differential drive pinion is splined directly to an automatic transmission. In this particular application, a front wheel drive, a pair of spiral bevel gears were chosen to avoid off-

412

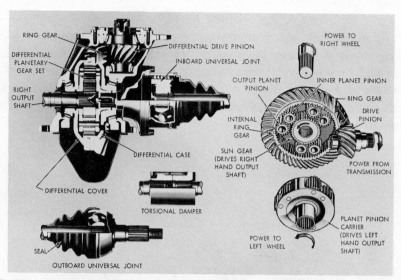

FIG. 21. A modern automotive final drive assembly. The differential is made up entirely of spur gears. When the car is traveling in a straight path, the entire train turns as a unit. A right turn causes the planet carrier (driving the left axle) to overspeed; a left turn causes the sun gear (driving the right axle) to overspeed. During either turn, there is relative motion between the internal ring, planets and sun (all spur gears), providing the differential action. (General Motors Engineering Journal)

setting the pinion from the center of the planetary train. (Hypoid gears, which are used to drive conventional differentials in order to locate the drive shaft below the axles, would be undesirable here.)

The spiral bevel gears produce a speed reduction of 3.21, and when the car is travelling in a straight path the entire planetary train turns as a unit. A right turn causes the planet carrier (driving the left axle) to overspeed, and a left turn causes the sun gear (driving the right axle) to overspeed. During either turn, there is relative motion between the ring, planets, and sun, providing the differential action. The planet gears must be in pairs, one contacting the ring and the other the sun, for proper rotation direction. The number of teeth in the gears are as follows: sun, 36; inner planets, 16; outer planets, 16; internal ring, 72; large spiral bevel, 45; and the spiral bevel pinion, 14. In order to make the axles flexible, Rzeppa-type constant velocity universal joints are used in the drive assembly.

Chain Drives

Chain drives, like gear drives, result in definite output to input speed ratios and have high power transmission capacity—over one-thousand horsepower for some designs operating at high speed. Unlike gear trains, however, distance between shafts is not a critical factor; shaft distance may even fluctuate during operation of a chain drive without adverse effect.

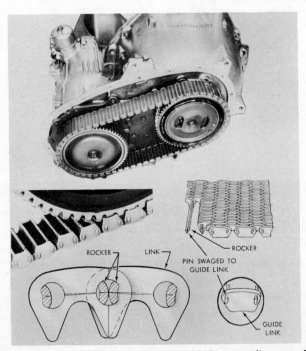

FIG. 22. Automotive chain drive. This inverted tooth chain transmits power from a torque converter (*left*) to a planetary transmission (*right*). It was selected in preference to a gear drive which would have required an idler. The links are designed for smooth engagement with the sprockets. Although timing chains are common in automobiles, development of a drive chain posed several problems including excessive noise. The manufacturer arrived at the above design after considerable analytical and experimental study, including the use of high speed motion pictures for analysis. (General Motors Engineering Journal)

Roller Chain Drives

Roller chain consists of sideplates and pin and bushing joints which mesh with toothed sprockets. Most high speed chain drives use roller type chain or an inverted-tooth type made up of pin-connected, inward-facing teeth. See Fig. 22. For maximum chain life, both sprockets are vertical and in the same plane. Although there is little restriction on center distances, the chain should wrap around at least 120° on both sprockets. Chain tension adjustment, if required, is made by moving one of the shafts or by using an idler sprocket.

Bead Chain Drives

For instrument drives and other very light load, low speed applications, bead chains, Fig. 23A, may be used. Sprockets need not be in

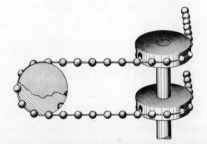

FIG. 23A. Bead chain drive. Shown is a close tolerance bead chain on pocketed sprockets for a positive, low-speed drive. The beads swivel on pins so that sprockets need not be in the same plane.

FIG. 23B. Complex instrument dial drive. Both bead chain and roller chain are used in this drive, assuring precise speed ratios with maximum flexibility. (Voland Corp.)

the same plane if idlers are provided where necessary to maintain chain-to-sprocket contact. The drive complex shown in Fig. 23B employs both bead chain and roller drives.

Sprocket speeds are inversely proportional to the number of teeth in each sprocket (or the number of pockets or indentation in bead chain sprockets). Both sprockets rotate in the same direction. Speed ratio is once again given by:

$$\frac{n_2}{n_1} = +\frac{N_1}{N_2},$$

where n_1 and n_2 are respectively driver and driven sprocket speeds, and N_1 and N_2 are respectively the numbers of teeth in driver and driven sprockets. Idler sprockets and center distance do not affect speed. When bead chain is used, the chain may be crossed between sprockets to reverse rotation direction.

Variable Speed Chain Drives

Speed ratio changing is generally *not* practical with high speed or high-load roller chain drives except by using two or more chains and sprocket pairs, with clutches to engage one set at a time. For low-load and low-speed, a movable idler sprocket may be used to shift the chain from one sprocket to another without interrupting the driving. One application for this type transmission is a racing bicycle having two driving sprockets with different numbers of teeth and a "cone" of five driven sprockets at the rear wheel with graduated tooth numbers. Thus, there are ten sprocket combinations available yielding ten different speed ratios. For most of the ratios, the sprockets and chain are not exactly in line (i.e. the sprockets in use are not in the same plane), but in this application, loads are light enough so that chain wear due to misalignment is slight.

A variable speed chain drive which provides essentially stepless speed ratio variation is shown in Fig. 24. Effective sheave diameter is changed by the spacing between the sides of the grooved sheaves. The chain has floating laminations which conform to the grooves. Thus, the output to input speed ratio is related to effective sheave diameter by Equation (3): $n_2/n_1 = d_1/d_2$.

FIG. 24. Variable speed chain drive. This drive provides essentially stepless speed ratio variation with a positive drive. Effective sheave (driving surface) diameter is changed by increasing or decreasing the spacing between the sides of the grooved sheaves. The chain has floating laminations which conform to the grooves, and thus output to input speed ratio depends on effective sheave diameters only. Speed ratio is independent of the number of grooves in the sheaves. (Link Belt Co.)

Belt Drives

While the low cost of belt drives is the most common reason for their selection over other means of power transmission, belts have other positive design features. Belts absorb shock which might otherwise be transmitted from the driven shaft back to the driver, and prevent vibrations in the driver from being transmitted to the driven shaft, thus reducing noise and damage from these sources.

Mechanism

In addition, a belt may act as a clutch, disengaging driver and driven shafts when loose and engaging them when tight. Belt tightening may be accomplished by moving either driver or driven shaft or, if both shafts are fixed, a movable idler pulley may be used to tighten the belt. This method is used to engage some power lawnmower drives to the gasoline engine and to drive punch presses and shears, in which case a belt is momentarily engaged to a large flywheel for the working stroke of the machine. An idler is the less desirable of the two methods from the standpoint of belt wear; if used, it should be as large as practical and, preferably ride on the inside of the slack span of the belt.

V-Belt Drives

V-belts, the most common type, are made of rubber reinforced with load-carrying cords. They operate in V-grooved pulleys or sheaves. The belt side-walls wedge into the pulley; the belt does not ride in the bottom of the groove. The effect of this wedging action is to improve driving traction by more than tripling the friction force over what it would be if the pulleys were flat. Output to input speed ratio is given by Eq. (3)

$$\frac{n_2}{n_1} = \frac{d_1}{d_2}$$

where d_1 and d_2 refer respectively to the driver and driven pulley pitch diameters, the diameters of the neutral surface of the belt riding in the pulley. (The neutral surface of the belt is the surface which is neither compressed nor extended due to bending around the pulleys.)

Since belt tension varies as an element of the belt turns about a pulley, there is some slippage; therefore speed ratios are not precise except with specially designed positive-drive belts and pulleys. If the belt does not cross itself, driver and driven pulleys turn in the same direction. For best results, the pulleys should be as large as practical and the belt should operate in a single vertical plane. Heavy loads may be carried by a multi-grooved V-pulley with a single backed multiple-V belt.

Variable Speed Belt Drives

For occasional speed ratio changing on light machinery, a "cone" of graduated diameter V-pulleys is matched with a similar "cone" (large pulley on one opposite the small pulley on the other). The belt is manually transferred from one pair of pulleys to the other when the machine is stopped.

A pair of belt-drive variable pulleys, similar in appearance and operation to the variable-speed chain drive pulleys shown in Fig. 24, may be used to change speed ratios on moving machinery without interrupting power. The sides of one pulley are moved apart to decrease its pitch diameter while the sides of the opposite pulley are moved together to increase its pitch diameter. Output to input speed ratio again equals the inverse ratio of pitch diameters, and may be continuously varied. Each variable pulley may change diameter by as much as a factor of three or four.

The variable pulleys may be varied manually, pneumatically, or hydraulically. Speed ratio change may be entirely automatic in response to a speed governor on the output shaft, output torque, engine vacuum, or a combination of the above. See Fig. 25.

FIG. 25. Pneumatically-controlled *belt* drive. The pneumatic control regulator at left responds to pressure signals, continuously varying speed for process control. Speeds may be varied, adjusted to remain constant, or a predetermined cycle of speed variation may be programmed. The ratio of minimum to maximum speed is 1 to 3 and units are rated at up to 25 horsepower. The linkage simultaneously moves both halves of the variable pitch pulley (foreground) in order to maintain belt alignment as speeds are changed. (Lewellen Mfg. Co.)

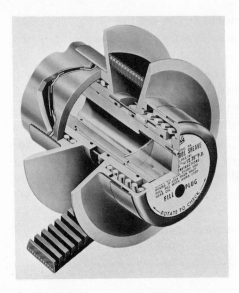

FIG. 26. Variable pitch pulley. This smooth-faced pulley is part of a variable speed *belt* drive. When the distance between pulley centers is increased, the spring loaded sides of the variable pulley separate to decrease its effective diameter. A cam at the left side of the pulley increases pressure on the pulley sides with increases in torque, compensating for the tendency of the pulley to separate at increased load. (T. B. Wood's Sons Co.)

Some variable-speed drives use a fixed-pitch diameter pulley opposite a *spring-loaded pulley* like that shown in Fig. 26. The sides of the spring-loaded pulley are separated simply by increasing the distance between the driver and driven shafts. A cam may be incorporated into the variable pulley to prevent separation of the sides when there is an increase in the driven load. The cam is visible on the left side of the pulley shown in Fig. 26.

Countershaft Pulleys

If the distance between driver and driven shafts is fixed, a variable double-pulley may be used on a countershaft, as shown in Fig. 27A. By moving the countershaft toward either the driver or driven shaft, Fig. 27A, the pitch diameters of the intervening double-pulley change simultaneously. One increases while the other decreases, giving a wide range of speed ratios.

When one or more countershafts are used, the output to input speed ratio again depends on the pitch diameters of the pulleys, and is given by Eq. (6B):

$$\frac{n_o}{n_i} = \frac{\text{Product of driving pulley pitch diameters}}{\text{Product of driven pulley pitch diameters}}.$$

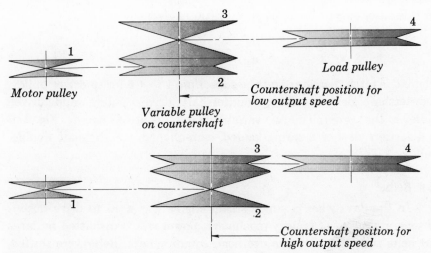

FIG. 27A. Variable-speed belt drive. When the countershaft is moved toward the load pulley, the spring-loaded faces of the countershaft double-pulley change the effective pitch diameters d_2 and d_3. Pitch diameter d_3 increases while d_2 decreases giving the output to input speed ratio $n_4/n_1 = d_1d_3/d_2d_4$ a higher value.

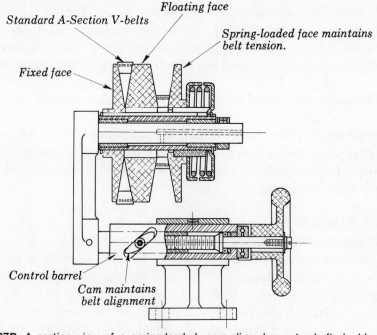

FIG. 27B. A section view of a spring-loaded, cam-aligned countershaft double-pulley for a compound variable-speed belt drive. (Speed Selector, Inc.)

Mechanism

In this case, output to input speed ratio is given by

$$\frac{n_4}{n_1} = \frac{d_1 d_3}{d_2 d_4}$$

where d is pitch diameter and the subscripts 1 to 4 refer to driver pulley, countershaft driven pulley, countershaft driver pulley, and driven pulley in that order. The two variable diameters are d_2 and d_3. Fig. 27B is a section view of a spring-loaded, cam-aligned, countershaft double-pulley.

Flat Belts

In the days when a single steam engine was used to drive dozens of separate pieces of factory machinery, power was transmitted by large flat belts turning pulleys on overhead countershafts. Belts were shifted, removed, and replaced by skilled operators who worked while the shafts were turning. While far less prominent now, flat belts have many modern, specialized applications. Light fabric belts and flat rubber-covered fabric belts are used at speeds up to 10,000 feet per minute and higher—speeds which are well above the operating range of ordinary V-belt drives. When used on balancing machine drives, light weight flat belts do not significantly affect the rotating mass and, in many high-speed applications, light flat belts are least likely to excite and transmit vibration.

Output to input speed ratio for flat belts is again given by $n_2/n_1 = d_1/d_2$, where pitch diameter d is measured to the center of the belt and equal to the pulley diameter plus one thickness of belt. As before, subscripts 1 and 2 refer to driver and driven pulleys, respectively. Either the driver or driven pulley of a flat belt drive is usually crowned to prevent the belt from riding off.

Positive Drive Belts

A special type of flat belt called a *timing belt* is used as a positive drive, insuring exact speed ratios. Teeth on the inside surface of the belt mesh with a grooved pulley and there is no slippage. See Fig. 28. Output to input speed ratio is given by Eq. (1), $n_2/n_1 = N_1/N_2$, where N_1 and N_2 are respectively, the *number of grooves* in the input and output pulleys. Timing belts may operate at high speeds and require only light tensioning since the drive does not depend on friction.

FIG. 28. Timing belt drive. Teeth on the inside surface of the belt mesh with grooves in the pulleys. Speed ratio depends on the number of grooves on the input and output pulleys. (T. B. Wood's Sons Co.)

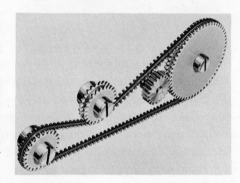

FIG. 29. Positive drive belt used with geared pulleys. This reinforced plastic belt was originally developed as a silent drive for sound and recording systems. The geared pulleys may be directly meshed with spur gears, eliminating intermediate components. An idler is usually used as shown to take up slack. The flexibility of this type belt allows for considerable shaft misalignment and, with idlers or guides, the belt may even be used between pulleys on perpendicular intersecting shafts. (PIC Design Corp.)

A patented drive system for instruments and other light-duty applications uses a reinforced plastic belt with side lugs, Fig. 29, which meshes with a gear-like pulley. The pulley has a central groove to accommodate the belt, but may be meshed with a 32 diametral pitch pinion. Output to input speed ratio is equal to the inverse ratio of the numbers of pulley teeth as with timing belts.

Disk Drives

For certain low-torque applications, disks may be used to transmit power from one shaft to another. See Fig. 30. When a pair of disks on parallel shafts contact at their outer edges, output to input speed ratio is equal to the inverse ratio of the disk diameters. For any number of disks, output to input speed ratio is again given by

$$\left| \frac{n_o}{n_i} \right| = \frac{\text{Product of driving disk diameters}}{\text{Product of driven disk diameters}}.$$

423

Mechanism

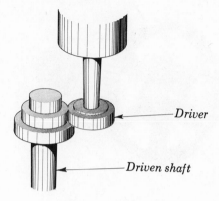

—Driver

—Driven shaft

FIG. 30. Friction drive. For this type of drive *the speed ratio equals the inverse ratio of disc diameters (or radii).* The drive is shifted to a new position to change ratios, and no clutch is required.

To maintain adequate friction force between the disks, alternate disks, or possibly all of the disks, might have rubber-covered driving surfaces.

Speed change in discrete steps may be accomplished by using a stepped set of disks on the driven shaft and changing the location of the driving disk to mesh with the driven disk giving the desired speed. Alternately, disk speed changers and reversers may employ an idler as is done with simple geared speed changers and reversing gear trains. Possible slippage between disks makes this type drive unsuitable for most instrument applications but permits a simple and inexpensive drive system for low-torque applications, eliminating the need for a clutch. Speed ratio may be changed by shifting disks from one location to another without stopping the drive since there is no problem of meshing teeth.

Variable Speed Wheel-Disk Drives

A wheel and disk type transmission provides stepless speed changing and reversing. The wheel (1) of Fig. 31 traces a path of radius r_2 on the disk (2), and output to input speed ratio is again given by

$$\frac{n_2}{n_1} = \frac{r_1}{r_2}$$

where r_1 is the radius of the driver and r_2 is the distance from the axis of the driven disc to the point of contact of the wheel and disc. When the wheel contacts the disk to the left of the disk center, the ouput direction is reversed.

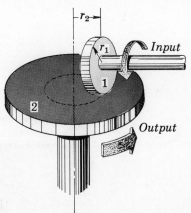

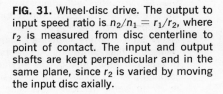

FIG. 31. Wheel-disc drive. The output to input speed ratio is $n_2/n_1 = r_1/r_2$, where r_2 is measured from disc centerline to point of contact. The input and output shafts are kept perpendicular and in the same plane, since r_2 is varied by moving the input disc axially.

While a wide range of speed ratios are available and the transmission is very simple in concept, the shifting process may pose problems. The drive wheel might be shifted by moving the input drive motor if the drive motor were small. Alternately, a splined shaft could be used and the drive wheel would then be slid along the disc by a shifting fork to change speeds. To provide adequate friction force for driving, one of the surfaces could be covered with rubber. Normally, the driving wheel would be covered since wear would then be distributed about it if the disk were stalled or if contact was made at the disk center.

An inexpensive alternative employs two disks and an idler wheel. Only the idler wheel is shifted while the input and output shafts rotate in place, as in Fig. 32. Since the velocity ratio is unaffected by idler diameter, speed ratio is again given by $n_2/n_1 = r_1/r_2$, where r_1 and r_2 vary simultaneously when the idler is shifted.

If a drive of this type were used on a phonograph, for example, the idler could be slid along between the input and output discs, producing turntable speeds of 16, 33⅓, 45, and 78 RPM with a single input speed. The drive shown is not reversible, but by simply moving the input and output shafts closer together, or by increasing the output disc diameter, a drive could be designed with positive, zero, or reverse output. When the idler is shifted to the center of the input disc, it does not turn and output speed is zero. When shifted farther to the left, the output is reversed.

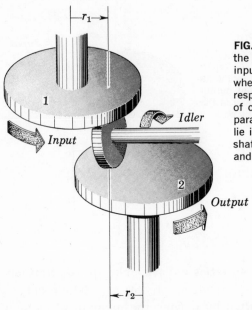

FIG. 32. Disc drive with idler wheel. As in the preceding illustration, the output to input speed ratio is given by $n_2/n_1 = r_1/r_2$ where both radii are measured from the respective disc centerlines to the points of contact. Input and output shafts are parallel and the axes of all three shafts lie in the same vertical plane. The idler shaft is perpendicular to the other two and is moved axially to change speed.

Variable Speed Cone Roller-Disc Drives

A commercially available disc drive which is similar in principle uses one or more *cone rollers*, shifed by an adjusting screw when the unit is running, Fig. 33A. Cam surfaces on the split output shaft respond to high output torque by increasing the normal force between the roller and discs to insure adequate driving traction. When the load decreases, the normal force is decreased so that wear is not excessive. A disc drive with four cone rollers is diagrammed in Fig. 33B. The larger model has an exceptional capacity when compared with other friction drives. It is rated at up to 60 H.P.

Variable Speed Ball-Disc Drives

Friction drives require relatively high normal forces where driver and driven parts contact. Optimum conditions for shifting, however, include low normal forces for drives of the type shown in Figs. 31 and 32, neither of which would be satisfactory if speed changing were frequent or continuous.

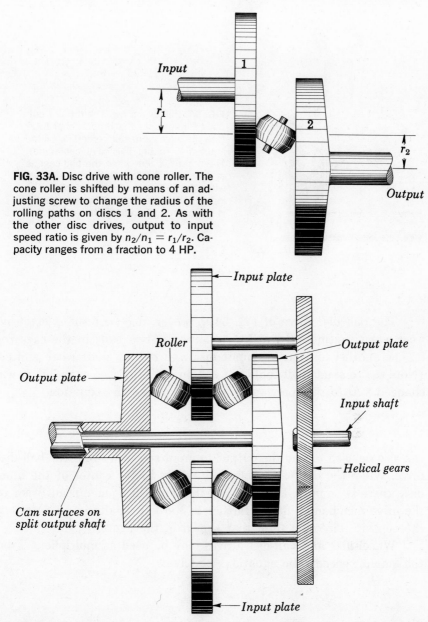

FIG. 33A. Disc drive with cone roller. The cone roller is shifted by means of an adjusting screw to change the radius of the rolling paths on discs 1 and 2. As with the other disc drives, output to input speed ratio is given by $n_2/n_1 = r_1/r_2$. Capacity ranges from a fraction to 4 HP.

FIG. 33B. Disc drive with four cone rollers. By using four adjustable rollers instead of one, the maximum power capacity is increased. This model may be used for up to 60 HP. The rollers are adjusted equally and the drive is kinematically equivalent to the single roller type shown in Fig. 33A. (Cone Drive Gears Div., Michigan Tool Co.)

Mechanism

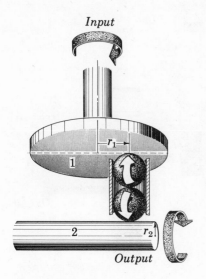

Input

FIG. 34. Ball-disc drive. The ratio of output to input speed is proportional to r_1 (the distance from the centerline of the input disc to the ball cage centerline). The output is zero when the ball cage is at the disc center. Direction reverses when the ball cage is moved past (to the left of) the disc center. This mechanism is often used as an integrator.

Output

The ball disc drive of Fig. 34, however, does not suffer extensive wear when continuously varied because the two balls in the cage *roll* on one another and on the input disk and output shaft when shifted. (Note that a single ball could not roll on both surfaces as radius r_1 was changed.) As for the previously discussed drives, the equation

$$\frac{n_2}{n_1} = \frac{r_1}{r_2}$$

can also be used to find the output to input speed ratio for the ball-disk drive. When the ball cage is shifted axially to the center of the input disk, there is no output motion but there is still no significant wear on the drive members. Shifting farther to the left results in an output in the opposite direction from that shown in the figure.

Wheel-disk and ball-disk drives may be used as multipliers. From the familiar speed ratio equation, we have

$$\theta_2 = \frac{r_1}{r_2} \theta_1$$

where the θ_1 and θ_2 are input and output angular displacement respectively (measured in degrees, radians or revolutions with both θ_1 and θ_2 in the same units). To multiply two numbers using the ball-disk

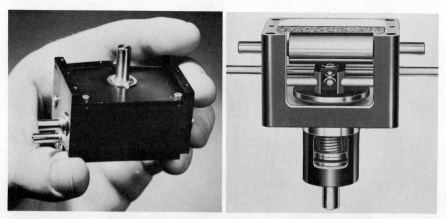

FIG. 35. Two views of a ball-disc integrator are shown. At *right* is a cutaway view of the ball-disc mechanism. The miniature integrator shown at *left* illustrates the compactness of this mechanism.

drive, we adjust r_1, the ball cage position, so that one of the numbers is represented by r_1/r_2, where r_2 is the radius of the output shaft. The driver is given a rotation θ_1 representing the other number and the product is given by θ_2, the rotation of the output shaft.

When r_1 is varied as a function of θ_1, then θ_2 is the integral of r_1/r_2 with respect to θ_1. Thus, the ball-disk drive is commonly used as an integrator. See Fig. 35. For example, let the ball cage position be automatically adjusted so that r_1/r_2 is numerically equal to the flow of liquid through a meter in pounds per hour. Disk 1 is turned at a rate of one degree per hour and the rotation of shaft 2, in degrees, gives the total amount of liquid which passed through the meter during the measuring period. Measurements could, of course, be scaled to keep both input and output values within a reasonable range.

Consider the disk drive of Fig. 32 with two offset disks, but with the idler wheel replaced instead by a single ball restrained in a cage. The variable speed ball-disk drive sketched in Fig. 36 operates on this principle except that, instead of a single ball, a cage of several steel balls rotates about its own center between the steel input and output disks. Each ball contacts both input and output disks at all times, permitting greater tractive forces between the two offset disks.

As far as input and output speeds are concerned, the rotating ball cage is kinematically equivalent to a single ball at the cage axis. When

429

Mechanism

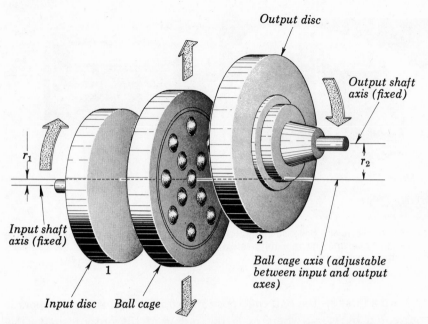

Output disc

Output shaft axis (fixed)

r_1

r_2

Input shaft axis (fixed)

1

2

Ball cage axis (adjustable between input and output axes)

Input disc   Ball cage

FIG. 36. The Graham *ball-disc* drive. This variation of the ball-disc drive employs a number of balls held in a rotating cage. The balls contact both the input and output discs. Output to input ratio is again given by $n_2/n_1 = r_1/r_2$ and may vary from 0 to 1.5. Output speed is increased as the ball cage centerline is moved toward the output disc axis. (Graham Transmissions, Inc.)

the ball cage axis coincides with the input axis, the output speed is zero. As the ball cage is moved toward the output shaft axis, output speed increases until, at the limit for this design, the output speed is 1.5 times the input speed. Speed ratios are changed when the unit is running. When recommended torque is not exceeded, there is pure rolling without sliding between the balls and disks except during speed changes. In general, the ratio of output to input speed is given by $n_2/n_1 = r_1/r_2$, where r_1 and r_2 are defined in Fig. 36. The angular velocity of the cage is half the sum of the input and output speeds:

$$\frac{n_1}{2}\left(\frac{r_1}{r_2} + 1 \right).$$

Although not available with this unit, a redesign would permit output to input speed ratios higher than 1.5 with further increase in r_1 or a reverse drive with the ball cage axis below the input shaft center.

430

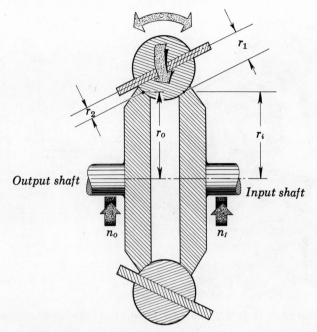

FIG. 37. Speed variator axle-mounted ball-disc drive. Since output and input disc radii are equal ($r_o = r_i$), output to input speed is given by $n_o/n_i = r_2/r_1$. A change in the angle of the ball axle simultaneously changes r_1 and r_2, the distances from ball axle to the point of contact of the ball surface with the beveled faces of the input and output discs respectively. (Cleveland Worm & Gear Div., Eaton, Yale, and Towne, Inc.)

Variable Speed Axle-Mounted Ball-Disc Drives. Another compact metal-to-metal friction drive employs axle-mounted balls which transmit power between beveled disks, as shown in Fig. 37. The ball axles are tilted uniformly by a slotted iris plate (acting as a set of cams) when it is desired to change speed ratios, Fig. 38. In analyzing this drive kinematically, we need consider only one ball and observe effective radii of driving and driven paths. When the ball axle is parallel to the input and output shafts (Fig. 38A) the distances r_1 and r_2 (from the ball axle to the points of contact of the ball with the beveled input and output discs) are equal. As the ball axle tilts either up or down (Figs. 38B and 38C) the radii r_1 and r_2 change simultaneously. Using the relationship for output to input speed ratio

$$\frac{n_o}{n_i} = \frac{\text{Product of effective driving member radii}}{\text{Product of effective driven member radii}},$$

431

Mechanism

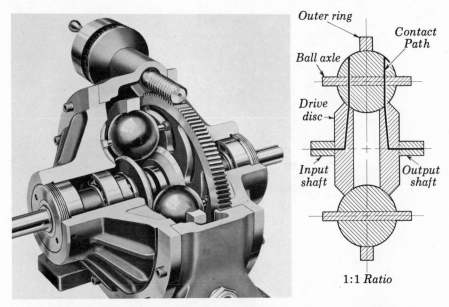

FIG. 38A. With the ball axle in the position shown, input speed equals output speed.

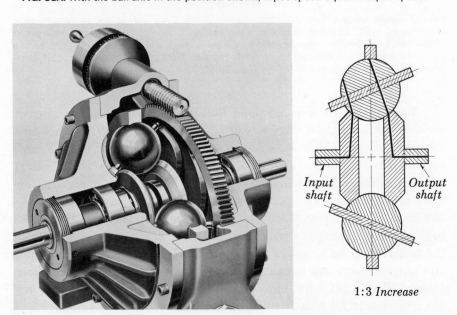

FIG 38B. The precision speed adjustment device (worm drive) at the top of the transmission is manually adjusted. The iris plate tilts the ball axle, simultaneously changing r_1 and r_2 as shown in the insert. The effect is a 1:3 input-to-output ratio.

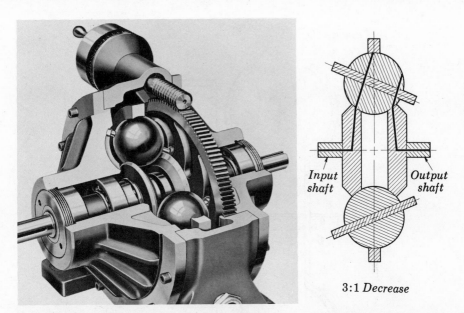

3:1 *Decrease*

FIG. 38C. With the axle tilted to the position shown, the input-to-output ratio becomes 3:1. For automatic process control or remote speed adjustment, the handwheel drive may be replaced by an electric or pneumatic actuator. The ring which encircles the balls balances radial forces, but runs freely and does not affect the speed ratio. (Cleveland Worm & Gear Div., Eaton, Yale, and Towne, Inc.)

we obtain

$$\frac{n_o}{n_i} = \frac{r_i r_2}{r_1 r_o} = \frac{r_2}{r_1}$$

after noting that the effective radii of the input and output discs are equal. Reversing is not possible with this mechanism alone, but speed ratio may be varied from ⅓ to 3 on commercially available units (while the unit is running). The actual drive unit is shown in a series of different positions in Fig. 38.

Variable Speed Roller-Torus Drives. A variation of the axle-mounted ball-disc drive is the roller-torus drive shown in Fig. 39. This drive employs two tiltable rollers within a split torus. The roller axes are shifted equally by gearing which includes a worm drive to provide fine speed adjustment. See Fig. 39B. The rollers act as idlers be-

433

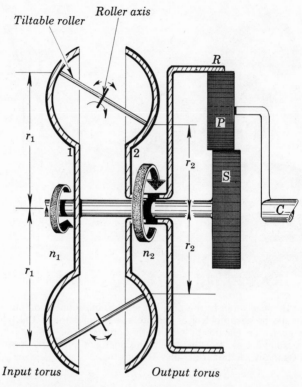

FIG. 39A. Roller torus drive. Roller axes are shifted to change r_1 and r_2. The input torus drives the sun gear, S; the output torus drives the ring, R. (Metron Instrument Co.)

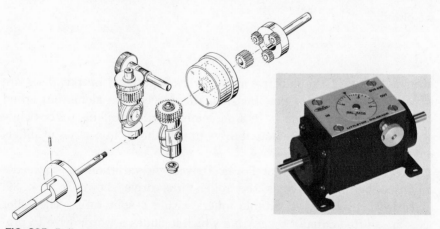

FIG. 39B. Roller torus drive. The roller torus drive is shown combined with a planetary gear transmission in an actual low power application. (Metron Instrument Co.)

tween the input and output tori. The output and input speed ratio is given by

$$\frac{n_2}{n_1} = -\frac{r_1}{r_2},$$

where r_1 and r_2 are measured from the drive shaft centerline to points of roller contact on the input torus and output torus respectively. The minus sign indicates that output rotation direction is opposite input. The roller-torus drive by itself cannot have a zero output and cannot be shifted to change the output direction. Commercially available roller-torus drives are used for low power instrument-type applications.

Friction drives and gearing are often combined to provide greater flexibility. Consider a simple planetary gear train with no fixed gears. From the section on planetary trains with more than one input, planet carrier speed is given by Eq. (16):

$$n_C = \frac{n_R + (n_S N_S/N_R)}{1 + (N_S/N_R)},$$

where n represents speed in RPM (or any other unit providing we are consistent), N represents numbers of teeth and subscripts C, R, and S refer to the carrier, ring, and sun respectively. Let the output torus of a roller-torus drive be directly connected to the ring gear of the planetary train and let the input torus shaft pass through the output torus to drive the sun gear. Then, the planet carrier may be used as output of the combined transmission so that a zero speed and a reverse are possible. Recall that, for all roller positions, the output torus rotates in a direction opposite the input torus. Referring to the roller-torus equation, $n_2/n_1 = -r_1/r_2$, and to the above equation for n_C, we have the ratio of output to input speed for the combined transmission:

$$\frac{n_C}{n_1} = \frac{-r_1/r_2 + (N_S/N_R)}{1 + (N_S/N_R)}$$

By rotating the rollers until r_1/r_2 is less than the fraction N_S/N_R, we obtain output and input in the same direction (with a considerable speed reduction). The roller adjustment at which $r_1/r_2 = N_S/N_R$ results in a zero output speed. Most of the range of the transmission is obtained with r_1/r_2 greater than N_S/N_R, resulting in an output direction opposite the input. The rollers may be adjusted to change speed *only* when the unit is running.

Mechanism

FIG. 40A. Multi-disc (viscous drag) drive. (Reliance Electric and Engineering Co.)

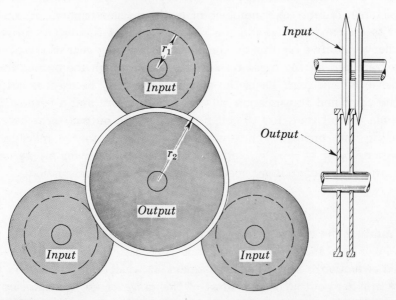

FIG. 40B. The sets of outer, (input) discs are tapered to fit into the variable-width slots of the center (output) discs. When the slots are widened, the outer discs move inward. This reduces the effective driving radius of the input discs and output speed is correspondingly reduced.

436

Variable Speed Multiple-Disc Drives

The multiple-disc drive (shown in Fig. 40A) is an interesting concept in drive train design, but is no longer commercially available. The output shaft is driven by a stack of rim disks which are thickest at their outer circumference. See the side view in Fig. 40B. The input to the rim disks consists of three stacks of thin cone shaped disks, all of which rotate at the same speed. A large number of disks are used to insure low forces between driver and driven disks and a lubricating film is maintained on the surfaces so that metal-to-metal contact does not occur. (Disk pressure is controlled by a torque-sensitive cam on the output shaft.) Power is transmitted by viscous drag between the disks.

The gear-driven cone disk stacks may be moved inward and outward between the rim disks to change the effective cone disk radius. Output speed is a function of input speed and the ratio of effective radii, r_1/r_2. When the cone disks are moved inward, r_1 decreases, reducing output speed; when moved outward, r_1 increases, and so does output speed. With constant input speed, the ratio of maximum to minimum output speeds is about four to one.

Planetary Traction Drives

Analysis of planetary traction drives differs little from the analysis of planetary gear trains. The same equations are applicable except that ratios of gear teeth are replaced by ratios of rolling path radii.

Planetary Disc Transmission

The planetary disc transmission shown in Fig. 41A has a split reaction ring R, a split sun S, and tapered planet discs P which are free to move radially in the planet carrier. When the reaction ring is adjusted to produce a larger gap, the planets move outward, and the spring-loaded sun reduces its gap. Since, in general, the rolling path of the sun on the planet and the rolling path of the ring on the planet have different radii, this drive is analyzed as if the planet were two separate planets, P_1 and P_2, rotating at the same speed. In Fig. 41B, P_1 refers to the contact of the planet with the sun, while P_2 refers to the contact of the planet with the split ring. When the reaction ring gap is adjusted, r_{P1} and r_{P2} change simultaneously.

Relative speeds are best computed by a superposition method. In the step I of Table 10, the entire train is given one positive (clockwise)

FIG. 41A. Dodge Disco *planetary disc transmission.* This Planetary Drive employs the operating principle of the multi-disc drive. The split, non-rotating ring has an adjustable gap. When the ring gap is increased, the planets move outward and the spring-loaded sun gap decreases. (Dodge Mfg. Co.)

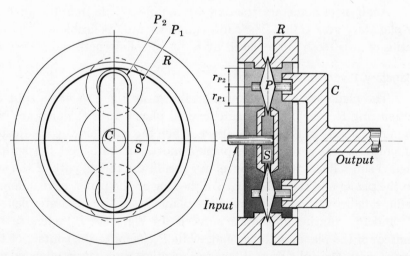

FIG. 41B. Schematic of the planetary disc drive. To solve for the output to input ratio using the superposition method, Table 10, effective radii are used instead of the tooth numbers used in the case of planetary gear drives. Note that the single planet disc is treated as if it were two separate discs, the first of radius r_{P1} and the second of radius r_{P2}.

438

rotation, disregarding the fact that the ring is fixed. In step II, the planet carrier is held stationary while the ring is given one negative rotation, so that total ring rotation equals zero in accordance with the constraints of the problem. In step II, the effect of the ring driving the planet, and the planet driving the sun, are noted in tabular form. *Note that effective radii are used here exactly as were numbers of teeth in the planetary gear section of this chapter.* Then, the first and second steps of Table 10 are added to obtain

$$1 + \frac{r_R r_{P1}}{r_{P2} r_S}$$

rotations of the sun for one rotation of the planet carrier while the re-

TABLE 10. SPEED RATIOS FOR A PLANETARY DISC TRANSMISSION WITH RING R FIXED, FIG. 41B

Disc	Sun S	Planet P		Ring R	Planet Carrier C
Driving Path Radius	r_S	r_{P1}	r_{P2}	r_R	
Step I. Rotations with Train Locked	$+1$	$+1$	$+1$	$+1$	$+1$
Step II. Rotations with Planet Carrier Fixed	$+ \dfrac{r_R r_{P1}}{r_{P2} r_S}$	$- \dfrac{r_R}{r_{P2}}$	$- \dfrac{r_R}{r_{P2}}$	-1	0
Total Rotations (Ring Fixed)	$1 + \dfrac{r_R r_{P1}}{r_{P2} r_S}$			0	$+1$

action ring has zero rotations. The ratio of planet carrier speed to sun speed is given by

$$\frac{n_C}{n_S} = \frac{1}{1 + (r_R r_{P1}/r_{P2} r_S)}. \tag{19}$$

A commercially available planetary disc transmission uses the sun shaft as input and the planet carrier as output, making the above ratio the output to input speed ratio. Allowing the planet discs to move outward by increasing the gap in the split reaction ring has the effect of reducing rolling path radius r_{P2} and increasing r_{P1}. The overall effect on the gear ratio is a decrease in output speed. Output to input speed ratio may be varied between $+0.12$ and $+0.72$ with this transmission by adjusting the reaction ring gap while the unit is running. Speed variation is stepless.

Planetary Cone Transmission

Another variable-speed planetary friction drive employs *cone* planets which make contact with a variable-position reaction ring, Fig. 42A. The drive motor may be directly connected to the planet carrier. A set of planet pinions (integral with the planet cones) drives a ring gear which serves as the output. At most input speeds, inertia forces hold the cones

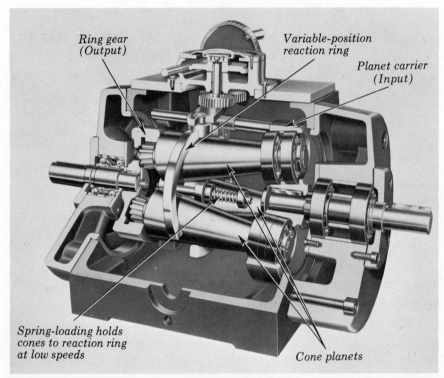

Ring gear
(Output)

Variable-position
reaction ring

Planet carrier
(Input)

Spring-loading holds
cones to reaction ring
at low speeds

Cone planets

FIG. 42A. Cutaway of planetary cone transmission showing speed control mechanism. The mechanism at the top of the transmission permits fine adjustment of reaction ring position and a wide range of speed ratios through zero and reverse speeds. Most models of this transmission depend on centrifugal force to hold the cone rollers against the ring. This model, however, is designed with a spring-loading assembly in the center to ensure traction between the cones and ring, even at low speeds. (Graham Transmissions, Inc.)

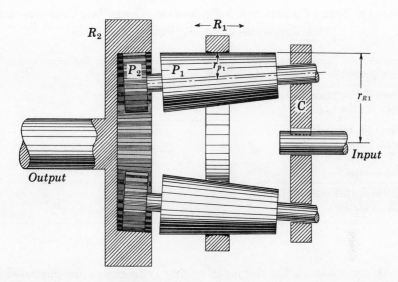

FIG. 42B. Schematic of the planetary cone transmission. The element of the planet cone P_1 which contacts ring R_1 is parallel to the input axis. The ring R_1 is moved left or right to increase or decrease the effective radius of the planet cone, r_{P1}, at the point of contact. Table 11 gives the output to input speed ratio.

against the friction ring, but if the input speed is low, auxiliary springs are used to insure contact. To change speeds, the reaction ring is shifted axially (Fig. 42B) to contact the planet cones at a different location (changing the effective planet radius, r_{P1}). Speeds may be changed when the unit is operating if the cone planets are spring loaded. For the unit without auxiliary springs on the planets, speeds may be changed when the drive is moving or stopped. Speed change is stepless.

Superposition will again be used to solve for relative speeds. In the first step of Table 11, the entire transmission is given one positive rotation. In step II, the reaction ring rotation is corrected by giving it one negative rotation with the carrier fixed. The effect is calculated for the cone planet and planet pinion (which turn as a unit) and for the ring gear. Adding steps I and II of Table 11, we have the required rotation of the reaction ring (zero) and one rotation of the planet carrier. The output to input speed ratio is given by the relative rotations of the ring gear divided by the carrier rotations:

$$\frac{n_{R2}}{n_C} = 1 - \frac{r_{R1}N_{P2}}{r_{P1}N_{R2}} \cdot \tag{20}$$

441

TABLE 11. SPEED RATIOS FOR A PLANETARY CONE TRANSMISSION WITH
THE REACTION RING R_1 FIXED, FIG. 42B

Component	C	R_1	P_1	P_2	R_2
Step I. Rotations with Train Locked	$+1$	$+1$	$+1$	$+1$	$+1$
Step II. Rotations with Carrier Fixed. (R_1 given (-1) Rotations)	0	-1	$-\dfrac{r_{R1}}{r_{P1}}$	$-\dfrac{r_{R1}}{r_{P1}}$	$-\dfrac{r_{R1}}{r_{P1}}\dfrac{N_{P2}}{N_{R2}}$
Total Rotations (R_1 Fixed)	$+1$	0			$1-\dfrac{r_{R1}N_{P2}}{r_{P1}N_{R2}}$

In one model, when the reaction ring (also called the control ring) is adjusted to approximately the middle of its range, the ratio of reaction ring radius to cone radius is equal to the ratio of the ring gear teeth to the pinion teeth (N_{R2}/N_{P2}). Then, the output speed is zero from Equation (20). As we move the reaction ring to the left, r_{P1} increases and output speed is in the same direction as input until, at its

TABLE 12. OPERATING CHARACTERISTICS OF TYPICAL TRACTION DRIVES[*][†]

Characteristic	Metron (Fig. 39)	Cleveland Variator (Fig. 38)	Cone-Trol (Fig. 33)	Graham Transmission (Fig. 42)	Dodge Disco (Fig. 41)
Over-all speed ratio	Infinite	9:1	6:1	Infinite	6:1
Maximum speed (rpm)	4000	3600	2040	9200	1260
Minimum speed (rpm)	0	100	380	0	104
Speed regulation (per cent)	5	4	......	......	......
Maximum input speed (rpm)	4000	1725	1725	3450	1725
Load range (hp)	Up to 0.016	½-10	½-60	¼-3	1-10
Motor driven	Yes	Yes	No	Yes	No
Efficiency (per cent)	......	75-90	90	65-85	90
Integral gear reduction	Yes	No	No	Yes	No
Transmission only	Yes	Yes	Yes	Yes	Yes
Constant torque ratings	Yes	Yes	Yes	Yes	Yes
Constant horsepower ratings	Yes	Yes	Yes	Yes	Yes
Change speeds—running	Yes	Yes	Yes	Yes	Yes
Change speeds—stationary	No	No	No	Yes	No

[*] Data does not necessarily apply to all units available from each manufacturer.

[†] Table courtesy of J. R. Burnett, Reliance Electric & Engineering Co.

maximum value, $n_{R2}/n_C = 1/5$. Moving the control ring to the right of the zero output position gives us an output rotation opposite the input until we reach a limited value of $n_{R2}/n_C = -1/5$. A similar transmission with a range of output to input speeds between $-1/100$ and $+1/3$ is also available.

The operating characteristics of several traction drives are compared in Table 12. The drives listed have been discussed in this section and the preceding sections and are referred to by figure number.

Impulse Drives and Flexible Spline Drives

A gear and linkage impulse drive driven by an eccentric is shown in Fig. 43. The sketch of the drive (Fig. 43B) is incomplete, showing only one of the three pinion and linkage assemblies of the unit shown in Fig. 43A, but we will first examine the drive as shown in part before considering the entire mechanism.

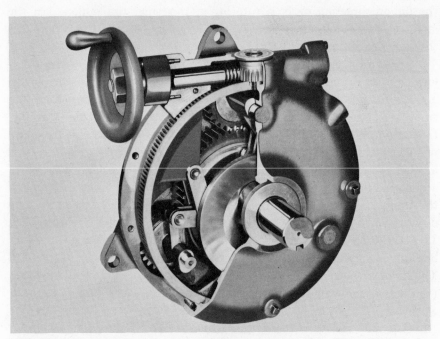

FIG. 43A. Cutaway view of the gear and linkage impulse drive. (Morse Chain Co.)

The eccentric drives a roller follower pinned to link 1. The follower in turn drives links 2 and 3. Link 3 turns a pinion counterclockwise through a one-way clutch, and the pinion drives the output gear. It is seen that the cam and follower will cause link 3 to oscillate through the same angle whether the input cam turns clockwise or counterclockwise. Thus, the orientation of the one-way clutch determines the directions the pinion and output gears will turn. In this case, the output is clockwise whether the input is clockwise or counterclockwise.

When links 2 and 3 are nearly perpendicular, the oscillation of link 3 is greatest and output speed is maximum. The pivot point of link 1 may be rotated about the drive axis, making the angle between links 2 and 3 quite small so that link 3 oscillates through a small angle and output speed is reduced.

The output shaft would be stationary for about half of each input shaft revolution if the drive had only one pinion and linkage assembly. The actual drive (Fig. 43A) with three such assemblies turns continuously, each linkage driving one third of the time. For a given linkage, during two thirds of each input cycle, link 3 is either rotating opposite the pinion direction or it is rotating slower than the pinion. (In the latter case, the pinion is being driven by one of the other linkages through the output gear.)

Instantaneous output speed is found by sketching the cam and follower (or its equivalent mechanism) and the linkage which is driving at a given instant. The procedure is illustrated in Fig. 43C. Since the roller track, which acts as a cam, and the cam follower are circular, the distance from the roller track center B to cam follower center C is fixed and will be considered rigid link 5. The axis of rotation of the roller track is labeled O_4 and O_4B is designated as link 4. For a specified position of adjustable pivot O_1, we form a four bar linkage with links 4, 5, 1 and the frame. Given ω_4, the angular velocity of the roller track, we may draw velocity polygon obc using the methods of Chapter Two. See Fig. 43D. We then note that links 1, 2, 3 and the frame also form a four bar linkage, permitting us to complete the polygon with velocity point d. The linkage shown is obviously driving the transmission at this instant (through a one-way clutch whereby link 3 drives the pinion counterclockwise). Thus pinion angular velocity is given by $\omega_3 = od/O_3D$.

Angular velocity of the output gear is related to the angular velocity of link 3 by the negative ratio of pinion teeth to output gear teeth. This

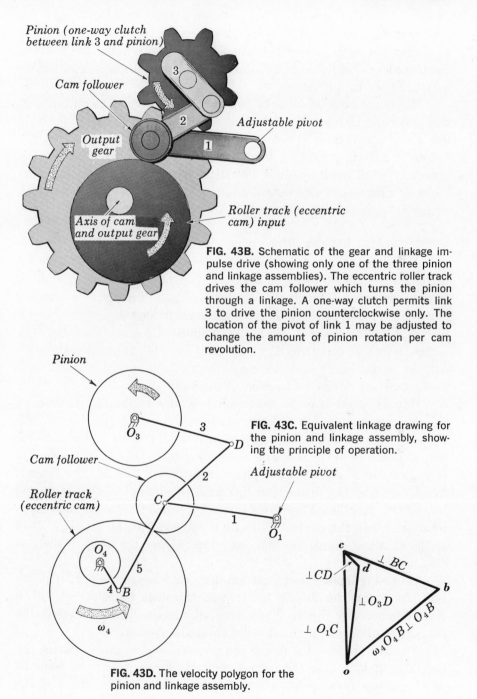

FIG. 43B. Schematic of the gear and linkage impulse drive (showing only one of the three pinion and linkage assemblies). The eccentric roller track drives the cam follower which turns the pinion through a linkage. A one-way clutch permits link 3 to drive the pinion counterclockwise only. The location of the pivot of link 1 may be adjusted to change the amount of pinion rotation per cam revolution.

FIG. 43C. Equivalent linkage drawing for the pinion and linkage assembly, showing the principle of operation.

FIG. 43D. The velocity polygon for the pinion and linkage assembly.

Mechanism

process is repeated at intervals for the entire time a given linkage drives to obtain a smooth plot of output speed. The same roller track drives the three identical linkages and thus, the output motion is repeated for every 120° of cam rotation.

If it is not obvious which of two linkages is driving the output gear at a particular instant, the problem is solved for both linkages; the linkage giving the highest speed is the actual driver. It is seen that the output is pulsating, making the drive practical only for relatively low speeds. Typical input speed is 180 RPM (necessitating a separate reducer in most cases) and output to input speed ratio may be adjusted to any value between 1:4.5 and 1:120.

Lamination-Type Impulse Drive

A similar impulse drive, called the *lamination-type*, is available for drives transmitting up to ¾ horsepower, Fig. 44A. Power is transmitted from an eccentric through an adjustable linkage directly to a one-way clutch on the output shaft. There are several linkage and clutch assemblies and, unlike the gear and linkage impulse drive, each assembly operates on its own eccentric. The eccentrics operate in sequence throughout the entire input cycle to insure continuous output motion, each linkage driving during its fraction of the input cycle.

Output speed may be determined at any instant by drawing a velocity polygon for the linkage which is driving at that time. Figs. 44C and 44D show the limiting positions. This process is repeated for several positions of the link which is driving to make a smooth velocity-time plot (which repeats itself when the next link becomes the driver). The location of O_3, the control link axis, is adjustable. If it is moved toward O'_3, then link 5 oscillates through a smaller angle for each input rotation. When the control link axis is adjusted to fall on O'_3, link 4 oscillates about its connection with link 5 and the output shaft is stationary.

Reversing input speed direction does not change the output direction. To reverse the output, the transmission may be equipped with a reversible one-way clutch. When the clutch mechanism is reversed, the magnitude of output to input speed ratio also changes.

The average speed of link 5 of a given linkage assembly during the time that it is driving the output shaft clockwise is not the same as when it drives counterclockwise. (A velocity plot verifies this.) If the

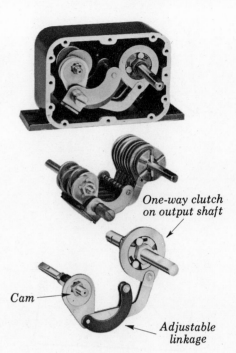

FIG. 44A. *Top:* Assembled view of a lamination-type impulse drive with cover plate removed. *Center:* The heart of the unit, which is a set of laminations phased to provide continuous driving. *Bottom:* A single lamination is shown with the important features identified. (Zero-Max Co.)

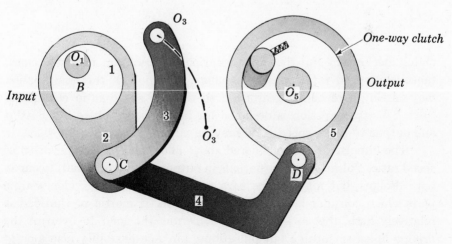

FIG. 44B. A single lamination of the lamination-type impulse drive is shown in detail. The location of control axis O_3 governs output rotation. When the control link axis is adjusted to position O'_3, the output shaft becomes stationary.

Mechanism

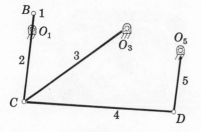

FIG. 44C. The equivalent linkage drawing for the single lamination-type drive
element shown in Fig. 44B. The linkage
is shown in one of its limiting positions.

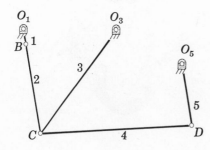

FIG. 44D. The other limiting position.

clutch mechanism and the input rotation direction are reversed simultaneously, speed ratio does not change. Alternately, the transmission
may employ a reversing gear train so that no speed ratio change results. This transmission is designed for input speeds up to 2000 RPM
and output to input speed ratio may be adjusted from zero to $\frac{1}{4}$.

The impulse drives considered above allow for stepless variation of
speed ratio. Pulsations (fluctuations in output torque or speed) occur in
both designs, but may not be as severe as indicated by velocity-time
plots which consider kinematic aspects alone. If inertia of the load is
relatively high, the one-way clutches permit the load to overrun the
driving links, smoothing out pulsations. Linkage flexibility also aids in
absorbing transmission pulsations so that their full effect is not transmitted to the driven machinery.

Flexible Spline Drives

The *flexible spline drive*, Fig. 45A, operates on a unique principle, employing a wave generator to deflect a flexible external spline. The flexible spline meshes with a slightly larger, rigid, stationary member having an internal circular spline. The major components are shown in exploded view in Fig. 45A. The wave generator, usually an ellipse-like cam, is ordinarily the input to the drive. The flexible spline serves as the output, rotating in a direction opposite the input as shown below.

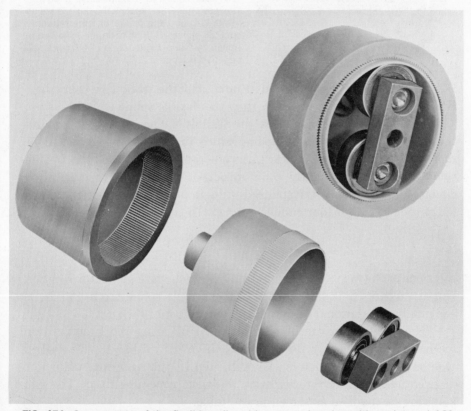

FIG. 45A. Components of the flexible spline drive are: a housing with an integral 162 tooth circular spline (fixed); a plastic 160 tooth flexible spline (the output member); and a 2-lobe ball-bearing wave generator (mounted on the input shaft). Other flexible spline drives are available for heavy-duty and high-precision applications. A combination of two rollers or an ellipse-like cam is used as the wave generator for drives of this type. (Harmonic Drive Div., United Shoe Machinery Corp.)

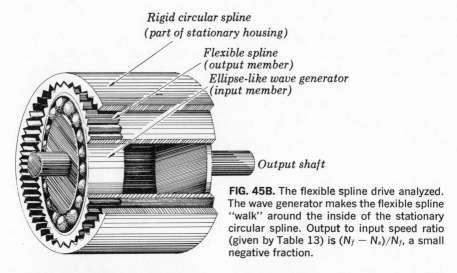

Rigid circular spline
(part of stationary housing)

Flexible spline
(output member)

Ellipse-like wave generator
(input member)

Output shaft

FIG. 45B. The flexible spline drive analyzed. The wave generator makes the flexible spline "walk" around the inside of the stationary circular spline. Output to input speed ratio (given by Table 13) is $(N_f - N_s)/N_f$, a small negative fraction.

Both splines have the same circular pitch, but the stationary spline has, typically, two or four more teeth than the flexible spline.

The wave generator causes the flexible spline to "walk" around the inside of the stationary spline. Since the splines mesh tooth for tooth, when the wave generator turns one rotation clockwise the flexible spline will advance slightly counterclockwise. The difference in pitch circumference between the splines results in a tangential motion with a magnitude of two or four circular pitches. In general, then, there are

$$\frac{N_f - N_s}{N_f}$$

rotations of the flexible spline (output) for each wave generator rotation (input), where N_f is the number of the flexible spline teeth and N_s is the number of stationary internal spline teeth, Fig. 45B.

The speed ratio can also be obtained by using the superposition method used previously for planetary drives. In Table 13, the locked train is given one rotation in step I. In step II, the rigid, internal spline is given one negative rotation with the wave generator fixed. The two steps are then added as shown in the table.

The wave generator of the flexible spline drive has two or more equally spaced lobes or rollers; the two splines mate where the lobes or rollers press the flexible spline unit against the rigid splines. The difference in tooth numbers, $N_s - N_t$, is a whole-number multiple of

TABLE 13. SPEED RATIOS FOR THE FLEXIBLE SPLINE DRIVE, FIG. 45

Component	Flexible Spline	Circular Spline	Wave Generator
Step I. Rotations with Train Locked	$+1$	$+1$	$+1$
Step II. Rotations with Wave Generator Fixed	$-\dfrac{N_s}{N_f}$	-1	0
Total Rotations	$1 - \dfrac{N_s}{N_f}$	0	$+1$

the number of lobes. An output to input speed ratio of $-1/80$, for example, is obtained by using a two-roller or two-lobe wave generator input and a flexible spline of 160 teeth meshing with a 162-tooth fixed internal spline. If output and input direction are to be the same, the wave generator is again used as the input member, but the output is taken from the rigid circular spline with the flexible spline fixed. Using the data from the above example, this condition would yield an output to input speed ratio of

$$\frac{N_s - N_f}{N_s} = + \frac{1}{81}.$$

Speed can be reduced to very low values with correspondingly great increases in output torque with compact, one- or two-stage, flexible spline drives. For this reason, they have been used in aircraft and space applications including vertical takeoff aircraft, short-takeoff and landing aircraft, and a meteor detection satellite. In the latter application, a two-stage 3 inch by 4½ inch flexible spline drive provides a 1 to 3840 speed reduction for a secondary drive to extend 15 foot by 48 foot detector "wings" (while orbiting).

Other Drive-Train Elements

There are many ways to convert rotational motion into rectilinear motion. Cams, linkages, rack and pinion combinations and a number of other devices are used.

Mechanism

Power Screws

Power screws, one of the most common and precise methods, are frequently used as machine tool drives in conjunction with gear trains. If a screw with a single thread engages a nut which is not permitted to rotate, the nut will move relative to the screw a distance equal to the pitch for each screw rotation. (The pitch is the axial distance between adjacent corresponding thread elements.) With a double-thread screw, the nut motion is two pitches and in general, the motion of the nut per screw rotation will be the lead (the pitch times the number of threads). When a right-hand screw turns clockwise, the relative motion of the nut is toward the observer; for a left-hand screw turning clockwise, the relative motion of the nut is away from the observer. The nut may be split through an axial plane if it is to be engaged and disengaged from the screw as in a lathe. A split nut also permits adjustment to compensate for wear and eliminate backlash.

Direction changing is usually accomplished by a geared reverse or an electrically reversible motor but there are other alternatives. For example, two counter-rotating screws of the same hand may be used with a grooved roller (acting as a nut) on a slider. The nut is shifted from one screw to the other to change the slider direction. If the roller is cam shifted at the end of each stroke, the slider has reciprocating motion of essentially constant velocity between direction shifts.

Differential Screws. When high-thrust, low-speed linear motion is required, a *differential screw* may be used. Fig. 46 shows a power screw with a lead L_1 for the left half and L_2 for the right half, both right hand threads. The motion of the slider equals the axial motion of the screw plus the axial motion of the slider with respect to the screw:

$$v = \frac{n}{60} (L_2 - L_1),$$

where v is slider velocity in in/sec
n is clockwise RPM of the screw
L_1 is the screw lead at the frame
L_2 is the screw lead in the slider.

For example, a single-thread screw may be cut with 11 threads per inch at the left end and 10 threads per inch at the right end. At 10 RPM, the slider velocity is

452

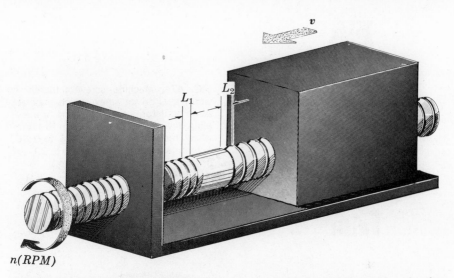

FIG. 46. Differential screw. If both of the threads shown are right-hand threads, the velocity v of the block is given by $v = (n/60)(L_2 - L_1)$, where L_2 is the lead of the thread on which the block is riding, L_1 is the lead of the thread turning through the frame, and n is the angular velocity of the screw.

$$v = \frac{10}{60}\left(\frac{1}{10} - \frac{1}{11}\right) = \frac{1}{660} \text{ in/sec.}$$

It is more common for power jacks, linear actuators, and other machinery controls to employ a worm drive for low-speed operation. In some cases, the outside of the nut has enveloping worm wheel teeth cut on it and it is restrained from axial motion by thrust bearings while the screw moves axially. See Fig. 47A. Hundreds of jacks of this type are used in a single installation; for example, a linear electron accelerator with a 4 inch diameter by 2 mile long waveguide which must be kept straight to within one millimeter. Fig. 47B illustrates a more conventional application of the power jack.

Ball Screws. Ball screws are used when friction must be reduced. The thrust load is carried by balls circulating in helical races, reducing typical friction losses to about 10% of transmitted power. Ball screws must include a ball return to provide a continuous supply to the nut. Preloading of the nut to eliminate backlash and reduce yielding is possible if the ball race in the nut is divided into two sections.

453

Mechanism

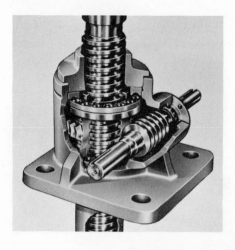

FIG. 47A. Machine screw actuator. A worm gear-driven screw which may act as an actuator, a precision jack, or a leveling device. The ratio of worm to worm-wheel teeth may be from 1:6 to 1:36. Actuators are available with up to 20 feet of screw travel. (Duff-Norton Co.)

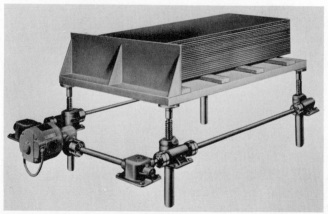

FIG. 47B. Four machine screw actuators are shown driven by a gear motor through bevel gear boxes. The actuators are self-locking. A *ball-screw* actuator is shown in Chapter 1. (Duff-Norton Co.)

Clutches and Brakes

Clutches and brakes are seldom the object of detailed kinematic analysis but they are essential drive train components.

Positive Clutches. Positive clutches rely on the engagement of jaws or teeth to transmit power between colinear (or nearly colinear) shafts. They cannot ordinarily slip and, in most cases, wear is insignificant. But since there is no slippage, the shafts to be joined by the clutch must both be stationary (or nearly so) at the time of engagement.

FIG. 48A. The positive clutch shown here is used to change speeds in a herring-bone gear speed reducer. (Horsburgh & Scott Co.)

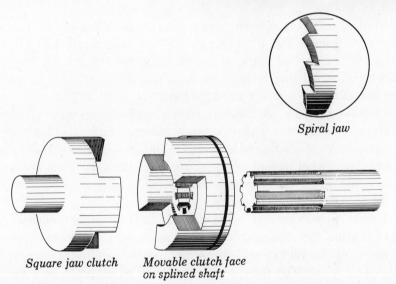

Spiral jaw

Square jaw clutch   *Movable clutch face on splined shaft*

FIG. 48B. Positive clutches. Since there is no provision for slippage, the square jaw clutch can be engaged only at shaft speeds of zero to a few RPM. However, the spiral jaw positive clutch is a design modification which permits engagement at greater speed differences.

Square and Spiral-Jaw Clutches. A square-jaw clutch, Fig. 48A, is ordinarily used only when the driver and driven shafts can both be stopped for engagement.

By using spiral jaws, Fig. 48B, engagement is possible at speed differences up to 100 RPM. However, if the driver and driven masses are high, repeated shock loading at engagement may cause failure in the shafting or elsewhere in the drive train. The spiral jaws are intended for driving in one direction only.

Multiple-Tooth Clutches. Multiple-tooth clutches permit engagement at a few hundred RPM speed difference between shafts, but they are sometimes used in conjunction with friction clutches to reduce relative speed. In automotive applications, the combination is called a synchromesh clutch, and consists of a conical friction clutch which first makes contact followed by a multiple-tooth positive clutch which slides into place an instant later when the relative speed is low. As noted earlier in this chapter, another clutch disengages the engine from the drive train during the process so that the synchronizing friction clutch is lightly loaded.

Most positive type clutches have one clutch-half directly connected to one of the shafts but the other clutch-half has an internal spline so that it may be shifted along a splined shaft for engagement and disengagement. A shifting linkage operates the clutch through a bearing or an annular groove in the movable half.

Friction Clutches. A common clutch application requires starting and stopping a machine while the prime mover is turning at high speed. Extreme shock loading due to large driver and driven masses would result if engagement were instantaneous. Thus, a *friction clutch* is ordinarily used so that the driven shaft is accelerated to driver speed at a safe rate while partial slippage occurs.

Drum-Type Friction Clutch. The drum-type clutch consists of a ring of friction elements which expands to contact the internal surface of a drum, or else an external ring which contracts to engage the outer surface of a drum. The friction elements may be attached to a flexible tube which is air actuated, as in Fig. 49.

The action of this type clutch is sensitive to velocity. When the friction elements and flexible tube are arranged as in Fig. 49, inertia forces resist clutch engagement and greater air pressure is required at higher velocities. When the friction elements and flexible tube are attached to the inner drum, high velocities aid engagement of the friction surfaces and may cause unintentional engagement.

Disc-Type Friction Clutch. The most common general purpose friction clutch, the *disk clutch*, is unaffected by inertia forces. If contact occurs on only one pair of disk faces, one disk may be moved

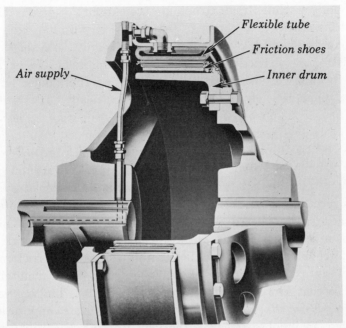

FIG. 49. Drum-type friction clutch. The air-actuated flexible tube expands to engage the clutch by forcing the friction shoes against the inner drum. The type shown is an industrial clutch designed for high-speed, high-torque applications. (Fawick Corp.)

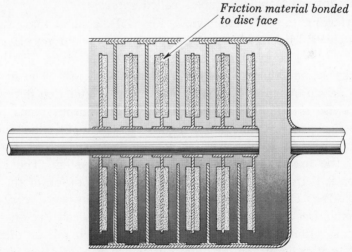

FIG. 50. Disc-type friction clutch. A friction material is bonded to both sides of alternate discs. An actuating mechanism (not shown) forces the discs together to engage the clutch.

axially along a splined shaft to actuate the clutch. For greater capacity, many disks are used to comprise the clutch, keyed alternately to the inside of a drum and to a shaft. See Fig. 50. Usually, both sides of alternate disks have a friction material bonded to them. To engage the clutch, the stack of disks is forced together by a mechanical linkage or actuated pneumatically, hydraulically or electrically. The rate of engagement is controllable so that the driven shaft may be accelerated uniformly to the speed of the driver.

Special Use Clutches. Special use clutches which are self-actuating include centrifugal, torque-limiting, and one-way or overrunning types. Centrifugal clutches are actuated by a mass which locks the clutch parts together at a predetermined speed. Torque-limiting clutches, as the name implies, release at a predetermined torque. The ball-detent type has a set of steel balls which are held in detents by means of a spring force which determines the limiting torque. Any friction clutch may act as a torque limiter if the contact force is maintained by springs so that slipping occurs at torques above the limiting value.

Sprag-Type Reverse-Locking Clutches. Certain applications require that an input shaft drive the load in either direction, but that the output shaft be prevented from driving the input shaft. This function is performed by the reverse-locking clutch, Fig. 51A, through specially-formed locking members called *sprags.*

Referring to the section view, Fig. 51B, assume that the input shaft (which drives the control member) turns counterclockwise. The control member contacts sprag A near the top, pivots it slightly counterclockwise, and thereby frees it from the outer race. The inner race is then driven by sprag A. (Sprag B performs no function during counterclockwise rotation.) Suppose, now, that the output tends to drive counterclockwise with *no* power applied to the input side. Then, the inner race slightly rotates sprag A, forcing it clockwise and jamming it against the fixed outer race, thus locking the system. The identical function is performed by sprag B for clockwise rotation of the clutch.

One-Way Clutches. One-way clutches drive in one direction only, but permit freewheeling if the driven side overspeeds the driver. The clutch operation depends on balls or sprags which roll or slide when relative motion is in one direction but jam if the direction of relative motion tends to reverse.

Ratchet and pawl drives perform a similar function except that

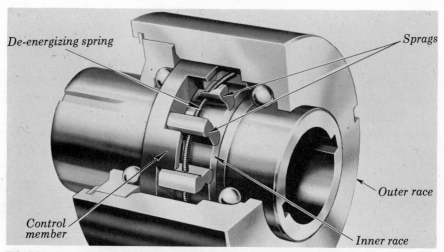

FIG. 51A. Sprag-type reverse-locking clutch. The input (left shaft) drives the load (right shaft) in either direction. When the output shaft tends to drive, the sprags lock it to the outer race. Other sprag configurations are available which permit operation with free-wheeling. (Formsprag Co.)

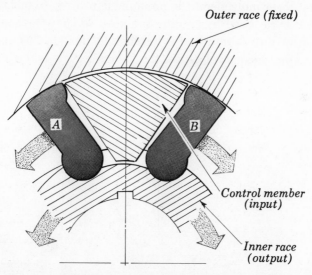

FIG. 51B. Section view of the sprag-type clutch. As the input begins to rotate counter-clockwise, it contacts sprag A. The sprag pivots slightly counterclockwise in its detent, separating from the outer race. The input pushes against the sprag, forcing the inner race (output shaft) to rotate. If the output begins to rotate faster than the input, the sprag is thereby given a slightly clockwise motion, jamming the sprag against the fixed outer race and, in turn, locking the output shaft. (Formsprag Co.)

the pawl may engage the ratchet between teeth only. Either a one-way clutch or a ratchet-pawl drive may be used to change oscillation into intermittent one-way rotation. Some machinery feed mechanisms operate in this manner.

Fig. 52 illustrates, in principle, the table feed mechanisms of a mechanical shaper. The lengths of the links are such that link 3 oscillates as link 1, the driver rotates. A spring-held pawl drives the ratchet during only the clockwise motion of link 3 (approximately, but not exactly, half of each cycle). The workpiece table is intermittently fed to the left by the power screw driven by the ratchet. The cutting tool (not shown) moves perpendicular to the velocity direction of the table, but only during the part of the cycle when the table is stationary, to insure straight cuts.

By increasing the driving crank radius r_1, the angle through which link 3 oscillates is increased. Feed is increased in discrete steps, i.e. the rotation of the ratchet per cycle will be an integer multiple of the pitch angle, where the pitch angle is $360°/N$ for N ratchet teeth. If link 3 oscillates through an angle of β degrees, the ratchet rotation per cycle will be the integer multiple of the pitch angle nearest to but not greater than β. Feed is reversed by turning the pawl so that the counterclockwise motion of link 3 rotates the ratchet. Although this results in a change in instantaneous velocities, the feed per cycle is unchanged.

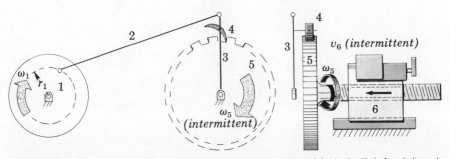

FIG. 52. Ratchet-pawl mechanism (applied to an intermittent drive). As link 1 rotates at constant angular velocity, link 3 oscillates. A pawl (link 4) on link 3 drives the ratchet (5) during the clockwise motion of link 3. The right-hand screw drives the work table intermittently to the left.

EXAMPLE—PROBLEM 1: Design an intermittent feed mechanism to provide rates of feed from .010 inches per cycle to .024 inches per cycle in increments of .002.

Solution: (There are several solutions to this design problem, each one involving many hours of work. We will take the first steps toward a practical design.)

1. A ratchet-pawl mechanism driving a power screw will be selected for this design. The required steps between minimum and maximum feed correspond to ratchet rotations of one pitch angle. For screw lead L inches, the feed per pitch angle is L/N inches. If we use a single-thread power screw with 5 threads per inch and a 100 tooth ratchet, the required .002 inch per cycle feed increments are obtained.

2. A linkage with rotating driver crank and oscillating driven crank (similar to Fig. 52) will be used to drive the pawl. The dimensions shown in Fig. 53 will be selected tentatively where link 1, the driving

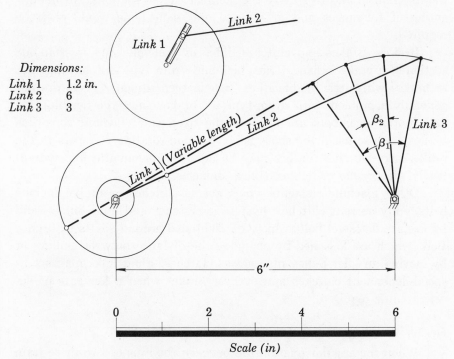

Dimensions:
Link 1   1.2 in.
Link 2   6
Link 3   3

FIG. 53. Example Problem 1 for a feed mechanism. Link 3 oscillates through angle β_1 with link 1 adjusted to 1.2 inches, and through angle β_2 with link 1 adjusted to 0.4 inches.

461

Mechanism

crank, is of variable length. Since the feed is .200 inches per rotation of the screw, the screw must turn through 1/20 rotation (18°) for the .010 inches per cycle feed. The .024 inches per cycle feed is obtained by a 43.2° rotation of the screw.

3. To give the required range of feeds, the oscillation of link 3 must be at least 43.2° when link 1 is adjusted to maximum length, and about 18° when link 1 is adjusted to minimum length. As a trial solution, we might design link 1 so that its length can be adjusted between .4 inches and 1.2 inches. Fig. 53 shows the mechanism with link 1 adjusted to 1.2 inches, at which setting link 3 oscillates through angle β_1. Angle β_2, the oscillation corresponding to a .4 inch length of link 1 is also shown. The trial design has a wider range of feeds than required and is therefore acceptable from that standpoint.

If we were to actually manufacture the mechanism, the next steps in the design process would be to find velocities and accelerations in the mechanism and to specify the members' cross sections. An investigation of tolerances and of stresses and deflections would then be required.

Brakes. Brakes and clutches differ in principle only in that one section of a brake is fixed. Thus, disk and drum type clutches may act as brakes with little modification. Inertia (centrifugal) effects are not generally a problem with drum-type air brakes since the flexible tube and friction members are used as the fixed side. Pivoted shoe-type brakes are also used, the shoes being the non-rotating members in the brake. Like clutches, brakes may be actuated pneumatically, hydraulically, electrically or by mechanical linkages.

Other machine elements which act as clutches or brakes include belts, eddy current clutches, hysteresis clutches and fluid links. Band brakes are flat steel belts which are tightened around shafts or drums. Belts which are loosened by changing the distance between pulleys or by moving an idler pulley may act as clutches. Fluid links may act as speed-dependent clutches and even as brakes when a low rate of deceleration is required.

Flexible Couplings

When the angular relationship between the axes of two drive train elements is variable, the elements may be joined by a flexible coupling, a flexible shaft or by a universal joint. Most flexible couplings are in-

462

American Technical Society

850 EAST 58TH STREET · CHICAGO, ILLINOIS 60637

ESTABLISHED 1898

FOR A BETTER FUTURE

Notes and errata for **Mechanism: Design Oriented Kinematics,**
Wilson and Michels

p. 7   15 in/sec × $\dfrac{1 \text{ in}}{10 \text{ in/sec}}$

p. 11 $B \sin \beta$, not $B \sin \alpha$

p. 29   above eq. 11: the *magnitude* of the acceleration

p. 97   line 5   *ac* must be horizontal

p. 169   above eq 1 . . . requires that the vector *direction* be . . . .

p. 176, 181   Figs. 2D, 3C, $A^n{}_{CB} = 16.6$

p. 184   Fig 4C: *b'c'* makes a 95° angle with the orientation of link *BC.*
         Vector *b'a'* is, therefore, drawn to form a 95° angle with *BD.*

FIG. 54. Universal joint. A pre-loaded universal joint is shown which is designed for use in a steering column tilting mechanism and similar applications where backlash is undesirable. The recommended maximum operating angle for this type of universal joint is 15°. (Automotive Div., Bendix Corp.)

tended only for small amounts of misalignment and flexible shafts have very limited torque capacity. Where high torque and large misalignments occur, a *universal joint*, Fig. 54, is the typical solution. The Hooke-type universal joint shown in Fig. 55 has a variable output speed ω_2 for misalignment ϕ unequal to zero when the input ω_1 is constant. For the position shown in Fig. 55A, the velocity of point A is $v_A = \omega_1 r$ where ω is given in radians per second.

The angular velocity of shaft 2 is maximum at this time and equal to

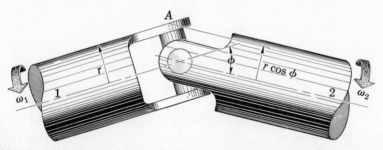

FIG. 55A. The Hooke-type universal joint. The misalignment is indicated by the angle ϕ. Velocity ratio ω_2/ω_1 varies instantaneously as the joint rotates.

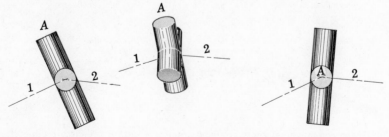

FIG. 55B. The cross-link of the universal joint is shown as it rotates through 90°.

$$\omega_2 = \frac{v_A}{r \cos \phi} = \frac{\omega_1}{\cos \phi}.$$

In 1, 2, and 3 of Fig. 55B, the cross link of the universal joint is shown as it rotates through 90°, the last position representing the minimum velocity of shaft 2: $\omega_2 = \omega_1 \cos \phi$.

At high shaft velocities, speed variations may be objectionable since acceleration and deceleration of the load may cause serious vibration and fatigue. Fig. 56A shows two Hooke type universal joints used to join shafts with a total misalignment of ϕ. If the shafts are in the same plane and each joint has a misalignment of $\phi/2$, Fig. 56B, the input shaft, 1, and output shaft, 3, travel at the same speed. The intermediate shaft, 2, turns at variable velocity, but if it is a short section, its mass will be low enough that serious vibration will not result.

An alternate method of avoiding acceleration and deceleration is through use of a constant-velocity universal joint. The constant-velocity ball joint, shown disassembled in Fig. 57A, is shown in the plane of the misaligned shafts, Fig. 57B. Each half of the joint has ball

FIG. 56A. An industrial Cordan-type universal joint for high torque applications. (Dana Corp.)

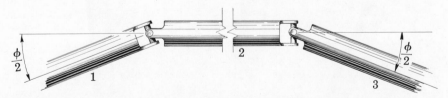

FIG. 56B. When two universal joints are used, input and output speeds are equal if each of the universal joints takes half of the misalignment, as shown.

FIG. 57A. A constant-velocity universal joint (Bendix-Weiss type) shown disassembled. (Bendix Corp.)

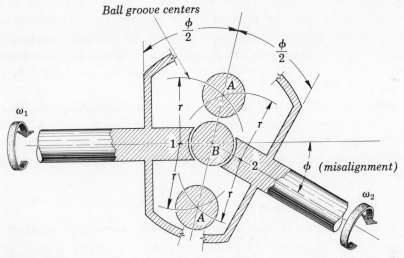

FIG. 57B. Balls designated by the letter A are held in intersecting ball grooves. The ball grooves in the input half of the joint intersect with the grooves in the output half so that the balls travel in a plane at an angle $\phi/2$ to perpendiculars to either shaft. The pinned center ball is designated by *B*.

grooves, the pairs of ball grooves intersecting in a plane which bisects the obtuse angle formed by the shafts. Thus, if all ball groove center radii equal r, the velocity of the center of ball *A* is given by

$$v_A = \omega_1 r \cos \frac{\phi}{2}$$

and

$$\omega_2 = \frac{v_A}{r \cos \phi/2} = \omega_1.$$

This constant velocity relationship holds at all times, even as misalignment ϕ changes.

Selection of Drive Train Components

A given set of design requirements might be satisfied by more than one of the gear train configurations, packaged speed reducers or drive train components considered above. A few of the most important design objectives will be discussed as an aid to optimum selection.

Shaft Geometry Considerations

One of the first requirements might involve *arrangement* of the input and output shafts. If the shaft center lines intersect as in an outboard motor drive, bevel gears might be used. For non-intersecting perpendicular shafts, an automobile rear end for example, hypoid gears are used. Power may also be transmitted between non-intersecting perpendicular shafts by special gears, or by a worm and worm-wheel if considerable speed reduction is desirable. If shaft centerlines do not intersect and are neither parallel nor perpendicular, crossed helical gears, bead chain and some types of belt drives are used. When the design requires parallel or colinear input and output axes, packaged speed reducers, belt and chain drives and spur and parallel helical gear trains may be considered.

Speed Ratio Considerations

If speed must be considerably reduced, worm and worm-wheel drives and some compound planetary drives are used. Rapid *speed ratio changing* (in discrete steps) suggests the use of clutches engaging and disengaging spur gears or helical gears on parallel shafts. An alternate method employs a planetary train with band brakes and clutches to lock certain elements.

When speed must be continuously variable, i.e., if stepless variation is required, friction drives are used. For low-power applications (phonographs and instrument-type applications), disk and wheel-disk drives are used. Some disk, roller-disk and ball-disk drives are variable through zero output speed to negative speed ratios.

Control Considerations

The method of *speed control* is an important factor in selection of a transmission. Spur and helical gear trains are ordinarily shifted manually through mechanical linkages, but speed changing may be actuated or assisted pneumatically, hydraulically or electrically. The bands and clutches in most planetary trains are automatically actuated by a speed-sensitive control.

Load (Horsepower) Considerations

Bead chain and plastic belts with lugs are limited to very low torque applications (chart drives, etc.). *High torque or power requirements* preclude the selection of these drives and most traction drives for many industrial applications. Drives available for high horsepower include chains, belts and gears.

The most severe power transmission and torque requirements are met by various forms of gearing. Using high speed double-helical gears, a single mesh has been used for loads as high as 30,000 to 40,000 horsepower. Two or more input pinions are used, (as in ship propulsion units) for higher horsepower drives.

Precision Drive Considerations

A requirement for *precision* in the transfer of motion is usually met by gear or power screw drives. Most high-precision instrument drives employ spur gear trains but for high velocity applications, helical gears are used. When considerable speed reduction is required, a single precision worm and worm wheel set will drive with less error than an equivalent train of several precision spur gears.

Sources of position error in gear drives include: error in tooth form and location; gear and shaft eccentricity, misalignment and deflection under load; thermal expansion and contraction; and looseness and deflection in couplings, bearings and other train components. When the output of a train must accurately reflect the input motion, the designer may use one or more of the following methods to control error:

(A) Select precision components.

(B) Use as few pairs of gears as possible to reduce integrated errors.

(C) Use larger diameter or shorter shafting and rigid supports to limit deflection under load.

(D) Replace alternate gears in the train with split anti-backlash gears. The split gear is spring loaded so that the halves rotate slightly with respect to one another and eliminate play.

(E) Attach one gear to a floating shaft which moves slightly to eliminate play between meshing teeth.

Mechanism

Noise, Shock, and Vibration Considerations

Noise, shock and vibration effects are usually reduced by nonmetallic drives. Belt drives absorb vibration and shock rather than transmitting these effects between the driver and driven shaft. For low loads, nylon or fiber gears are used to reduce noise.

Noise and vibration result as the load is transferred from one pair of gear teeth to another. The load transfer in helical gears on parallel shafts is smoother and more pairs of teeth are in contact at a given time than for similar spur gears. For this reason, helical gears are chosen for most high-power, high-speed drives.

Efficiency Considerations

Efficiency is an important factor in continuously operated drive trains. Over a period of years, losses of a few percent of transmitted power can be expensive. Low efficiency may exact additional penalties since friction losses represent (1) *heat* which must be dissipated and (2) addition fuel *weight* to be carried (a problem in surface vehicle design as well as aircraft and space vehicles).

Spur gears, helical gears on parallel shafts, and bevel gears have efficiencies of 98 to 99% at rated power (for each mesh). If lubrication is poor or if the drive operates at lower than rated speed, the losses may be greater. Efficiency is considerably reduced in pairs of gears with high sliding velocity; with high-reduction worm drives, losses may exceed 50% of transmitted power. Belt drive efficiencies are typically about 95% for single V-belts. Traction drives have efficiencies from 65 to 90% (lower at very low output speeds).

Miscellaneous Considerations

Other major selection criteria include *size, weight, reliability and cost*. On a cost-per-transmitted-horsepower basis, belt drives usually have the advantage. If speed is to be reduced by a large factor, a worm and worm wheel drive may be selected on the basis of its compactness and low cost, as compared with more complicated drive trains. Reliability is an important positive characteristic of gear trains, particularly spur gears and helical gears on parallel shafts. Planetary gear trains offer a compact package, taking up little space in an axial direction, even for high power drives.

Vectors

Vector Components

The location of a point in space may be described by a vector extending from the origin of a coordinate system to the point. Point P in Fig. 1 is located by the vector R. The X, Y, and Z coordinate axes in that figure are mutually perpendicular. Any motion of P will result in a change in the vector R, either in its magnitude or direction or both. Vectors will be shown in **boldface** type to distinguish them from scalar quantities. Vectors may also be identified by a line above or below the letter symbol.

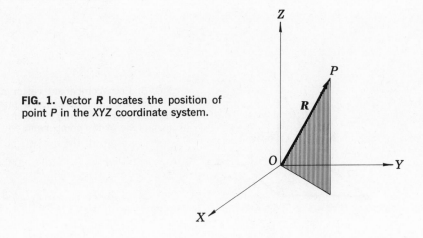

FIG. 1. Vector R locates the position of point P in the XYZ coordinate system.

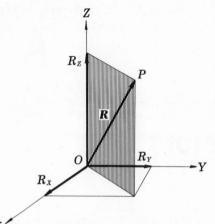

FIG. 2. The vector *R* can be resolved into vector components along the X, Y, and Z axes.

A line through P perpendicular to the X-axis intersects the X-axis at a distance R_x from the origin O. (See Fig. 2). The distance R_x is called the *projection* of the vector **R** on the X-axis, or the X-component of **R**. The projections of **R** on the Y-axis and Z-axis are labeled R_Y and R_Z. Vectors **I**, **J**, and **K** are *unit vectors* in the X, Y and Z directions respectively as shown in Fig. 3. That is, each has unit length and is used only to assign a direction. The scalar length R_x multiplied by the unit vector **I** gives us the vector IR_x of length R_x parallel to the X-axis. Forming the vector sum of the three components times their corresponding unit vectors, we obtain the original vector:

$$R = IR_X + JR_Y + KR_Z. \tag{1}$$

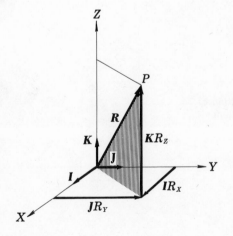

FIG. 3. Each component vector can be considered the product of a unit vector (magnitude of one) times the scalar magnitude of the component.

470

Velocity and Acceleration

Let point P in Fig. 4 move along a space curve C through a displacement dR during a time interval dt. The new position vector is then $R + dR$ representing a change in the direction of R or the magnitude of R or both. If the curve C is sufficiently smooth and if the velocity does not change rapidly, the rate of change of displacement, the velocity of P, is approximated by dR/dt. If we allow the time interval dt to become infinitesimal, the corresponding infinitesimal displacement dR lies in the curve C. Then, the instantaneous velocity of point P is given by

$$v_P = \frac{dR}{dt} \tag{2}$$

where the direction of v_P is given by a tangent to curve C at P. A dot above a vector or scalar quantity is sometimes used to indicate differentiation with respect to time; thus, dR/dt becomes $\dot{R}$.

In general, the vector dR represents a change in the X, Y and Z components of R. The velocity of point P is given by:

$$R = I\dot{R}_X + J\dot{R}_Y + K\dot{R}_Z + \dot{I}R_X + \dot{J}R_Y + \dot{K}R_Z \tag{3A}$$

where $\dot{R}_X = dR_X/dt$, etc. In this case, it is assumed that the X, Y, and Z coordinate axes are fixed so that there is no change in unit vectors I, J and K ($\dot{I}R_X = \dot{J}R_Y = \dot{K}R_Z = 0$). Therefore, Eq. (3A) becomes simply

$$\dot{R} = I\dot{R}_X + J\dot{R}_Y + K\dot{R}_Z. \tag{3B}$$

Using two dots to represent the second derivative with respect to time, d^2/dt^2, we have the rate of change of velocity, or the acceleration of P:

$$\ddot{R} = I\ddot{R}_X + J\ddot{R}_Y + K\ddot{R}_Z. \tag{4}$$

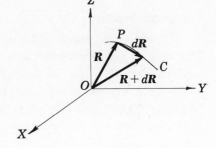

FIG. 4. The changed position of point P, graphically represented by the vector sum of the original position vector, R, and the vector representing the change in position, dR.

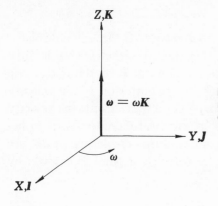

FIG. 5. Angular velocity can also be represented by a vector. Vector direction is determined by the right-hand rule.

Angular Velocity

Infinitesimal angular displacement and angular velocity may be considered vector quantities. Vector direction is defined as in Fig. 5. If a link rotates in the XY plane as shown, the angular velocity vector $\boldsymbol{\omega} = \omega K$ in the Z direction. In general, $\boldsymbol{\omega}$ is perpendicular to the plane of rotation and its sense is given by the RIGHT HAND RULE: *The fingers of the right hand are curved in the direction of rotation, ω, and the thumb points in the direction of the vector $\boldsymbol{\omega}$.* Alternately, consider a right hand screw which advances in the vector $\boldsymbol{\omega}$ direction when its direction of rotation is ω. The vector direction of $\boldsymbol{\omega}$ need not coincide with one of the coordinate axes as in Fig. 5. In general, the angular velocity vector is given by its components in the X, Y and Z directions:

$$\boldsymbol{\omega} = I\omega_X + J\omega_Y + K\omega_Z$$

(by analogy to R in Fig. 3).

The Vector Product

Consider a bent link which rotates in a fixed vertical bearing (Fig. 6). The angular velocity vector is vertically upward and we will select the radius vector $\boldsymbol{R} = \boldsymbol{OP}$ to describe the location of point P on the end of the link. We see in this simple case that point P describes a circle of radius $R \sin \theta$ and that its velocity is given by

$$v = \omega R \sin \theta \qquad (5)$$

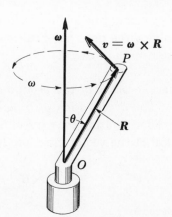

FIG. 6. The vector product (or *cross product*) of vector **R** (the position vector of point *P*) and the angular velocity of position vector **R** is itself a vector perpendicular to the plane formed by the two vectors. The cross product is the first time derivative of position vector **R**, i.e., the velocity of point *P*: $v = \dot{R} = \omega \times R$.

perpendicular to the plane of **ω** and **R** where θ is the angle between vectors **ω** and **R**. Thus, vector *v* corresponds to the definition of the *vector product* or *cross product* of vectors **ω** and **R**:

$$v = \omega \times R = \omega R \sin\theta, \tag{6}$$

a *vector* perpendicular to the plane of **ω** and **R** with its sense given by the right hand rule. (The vector product **ω** × **R** is read **ω** *cross* **R**.) An alternate expression of the right hand rule is convenient in this case. The right hand is held with the thumb in the vector **ω** direction and the index finger in the **R** direction (Fig. 7). The next finger is pointed in the direction of **ω** × **R**, perpendicular to the thumb and index finger. The velocity of a point on a rotating link is given by **ω** × **R** for any radius vector of constant length measured from the axis of rotation. If **R** changes in length, another velocity component is added. Incidentally, the vector product is defined by Equation (6) for any pair of vectors;

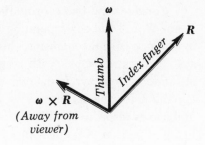

FIG. 7. Using the right-hand rule to find the direction of the vector cross product.

473

Mechanism

they need not be angular velocity and radius. The reader will note from applying the right hand rule that

$$B \times A = -A \times B;$$

thus *the order of the vectors in the expression is important.*

The *acceleration of a point in a fixed coordinate system* is found by differentiating the expression for the velocity, $\dot{R} = \omega \times R$. The differential of the vector cross product is given by the general expression

$$\frac{d}{dt}(A \times B) = \frac{dA}{dt} \times B + A \times \frac{dB}{dt}.$$

Therefore,

$$\ddot{R} = \frac{d}{dt}(\omega \times R)$$

$$= \dot{\omega} \times R + \omega \times \dot{R}$$

and, since $\dot{R} = \omega \times R$, we obtain

$$\ddot{R} = \dot{\omega} \times R + \omega \times (\omega \times R) \tag{7}$$

for any radius vector of constant length measured from the axis of rotation. Equation (7) is a vector expression for the relationship which we found geometrically in Chapter 3: $a = a^t + a^n = \alpha R + \omega^2 R$. Vector directions are given by applying the right hand rule to the terms in Eq. (7).

Moving Coordinate Systems

In mechanisms and dynamics it is sometimes convenient to establish a coordinate system which translates and/or rotates along with a moving link. In most cases, we then refer our velocities and accelerations back to a fixed coordinate system.

Consider the two coordinate systems of Fig. 8. Coordinate axes X, Y and Z and the corresponding unit vectors I, J and K are fixed. (For most work with mechanisms, this would mean that the XYZ coordinate system does not move with respect to the earth.) The origin o of coordinate system xyz is defined by the position vector R_o. Unit vectors i, j and k for the set of moving axes lie along, and move with, the x, y and z axes respectively. The xyz-ijk system may translate and/or rotate in any direction. A point P in a linkage is described by the vector r (the

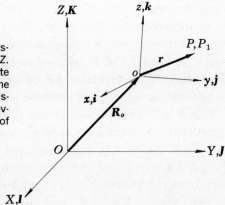

FIG. 8. A moving coordinate system. System xyz moves within fixed system XYZ. Point P moves within xyz. The absolute displacement of point P is given by the vector sum $R_o + r$, where r is the displacement of P with respect to the moving system and R_o is the displacement of the moving system.

position vector oP) in the moving coordinate system xyz. The total *radius vector* of P is

$$R = R_o + r \qquad (8)$$

measured from the origin of the fixed coordinates. For convenience, another point, P_1 is included in the sketch. Point P_1 is instantaneously coincident with P, but P_1 is *fixed* in the moving coordinate system. It moves with the xyz system, *but does not move with respect to it.*

Expressing vectors R_o and r in terms of their components and corresponding unit vectors, the radius vector to point P is given by:

$$R = R_o + r = R_{ox}I + R_{oY}J + R_{oZ}K + r_xi + r_yj + r_zk. \qquad (9)$$

Note that, in Eq. (9), R_o is written in terms of the fixed coordinate system, while r is written in terms of the moving coordinate system. The *velocity* of point P is given by the time rate of change in R:

$$\dot{R} = \dot{R}_{ox}I + \dot{R}_{oY}J + \dot{R}_{oZ}K$$
$$+ \dot{r}_xi + \dot{r}_yj + \dot{r}_zk$$
$$+ r_x\dot{i} + r_y\dot{j} + r_z\dot{k}. \qquad (10)$$

The first vector on the right side of the equation is the rate of change of R_o in the X direction, the X component of the velocity of o. As seen in Eq. (3B), since the X, Y and Z coordinates are fixed, unit vectors I, J and K do not change and the velocity of o is given completely by the first

475

three vectors on the right in Eq. (10). The sum of the first three will be identified by the symbol $\dot{\boldsymbol{R}}_o$. The next three vectors, $\dot{r}_x\boldsymbol{i}$, etc., represent the rate of change in the $\boldsymbol{r}$ vector *with respect to the moving coordinates*, or velocity of P relative to the moving coordinate system xyz. Their sum will be identified by the symbol $\dot{\boldsymbol{r}}_r$. (The velocity of P relative to xyz will be subscripted with the letter r, for *relative*.)

The last three vectors of Eq. (10) represent the effect of the rotating coordinate system (xyz) in any expression for the absolute velocity of P. Unit vectors $\boldsymbol{i}, \boldsymbol{j}$, and $\boldsymbol{k}$ are fixed relative to the moving xyz system (i.e., $\boldsymbol{i}, \boldsymbol{j}, \boldsymbol{k}$ move *with* the xyz system.) Relative to the fixed XYZ system, however, unit vectors $\boldsymbol{i}, \boldsymbol{j}$, and $\boldsymbol{k}$ rotate; thus their positions relative to fixed system XYZ are functions of time.

Another way of accounting for the last three terms of Eq. (10) is to consider the differentiation of the vector $\boldsymbol{r}$ with respect to the fixed XYZ system. In Fig. 8 we see that the vector $\boldsymbol{r}$ is the position vector of P in the xyz system. Thus in Eq. (9) vector $\boldsymbol{r}$ is described in terms of that system:

$$\boldsymbol{r} = r_x\boldsymbol{i} + r_y\boldsymbol{j} + r_z\boldsymbol{k}.$$

The rate of change of the position vector of P relative to the moving xyz system is given by $\dot{r}_x\boldsymbol{i} + \dot{r}_y\boldsymbol{j} + \dot{r}_z\boldsymbol{k}$, where $\boldsymbol{i}, \boldsymbol{j}$, and $\boldsymbol{k}$ are constant in magnitude and direction relative to the moving system. However, since the xyz system is moving within the fixed XYZ system, unit vectors $\boldsymbol{i}, \boldsymbol{j}$, and $\boldsymbol{k}$ are variables relative to XYZ. Thus, the rate of change of $\boldsymbol{i}, \boldsymbol{j}$, and $\boldsymbol{k}$ relative to XYZ must be added when considering any change in $\boldsymbol{r}$ relative to XYZ, or:

$$\dot{\boldsymbol{r}}_{XYZ} = \dot{r}_x\boldsymbol{i} + \dot{r}_y\boldsymbol{j} + \dot{r}_z\boldsymbol{k} + r_x\dot{\boldsymbol{i}} + r_y\dot{\boldsymbol{j}} + r_z\dot{\boldsymbol{k}}$$
$$= \dot{\boldsymbol{r}}_r + r_x\dot{\boldsymbol{i}} + r_y\dot{\boldsymbol{j}} + r_z\dot{\boldsymbol{k}}.$$

Note that the rate of change of $\boldsymbol{r}$ with respect to XYZ does *not* represent in itself the velocity of P with respect to XYZ. The position vector of P in XYZ is the vector sum of $\boldsymbol{r}$ and $\boldsymbol{R}_o$. Thus the velocity of P relative to XYZ must include *both* $\dot{\boldsymbol{r}}$ and $\dot{\boldsymbol{R}}_o$.

The first derivative of a vector of constant magnitude is the cross product of the angular velocity of the vector and the vector itself. Thus, for the last three vectors in Eq. (10):

$$r_x \dot{i} = r_x(\omega \times i)$$
$$r_y \dot{j} = r_y(\omega \times j)$$
$$r_z \dot{k} = r_z(\omega \times k),$$

so that,

$$r_x \dot{i} + r_y \dot{j} + r_z \dot{k} = r_x(\omega \times i) + r_y(\omega \times j) + r_z(\omega \times k)$$
$$= \omega \times (r_x i + r_y j + r_z k)$$
$$= \omega \times r.$$

Thus, the last three vectors of Eq. (10) can be replaced by the vector product $\omega \times r$, where ω is the angular velocity of the xyz coordinate system and r is the position vector of P in the xyz system. Thus, a more convenient form for Eq. (10) is

$$\dot{R} = \dot{R}_o + \dot{r}_r + \omega \times r \qquad (11)$$

where

$\dot{R}$ = absolute velocity of point P relative to XYZ,

$\dot{R}_o$ = velocity of the origin o of the xyz system,

$\dot{r}_r$ = velocity of point P relative to the xyz system,

$\omega \times r$ = cross product of the angular velocity of the rotating system xyz in the XYZ system and the position vector r.

The moving coordinate system also affects our expression for $\ddot{R}$, the *acceleration* of point P (the rate of change in $\dot{R}$). Using Equation (11), the first term on the right becomes simply $\ddot{R}_o$, the acceleration of o in the fixed coordinate system.

In progressing from Eq. (8) to Eq. (11) we saw that the derivative of position vector r in the moving coordinate system *with respect to the fixed system* was given by the derivative of the position vector with respect to the moving system *plus* the cross product of the angular velocity of the moving system and the position vector itself:

$$\dot{r}_{XYZ} = \dot{r}_r + \omega \times r.$$

477

Mechanism

By the same process, then, the second term of Eq. (11) becomes

$$\ddot{r}_r + \boldsymbol{\omega} \times \dot{r}_r.$$

Using the last term of Eq. (11), changes in $\boldsymbol{\omega}$, r, and the rotational effect give us

$$\dot{\boldsymbol{\omega}} \times r + \boldsymbol{\omega} \times \dot{r}_r + \boldsymbol{\omega} \times (\boldsymbol{\omega} \times r).$$

Then, the *total acceleration of Point P* is:

$$\ddot{R} = \ddot{R}_o + \dot{\boldsymbol{\omega}} \times r + \boldsymbol{\omega} \times (\boldsymbol{\omega} \times r) + \ddot{r}_r + 2\boldsymbol{\omega} \times \dot{r}_r. \tag{12}$$

The first term on the right of Equation (12) is the total acceleration of the origin o of the moving coordinates; the next two give the acceleration of P_1 relative to o where P_1 is a point instantaneously coincident with P having no motion relative to the moving coordinates xyz. The last two terms are the motion of P relative to P_1. The sum, $\ddot{R}$ is the total acceleration of P relative to fixed coordinates XYZ. It is important to remember that $\boldsymbol{\omega}$ and $\dot{\boldsymbol{\omega}}$ refer, respectively, to the angular velocity and the angular acceleration of the moving coordinate system.

Problems involving spatial linkages (mechanisms involving motion which does not lie in a plane or in a set of parallel planes) require that Equation (12) be applied in its general form. In plane mechanisms, the vector products have more familiar forms: $\dot{\boldsymbol{\omega}} \times r$ becomes αr, the tangential acceleration; $\boldsymbol{\omega} \times (\boldsymbol{\omega} \times r)$ becomes $\omega^2 r$, the normal acceleration and $2\boldsymbol{\omega} \times \dot{r}_r$ becomes $2\omega v$, the Coriolis acceleration.

Let us consider the problem of velocity and acceleration in a planetary gear train (Fig. 9). Let the planet carrier (4) rotate counterclockwise with constant angular velocity $\omega_4 = \omega_4 k$ (given). Note in Fig. 9C that while I and i and J and j differ, in this problem K and k are identical. Ring gear (3) is to be fixed. By the familiar tabular method, Fig. 9B, we find the sun gear speed $\omega_1 = (1 + N_3/N_1)\omega_4$ and the planet speed $\omega_2 = (1 - N_3/N_2)\omega_4$. Since the sun gear and arm rotate about fixed centers, velocities and accelerations of points on these members are given respectively by

$$\dot{R} = \boldsymbol{\omega} \times R \quad \text{and} \quad \ddot{R} = \boldsymbol{\omega} \times (\boldsymbol{\omega} \times R)$$

respectively when the sun gear and arm have no angular acceleration.

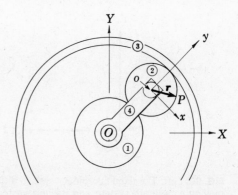

FIG. 9A. Planetary gear train.

Gear	Sun (1)	Planet (2)	Ring (3)	Carrier (4)
No. of Teeth	N_1	N_2	N_3	N_4
Step I. Rotations with Train Locked	$+1$	$+1$	$+1$	$+1$
Step II. Rotations with Planet Carrier Fixed	$+\dfrac{N_3}{N_1}$	$-\dfrac{N_3}{N_2}$	-1	0
Total Rotations	$1+\dfrac{N_3}{N_1}$	$1-\dfrac{N_3}{N_2}$	0	$+1$

$$\omega_2/\omega_4 = (1 - N_3/N_2)/1$$
$$\omega_2 = (1 - N_3/N_2)\,\omega_4$$
$$\Omega = \omega_2 - \omega_4 = (-N_3/N_2)\,\omega_4$$

FIG. 9B. Speed ratio table for the planetary train.

The motion of a point on the planet is more complicated; we will apply Equation (11) with the following substitutions:

$$\dot{\boldsymbol{R}}_o = \omega_4 \boldsymbol{k} \times R_o \boldsymbol{j} = -\omega_4 R_o \boldsymbol{i}$$

(Scalars ω_4 and R_o are the magnitudes of vectors $\boldsymbol{\omega}_4$ and $\boldsymbol{R}_o$. The moving coordinate system xyz is fixed to the planet carrier with origin o at the center of the planet. See Fig. 9D. We have applied the right hand rule to obtain $\boldsymbol{k} \times \boldsymbol{j} = -\boldsymbol{i}$. A similar procedure is followed in each substitution.)

479

Mechanism

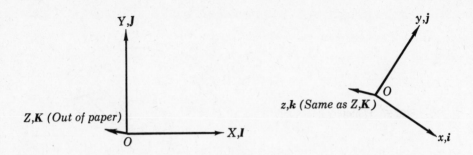

FIG. 9C. *Left:* The fixed coordinate system and its corresponding unit vectors. *Right:* The moving coordinate system and its unit vectors, for the position shown in Fig. 9A. The moving system rotates with the planet carrier (4) at ω rad/sec and zero angular acceleration.

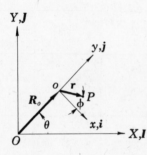

FIG. 9D. The position of the moving coordinate system relative to the fixed system. The absolute displacement of point P is given by $R_o + r$.

There are no angular acceleration terms corresponding to $\dot{\boldsymbol{\omega}}$ since the angular velocity of the gears is constant due to the (given) constant angular velocity of the carrier. Position vector r defines the position of point P on the planet. The relative velocity of P is given by

$$\dot{r}_r = \Omega \times r$$

where Ω, the angular velocity of the planet relative to the carrier, is given by

$$\Omega = \boldsymbol{\omega}_2 - \boldsymbol{\omega}_4 .$$

The velocity of P relative to xyz is therefore given by

$$\dot{r}_r = (\boldsymbol{\omega}_2 - \boldsymbol{\omega}_4) \times r .$$

480

The relative velocity of P with respect to point o is given by

$$\dot{r} = \dot{r}_r + \omega_4 \times r$$
$$= (\omega_2 - \omega_4) \times r + \omega_4 \times r$$
$$= \omega_2 \times r.$$

Continuing with the unit vector substitutions, the relative velocity of P with respect to point o can be expressed in terms of the angular velocity (ω_4) of the rotating system and the components of r. From Fig. 9D, we obtain

$$r = r\,(i \cos \phi + j \sin \phi).$$

Substituting these vector expressions into the speed ratios for the sun and planet obtained by the table in Fig. 9B, we obtain

$$\omega_2 = \left(1 - \frac{N_3}{N_2}\right)\omega_4$$

$$\omega_2 \times r = \left(1 - \frac{N_3}{N_2}\right)\omega_4 \times r$$

$$= \left(1 - \frac{N_3}{N_2}\right)\omega_4 k \times r\,(i \cos \phi + j \sin \phi).$$

Since, by the right hand rule, $k \times i = j$ and $k \times j = -i$,

$$\omega_2 \times r = \left(1 - \frac{N_3}{N_2}\right)\omega_4 r\,(j \cos \phi - i \sin \phi).$$

Combining terms, then, the velocity of point P on the planet with respect to the fixed coordinates of the train (XYZ) is finally given by

$$\dot{R} = \dot{R}_o + \dot{r}$$
$$= -\omega_4 R_o i + \left(1 - \frac{N_3}{N_2}\right)\omega_4 r(j \cos \phi - i \sin \phi)$$
$$= \omega_4 \left[\left(\frac{N_3}{N_2} - 1\right) r \sin \phi - R_o\right] i - \omega_4 \left[\left(\frac{N_3}{N_2} - 1\right) r \cos \phi\right] j.$$

$$(13)$$

The acceleration of point P is determined using Eq. (12) as follows:

$$\ddot{R} = \ddot{R}_o + \dot{\omega} \times r + \omega \times (\omega \times r) + \ddot{r}_r + 2\,\omega \times \dot{r}_r.$$

Recalling that the given angular velocity of the carrier is constant, the $\dot{\omega}$ and $\dot{\Omega}$ terms in the acceleration equation are zero. We can further make the following substitutions in Eq. (12):

$$\begin{aligned}
\ddot{R}_o &= \omega \times (\omega \times R_o) \\
&= \omega_4 k \times (\omega_4 k \times R_o j) \\
&= \omega_4 k \times (-\omega_4 R_o i) \\
&= \omega_4{}^2 R_o (-j) \\
&= -\omega_4{}^2 R_o (j)
\end{aligned}$$

(using the right hand rule where the term in parenthesis is evaluated first). The next term, $\dot{\omega} \times r$, is zero (ω is constant). The next term, $\omega \times (\omega \times r)$, becomes

$$\begin{aligned}
\omega \times (\omega \times r) &= \omega_4 k \times [\omega_4 k \times r(i \cos \phi + j \sin \phi)] \\
&= \omega_4 k \times [\omega_4 r\, j \cos \phi - \omega_4 r\, i \sin \phi] \\
&= \omega_4{}^2 r\, (-i) \cos \phi - \omega_4{}^2 r\, j \sin \phi \\
&= -\omega_4{}^2 r\, (i \cos \phi + j \sin \phi).
\end{aligned}$$

The next term to be considered is the derivative of the relative velocity, $\ddot{r}_r$. Recall that $\dot{r}_r = \Omega \times r$. The derivative of this expression is then given by

$$\ddot{r}_r = \Omega \times (\Omega \times r)$$

where relative angular velocity

$$\Omega = \omega_2 - \omega_4 = -\frac{N_3}{N_2}\,\omega_4 k.$$

Thus

$$\ddot{r}_r = \left(-\frac{N_3}{N_2}\,\omega_4 k \right) \times \left(-\frac{N_3}{N_2}\,\omega_4 k \times r \right)$$

$$\ddot{r}_r = -\left(\frac{N_3}{N_2}\,\omega_4 \right)^2 r(i \cos \phi + j \sin \phi).$$

Finally, the last term of Eq. (12) is given by

$$2\boldsymbol{\omega}\times\dot{\boldsymbol{r}}_r = 2\omega_4\boldsymbol{k}\times\left[-\frac{N_3}{N_2}\,\omega_4\,\boldsymbol{k}\times r\,(\boldsymbol{i}\cos\phi + \boldsymbol{j}\sin\phi)\right]$$

$$= 2\,\frac{N_3}{N_2}\,\omega_4{}^2\,r\,(\boldsymbol{i}\cos\phi + \boldsymbol{j}\cos\phi).$$

Combining all of the above terms, we obtain the total acceleration of a point on the planet with respect to the fixed coordinates:

$$\ddot{\boldsymbol{R}} = \omega_4{}^2\left[-R_o\boldsymbol{j} + \left(2\,\frac{N_3}{N_2} - \frac{N_3{}^2}{N_2{}^2} - 1\right) r\,(\boldsymbol{i}\cos\phi + \boldsymbol{j}\sin\phi)\right]$$

which may be written as

$$\ddot{\boldsymbol{R}} = \omega_4{}^2\,(-\boldsymbol{R}_o) + \omega_4{}^2\,(N_3{}^2/N_2{}^2 - 2\,N_3/N_2 + 1)\,(-\boldsymbol{r}).$$

We see that the term $N_3{}^2/N_2{}^2 - 2\,N_3/N_2 + 1 = (1 - N_3/N_2)^2$ which is equal to $(\omega_2/\omega_4)^2$ from the tabular analysis. Using this, we find the following simple expression for the acceleration of P:

$$\ddot{\boldsymbol{R}} = \omega_4{}^2\,(-\boldsymbol{R}_o) + \omega_2{}^2\,(-\boldsymbol{r}).\qquad(14)$$

EXAMPLE PROBLEM: In Fig. 9, let the planet carrier speed be $\omega_4 = 100$ rad/sec counterclockwise (constant). The ring gear is fixed. Numbers of teeth are $N_1 = 30$, $N_2 = 25$ and $N_3 = 80$. The distance Oo on the planet carrier is $R_o = 5.5$ inches and the planet pitch radius is $r = 2.5$ inches. Find the velocity and acceleration of a point P on the planet *at the instant when P is the pitch point of the planet and ring.* **Solution:** The vector directions of $\boldsymbol{R}_o$ and $\boldsymbol{r}$ are the same when we consider the instant when P is the pitch point of the planet and ring. For the velocity of the moving coordinate system (the axis of the planet gear) relative to the fixed axis, we obtain

$$\dot{\boldsymbol{R}}_o = \boldsymbol{\omega}_4\times\boldsymbol{R}_o.$$

For the point P on the planet relative to the moving axis (moving system xyz), we obtain

$$\dot{\boldsymbol{r}}_r = \boldsymbol{\Omega}\times\boldsymbol{r} = (\boldsymbol{\omega}_2 - \boldsymbol{\omega}_4)\times\boldsymbol{r} = \boldsymbol{\omega}_2\times\boldsymbol{r} - \boldsymbol{\omega}_4\times\boldsymbol{r}.$$

From the table in Fig. 9B we know that

$$\omega_2 = \left(1 - \frac{N_3}{N_2}\right)\omega_4.$$

Mechanism

Therefore,

$$\dot{r}_r = (1 - \frac{N_3}{N_2})\, \boldsymbol{\omega}_4 \times r - \boldsymbol{\omega}_4 \times r$$

$$= \boldsymbol{\omega}_4 \times r \,(1 - \frac{N_3}{N_2} - 1)$$

$$= \boldsymbol{\omega}_4 \times r \,(- \frac{N_3}{N_2}).$$

Using Eq. (11), the velocity of point P relative to the fixed axis XYZ becomes

$$\dot{R} = \dot{R}_o + \dot{r}_r + \boldsymbol{\omega}_4 \times r$$

$$= \boldsymbol{\omega}_4 \times R_o - \frac{N_3}{N_2} \boldsymbol{\omega}_4 \times r + \boldsymbol{\omega}_4 \times r$$

$$= \boldsymbol{\omega}_4 \times \left[R_o + r + \left(- \frac{N_3}{N_2} \right) r \right].$$

But $R_o + r$ is the pitch radius of the ring gear, which is precisely $(N_3/N_2)\, r$. Since R_o and r have the same direction in this problem, the term in brackets is zero, and we have $\dot{R} = 0$. We obtain the same result from Eq. (13) with $\phi = 90°$, or by inspection, observing that P is the instant center of the planet in this special case.

Acceleration of P is given by Eq. (14). Noting that

$$\omega_2 = \left(1 - \frac{N_3}{N_2} \right)\, \omega_4 = 220 \; rad/sec,$$

we obtain

$$\ddot{R} = (100)^2 (5.5) + (220)^2 (2.5),$$

the first term in the $-R_o$ direction; the second in the $-r$ direction. The result is

$$\ddot{R} = 176{,}000 \; in/sec^2$$

toward O, the center of the planetary train.

Appendix

B

Dynamics of Linkages

As stated at the conclusion of Chapter Three, dynamics is a study of the relationship between force and motion. The word *force* is used in a general sense to include moments or torques in inch-pounds as well as forces in pounds. *Motion* refers to both translation and rotation. Kinematics treats motion without considering the associated forces. The study of mechanisms is, traditionally, a study of kinematics of machinery—the motion of linkages but not the forces which cause the motion or arise from it. At this point, we will deviate from the subject of pure kinematics and take a look into the closely related problems of dynamics of machinery.

Static Force Balances

Let us introduce the problem of forces on linkages with *statics*, the special case of dynamics where the effects of motion may be neglected. A force balance (in the general sense) gives us the force in each link and the reactions of the frame. We will use one basic law of statics: *A rigid body is in equilibrium when the resultant of all forces acting on it equals zero.*

Consider the rigid link of Fig. 1, which has pin joints at either end. For simplicity, the joints are assumed to be frictionless and the link

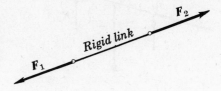

FIG. 1. The rigid link shown is in equilibrium. It is acted on by two equal and opposite forces along its axis which balance each other. The link, in this case, is called a two-force member.

Mechanism

weightless. This idealized link can only be in equilibrium under a pair of axial forces, say F_1 and F_2, where these forces are equal but opposite. If the forces are positive as shown, the link is in tension; if the forces are directed inward, the link is in compression In either case, the link is referred to as a two-force member.

Moments of Force. In general, if the weight of the link is considered the pin forces are no longer axial. We must then consider (1) the equilibrium of forces as in Fig. 1, and also (2) a balance of moments. The *moment of force* about a point is equal to the magnitude of the force vector times its perpendicular distance to the point. Consider the link of Fig. 2 where point C is the *center of mass. (The entire weight of the link may be assumed to act at the center of mass if we are interested in forces at the pin joints. But if internal stresses, which are not discussed here, must also be determined accurately a more sophisticated approach is required.)* Since we assume frictionless pin joints at B and D, we may balance moments about either end of the link, i.e., the sum of the clockwise moments equals the sum of the counterclockwise moments, or the sum of all the moments is zero. Taking moments about B in Fig. 2, we have the clockwise moment aW equal to the counterclockwise moment bR_2, from which we obtain the reaction

$$R_2 = \frac{a}{b} W.$$

(Note that R_1 has no moment about pin B.) We obtain the other reaction by balancing moments about point D, or by balancing vertical forces. Its value is

$$R_1 = W - R_2.$$

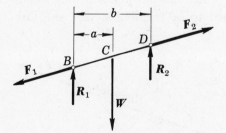

FIG. 2. Force and moment equilibrium. The forces shown act on the link in directions other than along the axis of the link. The link is in equilibrium only when (1) the sum of the forces in any direction equals zero (*force balance*), and (2) the sum of the moments about any point equals zero (*moment balance*).

If the link of Fig. 2 is uniform over its length, then the center of mass is at the midpoint and $R_1 = R_2 = W/2$ (one half W). Axial forces, F_1 and F_2, are again equal and opposite.

Free Body. The total force at each pin is given by the vector sum of the forces acting on the pin. The key to static and dynamic analysis is the isolation of a *free body* together with all of the forces acting on that body. In the examples considered above, we have made a sketch of the link in question, showing forces which act *on* the link, but not forces which are *applied by* the link. Thus, the single link forms the free body. A group of links, an entire mechanism, or even a single pin may also be treated as a free body.

Torque. A twisting moment about a shaft may be called a torsional moment or, simply, a *torque*. When in the same plane, torque and moment are equivalent. In the case of a plane mechanism acted on by forces and torques within its plane of motion, we need only equate clockwise moments to counterclockwise moments and equate forces in each of two directions in the plane. We say, for example, that the sum of the forces in the X direction equals zero and that the sum of the forces in the Y direction equals zero. The "rigid body" which we consider may be a link in a mechanism, a part of a link, or any point in the mechanism.

In Fig. 3, for example, let torque T be given along with the direction of force F_1 acting on link OB at B. Balancing moments about point O, we find the magnitude of the force at B:

$$F_1 = \frac{T}{b}.$$

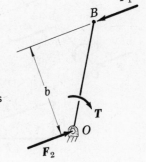

FIG. 3. For plane mechanisms, torque is equivalent to a moment of force.

Mechanism

There is also a force F_2 at the bearing which is equal to but opposite F_1, satisfying the equilibrium condition. Due to the simplicity of this problem, however, it was not necessary to break the forces into horizontal and vertical components.

Although the mechanism as a whole is not a rigid body, a necessary condition for equilibrium is that the external forces and torques acting on it balance. We will therefore find it most practical to balance the forces at each pin joint and the forces and moments on each link, working progressively from known forces to unknown forces. Bending moments and stresses within a link will not be considered in this work.

Consider, for example, the slider crank linkage shown in Fig. 4, representing a compressor or piston engine, which is operating at so low a

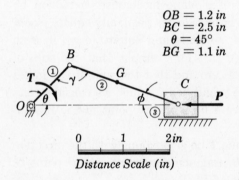

$$OB = 1.2 \ in$$
$$BC = 2.5 \ in$$
$$\theta = 45°$$
$$BG = 1.1 \ in$$

FIG. 4A. We will set up a *static* force balance for the slider crank linkage, which is acted on by piston force **P** and crank torque **T**.

Distance Scale (in)

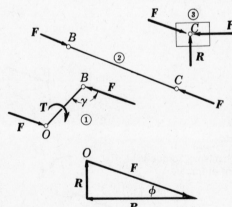

FIG. 4B. Static force balances are shown for each of the three links, each considered a free body. External forces are balanced by reaction forces. Note the application of reaction force **F** in solving each of the free body diagrams.

488

speed that inertia effects are negligible. *To simplify the discussion, we will assume that gravity forces are small compared with other forces and that all forces lie in the same plane in this and the following examples.* External forces on the linkage are the piston force **P** and crank torque **T**, with reactions at the piston and crank. Let us find torque **T**, the forces in each link, and the reactions, assuming that **P** is known.

The static force balance assumes a *state of equilibrium* where each external force is balanced or nullified by an opposite force so that the net effect produces *no motion change* in the linkage. Although an object can move at uniform velocity and still be in a state of equilibrium (static balance), the student will find it convenient to consider the linkage completely motionless. Having eliminated gravity and inertia forces we note that link 2, the connecting rod, is loaded only by pins at B and C. Pins transmit no torque, i.e., bearing torque is negligible. Link 2 is thus a two-force member loaded only by (unknown) forces **F** at each end, as shown in Fig. 4B. Forces **F** lie along the link, producing zero net moment, and are equal and opposite, balancing link 2. *(We have assumed positive directions of forces and reactions as shown in Fig. 4B; if one of our guesses is wrong we will obtain a negative value, indicating that we should reverse the sense of that vector.)*

The pin C which joins the connecting rod (2) to the slider (3) applies an equal and opposite force to the slider, which is balanced by the given force **P** and a reaction **R** (normal to the slider path since we again assume negligible friction). The existence of a reaction (force) **R** to force **F** might be guessed at as the student observes the directions of **F** and **P** at pin C (Fig. 4B). An additional force is needed to balance the vertical component of **F**. *(P, being horizontal, cannot provide the balancing vertical component.)* A glance at the force diagram confirms this guess. The vector force balance at C is

$$\boldsymbol{F} + \boldsymbol{P} + \boldsymbol{R} = 0.$$

The above vector equation may be solved graphically to find the magnitude of **F** and **R**, or we may write

$$F = \frac{P}{\cos \phi} \quad \text{and} \quad R = P \tan \phi.$$

Pin B, which joins the connecting rod (2) to the crank (1), applies an equal and opposite force **F** to the crank, which is balanced by an

489

equal and opposite reaction F at the crankshaft bearing O. We note the forces F, which appear in several places in Fig. 4B, are identical vectors except for sense. The magnitude in each case is given by $F = P/\cos \phi$, and the direction is parallel to link 2 in each case. The force F is, in general, neither parallel nor perpendicular to link 1. *(Since link 1 has a torque acting at one end, it is not a simple two-force link like link 2.)* It is convenient to break up F into an axial force, $F \cos \gamma$ along link 1, and a bending force, $F \sin \gamma$ perpendicular to link 1. The force perpendicular to link 1 results in the torque:

$$T = (OB)\ F \sin \gamma.$$

An identical result is obtained by multiplying F by its perpendicular distance to point O, as in Fig. 3.

EXAMPLE—PROBLEM 1: Static Force Balance. Suppose Fig. 4 is a schematic representation of a miniature compressor with dimensions $OB = 1.2$ in. and $BC = 2.5$ in. Let us find the required crank torque, the load in each link, and the bearing forces if total gas force $P = 10$ lb at the instant that the crank angle $\theta = 45°$. The speed is low and inertia forces will be neglected. Although weight is normally important to a static force balance, the weights of the links will be considered small compared to the applied forces and will be neglected. Finally, all forces will be assumed to lie in a plane.

Solution. The linkage may be drawn to scale (Fig. 4A) to find angles γ and ϕ, or we may use the law of sines:

$$\frac{\sin \theta}{BC} = \frac{\sin \phi}{OB}.$$

We can then use the triangle relationship

$$\theta + \phi + \gamma = 180°$$

to obtain $\phi = 20°$ and $\gamma = 115°$ (approx.). The reaction of the cylinder on the piston is therefore

$$R = P \tan \phi = 10 \tan 20° = 3.6 \text{ lb}$$

and the compressive force in link 2 becomes

$$F = P/\cos \phi = 10/\cos 20° = 10.6 \text{ lb}.$$

The total crankshaft bearing load at O is also 10.6 lb (possibly divided between two bearings). The axial load on link 1 (that component of F along the axis of link 1) is given by the magnitude of

$$F \cos \gamma = 10.6 \cos 115° = 4.5 \, \text{lb}$$

(a *compressive* load as we see from Fig. 4B). The bending load (that component of F perpendicular to the axis of link 1 and acting through point B) is $10.6 \sin 115° = 9.6$ lb, from which we obtain the required crankshaft torque:

$$T = (OB) \, (F \sin \gamma) = (1.2) \, (10.6 \sin 115°) = 11.5 \, \text{lb-in.}$$

All of the above forces, it should be noted, could have been found graphically as well.

If we did not require the loads in links 1 and 2, torque T could have been obtained directly by balancing torques on the linkage as a whole. Doing this, we obtain

$$T = (OC) \, R = (3.25 \, \text{in.}) \, (3.6 \, \text{lb}) = 11.5 \, \text{lb-in,}$$

the same result we obtained above, allowing for the small error introduced by rounding off forces and angles.

Dynamic Force Balance

In the above example problem, it was assumed that the operating speed of the linkage was very low. Suppose we now consider the dynamic case—the case in which there are high linear and angular accelerations.

Inertia Effects. We know that a body resists any change in its velocity. This resistance will be called an inertia effect. The most convenient treatment of inertia effects is to consider them *reverse effective forces* and *reverse effective torques*, and to include them in the usual force or torque balance. Thus, *the dynamic problem is reduced in form to a static force and torque balance* where inertia effects are treated in the same manner as pin forces or crankshaft torque.

A body resists any change in velocity by an inertia force proportional to the mass of the body and its acceleration. The inertia force direction is exactly opposite the acceleration. If a body is accelerated at a rate equal to the acceleration of gravity (g), the inertia force will equal the weight of the body. Thus, a body falling without friction has an inertia force directed upward which is equal in magnitude to the body weight. In general, if we define mass as the weight of a body divided by the acceleration of gravity,

$$m = \frac{W}{g},$$

then the inertia force has the simple form

$$F_i = -ma.$$

Mass m is a scalar, and the minus sign in the above equation indicates that the inertia force vector is directly opposite the acceleration vector. In dynamic analysis of machinery, weights are given in pounds and acceleration are given in in/sec^2. Thus, we divide the weight by 386 in/sec^2, the acceleration of gravity, to obtain mass in lb-sec^2/in. Inertia forces are given simply in pounds.

For purposes of dynamic analysis, the mass of a body is assumed to be concentrated at the *center of mass* of the body. We then find the acceleration of the center of mass and locate the inertia force at that point. As an example, let the link in Fig. 2 weight 3.86 lb and accelerate horizontally at $a = 500$ in/sec^2 to the left. The mass of the link is given by

$$m = \frac{W}{g} = \frac{3.86\,\text{lb}}{386\,\text{in/sec}^2} = 0.01\ \text{lb-sec}^2/\text{in},$$

and is assumed to be concentrated at point C. The inertia force is given by

$$F_i = -ma = -(0.01\ \text{lb-sec}^2/\text{in})\,(500\ \text{in/sec}^2) = 5\ \text{lb (to the right)},$$

and is assumed to act at C. This 5 lb inertia force is added in the same manner as any applied force and must be accounted for in the force balance.

Let us now consider inertia effects associated with rotation. In order to avoid unnecessary complications, we will examine a link of length $2L$ and of weight $2W$, with half of the weight concentrated at each end. The link rotates about its center point as in Fig. 5. The link center of mass coincides with O, the center of rotation. Thus, the center of mass cannot have an acceleration. But, if the link has an angular acceleration

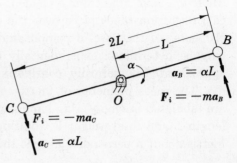

FIG. 5. Inertia effects due to rotation. Half the weight of the link shown is assumed concentrated at each end. The acceleration of points B and C gives rise to inertia forces which oppose the acceleration. While the inertia forces balance out ($F_{iB} + F_{iC} = 0$), a net inertia torque results ($T_i = -2F_iL$).

α as shown, the mass at point B has a tangential acceleration, $a_B = L\alpha$, and the inertia force at B is given by

$$F_i = -ma_B = \frac{W}{g} L\alpha$$

in a direction opposite a_B. (We ignore normal acceleration effects, which balance for this link.) The inertia torque arising from the inertia force at B is

$$T_i = F_iL = \frac{W}{g} L^2\alpha \text{ (counterclockwise).}$$

The inertia force due to the mass at C is equal to, but directly opposite, the inertia force at B. Thus, there is no net inertia force. The inertia torque arising from the acceleration of the mass at C, however, is also counterclockwise and the total inertia torque due to angular acceleration of this idealized link is

$$T_i = -2 \frac{W}{g} L^2\alpha$$

(i.e., in a direction opposite α).

Mass Moments of Inertia. In the above example, we saw that the inertia torqe due to rotation of a concentrated mass about point O is given by mass *times* the square of the distance between the mass and the point O *times* angular acceleration. In the case of a real link (with *distributed* mass) rotating about a point O, the corresponding expression for inertia torque is

$$I = \int r^2\, dm$$

where dm is an infinitesimal element of mass at a distance r from point O. Integration takes place over the entire body and includes all such elements. In the case of complicated shapes, mass moment of inertia may be determined experimentally or the above expression may be approximated numerically, considering a finite number of small masses.

The mass moments of inertia of many regular geometric shapes are tabulated in engineering handbooks. In the case of a slender rod of length L and total weight W rotating in a plane, the mass moment of inertia about a perpendicular axis through the center-point is given by

$$I = \frac{WL^2}{12g}.$$

The mass moment of inertia for the same rod about a perpendicular axis through one end is given by

$$I = \frac{WL^2}{3g}.$$

The mass moment of inertia of a circular disc of radius R and total weight W about a perpendicular axis through the center is given by

$$I = \frac{WR^2}{2g},$$

where the units are W (lb), L and R (in), and I (lb-sec²-in) where $g = 386$ in/sec².

To summarize, if a link translates (a piston, for example) there is an inertia force created equal to

$$F_i = -\frac{W}{g}\, a$$

applied at the center of mass where a is the acceleration of the center of mass. If a link rotates about its center of mass (a balanced crank, for example) then there is an inertia torque

$$T_i = -I\alpha.$$

A more general case is represented by a connecting rod or another link in which, simultaneously, the center of mass accelerates as the link is undergoing angular acceleration. We then have both an inertia force at the center of mass and an inertia torque about the center of mass.

EXAMPLE — PROBLEM 2: Dynamic Analysis. Consider the slider crank linkage shown in Fig. 6A. The linkage is identical to that shown in Fig. 4. In this case we will assume that link 1 rotates at a constant angular velocity of 100 rad/sec clockwise, i.e., we assume negligible angular acceleration of link 1. Let us now consider the forces acting on the linkage, this time *including* the inertia effects.

Solution. The velocity polygon constructed to scale in Fig. 6B satisfies the following vector equation:

$$oc = ob + bc,$$

where *oc* is directed to the right along the path of C,

   ob equals $\omega_1\,OB$ perpendicular to OB, and

   bc is perpendicular to BC.

As in the acceleration studies of Chapter Three, the results of the velocity polygon are then used to compute normal accelerations in order to construct the acceleration polygon shown in Fig. 6C. The acceleration polygon corresponds to the following acceleration vector equation:

$$a_C = a^n{}_B + a^t{}_B + a^n{}_{CB} + a^t{}_{CB},$$

where a_C is of unknown magnitude and lies along the path of C,

   $a^n{}_B$ equals $(ob)^2/OB$ and lies along OB directed toward O,

   $a^t{}_B$ equals zero since $\alpha_1 = 0$,

   $a^n{}_{CB}$ equals $(bc)^2/BC$ and lies along BC toward B, and

   $a^t{}_{CB}$ is of unknown magnitude perpendicular to BC.

When the acceleration polygon is completed, acceleration points b' and c' are located. Acceleration point g', the acceleration image of the center of mass G of link 2, is found by the proportion $b'g'/b'c' = BG/BC$. (The location of the center of mass is given in Fig. 6A.) We then use the acceleration scale to determine the values of a_C (or $o'c'$), a_G ($o'g'$), and $a^t{}_{CB}$, from which we find the angular acceleration of link 2

$$\alpha_2 = \frac{a^t{}_{CB}}{CB}.$$

We will now consider the inertia effects of the linkage. Let the

495

Mechanism

weight of link 2, the connecting rod, be 0.4 lb, and let link 3, the piston, weigh 0.2 lb. Link 1, the crank, is assumed to rotate at constant angular velocity and will be counterbalanced so that its center of gravity falls at O, the axis of rotation, thus eliminating the inertia effects of link 1. (The drawing does not show the crank counterweight.) We will work con-

$$OB = 1.2\ in$$
$$BC = 2.5\ in$$
$$\theta = 45°$$
$$BG = 1.1\ in$$

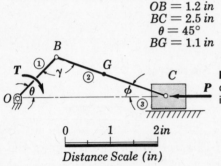

FIG. 6A. *Dynamic* analysis of the slider crank linkage of Fig. 4. The analysis will include inertia effects.

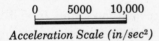

Distance Scale (in)

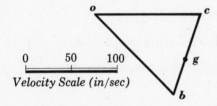

Velocity Scale (in/sec)

FIG. 6B. The velocity polygon for the slider crank linkage is required in order to find the velocities of points B and C. The velocities are used in turn to compute the normal accelerations of the linkage.

0   5000   10,000

Acceleration Scale (in/sec²)

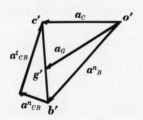

FIG. 6C. The acceleration polygon is constructed to find the total acceleration of points B, C, and G (center of gravity), and the angular acceleration of link 2.

FIG. 6D. Torque balance on link 2. Link 2 is drawn as a free body in equilibrium. The free body diagram must include the external forces acting on the link, the reactions, and the inertia forces (since this is a dynamic analysis). Since two forces are unknown (*F* at *B*, *R* at *C*), a torque balance about *B* can be used to determine the unknown force *R*.

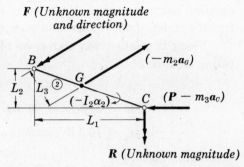

FIG. 6E. Force balance for link 2. A force polygon can be constructed to determine the remaining unknown force, *F* at *B*.

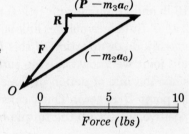

FIG. 6F. Torque balance on link 1. The force acting on link 1 at *B* is the *reaction* of force *F* acting at *B* on link 2. Its direction is therefore opposite to the direction as determined in the force polygon.

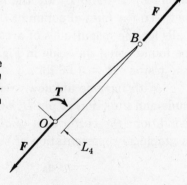

sistently in an inch-pound-second system of units. Thus, mass is given by dividing the weight (lbs) by 386 in/sec², the acceleration of gravity. Let the mass moment of inertia of link 2 be $I_2 = 0.0005$ lb-sec²-in, about G, determined experimentally or computed as described above. Conveniently, the mass moments of inertia of the other links are not

497

required since the crank (link 1) rotates at constant angular velocity and the slider (link 3) moves in pure translation.

Using the data given above, we obtain the following inertia forces acting on link 2:

$$-m_3 a_c = 4.55 \text{ lb to the right (opposing } P \text{ at } C),$$

$$-m_2 a_G = 10.3 \text{ lb opposite } a_G \text{ (at } G),$$

and an inertia torque,

$$-I_2 \alpha_2 = 1.6 \text{ in-lb clockwise (on link 2)}.$$

These forces are applied to link 2 (Fig. 6D) along with gas force $P = 10$ lb and an unknown vertical reaction R. Link 1 applies a force to link 2 at B. But since neither link is a two force member, we do not know the magnitude or direction of this force. However, since B does represent a pin joint we know that the sum of the moments about B is zero. Also, since the line of action of force F goes through B, the torque due to F at point B is zero. Thus, considering clockwise moments and torques positive, we set up the torque balance about pin B:

$$RL_1 + (P - m_3|a_c|) L_2 - m_2|a_G|L_3 + I_2|\alpha_2| = 0,$$

where L_1, L_2, and L_3 are the moment arms or perpendicular distances between the lines of action of the forces and pin B. The above equation calls for the magnitudes of accelerations a_c, a_G and α_2. The lengths can be found using the scale in Fig. 6A. The result is a downward force on the piston: $R = 1.06$ lb.

With but one unknown remaining, the force F of unknown magnitude and direction at pin B, we may find it using the force equilibrium condition: *the vector sum of all forces on link 2 equals zero*. Fig. 6E is a graphical representation of the equation

$$-m_2 a_G + (P - m_3 a_c) + R + F = 0$$

from which $F = 5.3$ lb in the direction shown.

The same force F is applied in the opposite direction to link 1 (the crank) at pin B. Since there are no inertia forces on link 1, the force F at B is balanced by an equal and opposite force at the crankshaft O as shown in Fig. 6F. Balancing torques about the crankshaft, $T - FL_4 = 0$, or $T = 0.6$ in-lb clockwise. The results of our analysis, then, include:

(1) the force between piston and cylinder, $R = 1.06$ lb; (2) the force on wrist pin C made up of the vector sum, $R + (P - m_3 a_C) = 5.6$ lb; and (3) the force on crankpin B and crankshaft bearing O, both of which are $F = 5.3$ lbs. Stresses within links 2 and 3 depend on actual inertia forces which, in turn, depend on the shape of the member.

We obtain an identical result (within the limits of our graphical and calculation accuracy) by balancing torques on the linkage as a whole about point O. This torque balance includes the applied torque, the inertia torque, the moment due to reaction R, and the moment due to inertia force at G on link 2. Pin reactions at B are internal to the system and are not considered in a torque balance on the entire mechanism.

The static effects of link weights were not considered in the above analysis (although the more significant inertia effects were). Weight forces may be included in the analysis by adding vertical (downward) forces equal to the weight of link 1 at O, the weight of link 2 at G, and the weight of link 3 at C. The weight of link 2 has a small effect on the reactions at O and C, on the force at B, and on the torque.

Relationship of Dynamic Analysis to Design

In some cases, accelerations are of interest without regard to the effects which they produce. Frequently however, dynamic effects on a mechanism must be studied, and the velocity and acceleration become only the first steps in our analysis. In the above example of dynamic analysis, inertia effects are of the same order of magnitude as the loading due to gas forces—they cannot be ignored.

A more complete picture of the dynamic loading is obtained by considering the linkage in a series of positions representing a complete cycle of motion. A dynamic analysis is then performed for each position to determine loads on each bearing or pin. At high speeds, some linkages transmit serious shaking forces to the foundation. These result from inertia loads which continually change direction. A careful dynamic analysis predicts problems of this type so that the mounting may be improved or the linkage redesigned while still in the "drawing board" stage.

499

Glossary

Only those terms of particular interest to the study of mechanisms are included. Many terms are used in more than one sense and there is little standardization in the literature, but the intended meaning is usually clear from the context. Some terms are followed by a typical symbol and suggested dimensional units.

Absolute acceleration (a): The instantaneous time rate of change in velocity with respect to a fixed reference. (a vector quantity)

Absolute velocity (v): The instantaneous time rate of change in displacement with respect to a fixed reference. (a vector quantity)

Acceleration: The absolute acceleration of a point. *Average acceleration* refers to the change in velocity over a finite time interval divided by that time interval. Accelerations are expressed in inches/second.^{2}

Acceleration image: A set of points in an acceleration polygon which correspond to points on a rigid link.

Acceleration polygon: A graphical representation of accelerations on a polar diagram. The absolute acceleration of a point is represented by a vector drawn from a pole point o'.

Addendum: The height of a gear tooth measured from the pitch circle.

Angles of action: The angles turned through by the driver and follower during contact between two meshing gear teeth.

Angles of approach: The angles turned through as two meshing gear teeth go from the point of initial contact to the pitch point.

Angles of recess: The angles turned through by the driver and driven gear as the contact progresses from the pitch point to the point of final contact.

Angular acceleration (α): The instantaneous time rate of change in angular velocity of a link (expressed in radians/second^2.)

Angular displacement *(θ):* The change in angular position of a link (expressed in radians.)

Angular velocity *(ω):* The instantaneous time rate of change in angular position of a link (expressed in radians/second.)

Axial pitch: In worm gear studies, the distance, measured axially, between corresponding points on adjacent threads of the worm.

Ball-disc drive: Variable-speed, friction drive employing a movable ball or ball cage to change effective radii of input and output discs.

Base pitch $(p_b):$ In gear design, the distance between corresponding points of adjacent teeth measured on the base circle.

Bearing: The part in which a pin or shaft turns, permitting rotation of one link relative to another or relative to a fixed frame.

Bevel gears: Gears used to transmit power between intersecting shafts. The pitch surfaces of mating bevel gears are rolling cones.

Centro (01, etc.): A point considered to be in two links, having the same velocity in both.

Centrode: The locus of a centro as a linkage goes through its usual cycle of motion.

Circular pitch *(p):* The sum of the *tooth width* and the *tooth space*, both arc distances measured along the pitch circle. Or, distance between corresponding points on adjacent gear teeth, measured along the pitch circle.

Clearance: In gear design, the distance between the addendum of one gear and the dedendum of the mating gear.

Common normal: A line perpendicular to two curves at their point of contact.

Component method: A study of velocities through examination of velocity components along a link and perpendicular to the link.

Connecting rod: The link between the crank and the piston of a slider crank linkage or between the crank and follower of a four bar linkage (the coupler.)

Conjugate action: See FUNDAMENTAL LAW OF GEARING.

Contact ratio: The average number of pairs of teeth in a contact in a pair of gears.

Continuous speed variation: Stepless changing of speed ratios.

Coriolis acceleration $(a^c):$ The component of acceleration which arises when we consider a velocity relative to a rotating path.

Coupler: The link connecting the input and follower cranks on a four bar linkage.

Crank: A link which rotates about a fixed center (the center of the *crankshaft.)*

Crank dead center: The limiting position of the slider crank linkage with the slider closest to the fixed center of the crank.

Crank pin: The joint between crank and connecting rod. The crankshaft and one or more cranks and crankpins are often manufactured as a single member.

Crank rocker mechanism: A four bar linkage having one crank which rotates through 360° and another which oscillates.

Crossed helical gears: Helical gears which transmit power between shafts which are non-parallel and non-intersecting. Crossed helical gears are usually of the same hand.

Cycle: A complete sequence of positions of the links in a mechanism (from some initial position back to the initial position).

Dead center: Either limiting position of a slider crank mechanism.

Dedendum: The depth of a tooth space measured from the pitch circle.

Diametral pitch *(P):* The number of teeth divided by the pitch diameter of a gear.

Differential gearing: A gear train to divide power between two shafts, permitting speed variation between the shafts.

Dimensions: Length, time, and force (inches, seconds, and pounds).

Displacement *(s):* The change in position of a point during a time interval represented by a vector directed from the initial position to the final position.

Displacement diagram: In cam studies, a plot of follower displacement vs. cam rotation.

Double rocker mechanism: A four bar linkage in which neither crank can rotate through 360°.

Drag link: A four bar linkage in which both cranks rotate through 360°.

Driver: The crank which ordinarily represents the input to a linkage. When the function of a linkage is not specified, the terms *driver* and *driven link* (follower) may be assigned arbitrarily.

Dynamics: The motion of a linkage under the influence of applied and inertial forces.

Equilibrium: A state of balance of forces on a member or linkage. A body at rest is in static equilibrium; a body in motion is in dynamic equilibrium.

Equivalent linkage: An arrangement of links with the same motion characteristics (but not the same form) as a linkage to be studied.

Face width *(w):* In spur gear studies, the length of the gear tooth measured along the gear axis.

Fixed center *(O_1 etc.):* The stationary point about which a link rotates.

Flexible coupling: Device used to transmit power between two shafts when the misalignment between the shafts is small but variable.

Follower: In cam studies, the link which is moved by a cam through a precise sequence of motion. Generally, any mechanical element driven by another.

Force *(F)*: In the general sense, an applied lineal force, a torque or an inertia effect.

Four bar linkage: A mechanism made up of a driving crank, a coupler, follower crank and a fixed link.

Frame: A fixed link which may be represented by the line between two fixed centers.

Friction drive: Drive which relies solely on friction forces between contacting members. Used in low-speed, low-power applications.

Function generator: A mechanism designed to produce a certain mathematical relationship between input and output motion.

Fundamental law of gearing: The shape (profile) of the teeth of a gear must be such that the common normal at the point of contact between two meshing teeth must always pass through a fixed point on the line of centers (the pitch point). When this condition is satisfied, the teeth are said to produce conjugate action.

Gear: A toothed wheel used to transmit power from one rotating shaft to another. *Spur gear* teeth are cut parallel to the shaft axis; *helical gear* tooth elements form a helix; *bevel gear* tooth elements lie on a cone.

Gear train: A set of meshing gears to produce one or more input to output speed ratios.

Hand: In helical gear studies, the slope of the teeth (to right or left) when viewed along the axis of the gear.

Harmonic motion: Motion which may be described by sine and cosine functions.

Helical gear: Gear whose teeth take the shape of a helix, or form an angle with the gear axis. Helical gears can be used with parallel shafts and with shafts which are non-parallel and non-intersecting.

Helical motion: Rotation combined with translation along the axis of rotation. (The motion of a screw)

Helix angle *(ψ)*: In gear studies, the angle that the gear teeth make with the axis of a helical gear.

Idler: A gear used to change direction of rotation in a train, but not directly connected to an input or output shaft.

Impulse drives: Drives which produce an intermittent or pulsating output with constant input.

Inertia loads: The reverse effective force due to acceleration of a mass.

In-line slider crank: A linkage in which the fixed center of the crank lies on the (extended) path of the wrist pin.

Instantaneous acceleration: See ABSOLUTE ACCELERATION.

Instantaneous center: (instant center) A point in a link which has zero velocity.

Instantaneous velocity: See ABSOLUTE VELOCITY.

Interference: In gear studies, the case where gear tooth contact is between two non-conjugate curves; i.e., the fundamental law of gearing is broken. Interference occurs when the tip of one gear tooth is in contact below the base circle of the mating gear tooth.

Internal gear: Gear with teeth formed on the inner rather than the outer surface.

Inversion: A new linkage made from another by fixing a different link from the fixed link in the original mechanism.

Involute: A curve traced by the end of a string unwrapped from a circle (the *base circle.*) Practically all gears in common use are based on an involute profile.

Jerk: The time rate of change in acceleration (a vector quantity).

Kennedy's theorem: For three bodies, there exist three centros which lie on a line.

Kinematics: The study of motion. Applied kinematics may be called "mechanism."

Lead *(L):* In worm gear studies, the axial pitch times the number of worm teeth. In the case of screw threads, the pitch times the number of separate threads.

Length of contact: The straight-line distance from the intersection of the driven gear addendum circle and the pressure line (initial contact) to the intersection of the driver addendum circle and the pressure line (final contact).

Limiting position: A linkage configuration at the instant the driven link has zero velocity while the driver has a non-zero velocity. An extreme position of the linkage.

Line of action: Locus of points of contact between two gear teeth from initial to final contact.

Line of centers: A line joining the fixed centers of two links.

Linear motion: The instantaneous displacement, velocity, and acceleration of a point. Also, rectilinear motion.

Link: A single machine part; a gear, cam, connecting rod, piston, or other rigid member. When the link has pin joints at either end, the distance between pins is considered the length of the link and the link itself may be represented by a line between the pins.

Linkage: A mechanism. A system of connected links.

Machine: A single mechanism or several mechanisms grouped together with a specific function.

Mass *(m):* The weight of a body divided by 386 inches/second^2 (the acceleration of gravity.) Thus mass is expressed in pound-second^2/inch. In the general sense, mass also refers to the rotational equivalent, *mass moment of inertia (I)* expressed in pound-inch-seconds^2.

Mechanical advantage: The ratio of output force to input force or the ratio of output torque to input torque.

Mechanism: A group of connected links. The links or elements of a mechanism are so arranged and constrained that the motion of one link produces certain predictable motion of the other links. Also, the study of kinematics of machines (the study of linkage motion.)

Moment *(M):* The magnitude of a force vector times its perpendicular distance to a point.

Non-standard gears: Mating gears specially cut with unequal but complimentary addenda and dedenda to eliminate interference. Gears of this type are not interchangeable with other gears.

Normal *(n* superscript): Perpendicular (to the path or velocity direction.)

Normal circular pitch *(p^n):* Distance between corresponding points on adjacent helical gear teeth measured normal to the helix angle of the gear.

Normal diametral pitch *(P^n):* The value of the ratio of π (pi) and the normal circular pitch of a helical gear.

Normal pressure angle *(ϕ^n):* The pressure angle for the tooth profile of a helical gear, obtained by passing a plane normal to the helix angle.

Offset: The (perpendicular) distance between the extended wrist-pin path and the fixed center of the crank in a slider crank mechanism.

One-way clutch: Clutch designed to permit motion in one direction and to prevent or limit motion in the opposite direction.

Oscillation: Back and forth rotation. Sometimes, back and forth rectilinear motion.

Parameter study: A study of the effect of changing a variable, e.g., the effect of the ratio of connecting rod to crank length on maximum acceleration.

Path: Actual movement of a point in moving from an initial to a final position.

Period: The time of one complete cycle.

Pin: A representation of a shaft or pivot in a fixed or moving bearing or support.

Pitch angle *(γ):* In bevel gear studies, the angle between an element of the pitch cone and the axis of the gear. In spur and helical gear studies, the pitch angle is the angular equivalent of the circular pitch.

Pitch circles: Circles on a pair of gears which theoretically roll on one another (at the *pitch point.*) The diameter of a pitch circle is the *pitch diameter (d).*

Pitch curve: In cam studies, the curve generated by the trace point as the follower is rotated about a stationary cam.

Pitch point: In cam studies, that point on the cam pitch curve having the largest pressure angle. In gear studies, the pitch point is the point of tangency of the pitch circles of meshing gears. Also, the point of intersection of the line of action and the line of centers.

Plane mechanism: Mechanism for which all motion occurs in a single plane or parallel planes.

Plane motion: Rotation and translation in a single plane or in several parallel planes.

Planetary train: An arrangement of gears such that the centers of one or more gears (called planets, *P*) are held in a *planet carrier, C,* and rotate about a sun gear, *S,* and/or within an internal gear *(ring gear, R).*

Positive clutch: Clutch which employs jaws or teeth to transmit power between colinear shafts. Positive clutches are often used in combination with friction clutches; such combinations are referred to as synchromesh clutches.

Positive drive: Drive employing toothed or grooved components to assure positive power transfer with no slippage.

Positive motion cam: Cam which drives follower at all times (even during return).

Pressure angle *(ϕ):* In cam studies, the angle between the line of action of the follower (which is usually vertical) and a normal drawn to the cam pitch curve. In gear studies, the pressure angle is the angle between the pressure line, or line of action, and the common tangent to the pitch circles of meshed gears.

Prime circle: In cam studies, the smallest circle, having its center at the cam center, that can be drawn tangent to the pitch curve.

Quick return mechanism: A linkage with a reciprocating member which moves slowly in one direction (usually the *working stroke*) and returns quickly.

Rack: A straight gear. The diameter of a rack is infinite.

Radian: An angle of $180°/\pi$ or about $57.3°$. Radians are dimensionless.

Reaction: The force applied by body *B* to body *A* in opposition to a force applied by *A* to *B*. The two forces are equal in magnitude and opposite in direction.

Reciprocating motion: Back and forth translation, as of a piston.

Rectilinear: In a straight line.

Reference frame: A fixed or moving set of coordinate axes.

Relative motion: A displacement, velocity, or acceleration measured with respect to a moving body or point. Motion as seen by an observer in a moving reference frame.

Revolution: One complete rotation.

Rigid link: Any machine element in which deformations are slight compared with other motion of the mechanism. Any element which acts instantaneously as a rigid link, e.g., a belt which is between a pair of pulleys.

Roller-disc drive: Variable-speed friction drive employing one or more rollers. Roller position is adjusted to vary effective radii of input and output discs.

506

Roller-torus drive: Variable-speed friction drive, similar to the axle-mounted ball-disc drive, employing adjustable rollers within a split torus. The roller axes are tilted to change effective radii of the input and output halves of the split torus.

Rolling motion: Absence of sliding motion along the common tangent, i.e., absence of relative motion.

Rotation: Motion about a fixed axis, whether continuous or oscillatory. General plane motion is made up of rotation and translation.

Scalar: A quantity without any associated direction (e.g., time).

Scale: The magnitude of a vector represented by a length of one inch on a vector polygon, e.g., 1 inch = 20 inches/second. Also, to convert measurements from a velocity or acceleration polygon to actual values of velocity and acceleration.

Schematic: A sketch intended to show linkage function without regard to actual physical appearance.

Scotch yoke: A linkage with rotating input motion and sinusoidally translating output motion.

Self-locking: The property of a screw or gear train which prevents the driven member from acting as driver. Almost all worm drives are self-locking.

Sense: An indication of which way a vector points when its direction is given by a line, e.g., if the direction of a vector is known to be horizontal, the *sense* may be *to the right*.

Sinusoidal motion: Displacement–time, velocity–time and acceleration–time relationships characterized by sine and/or cosine functions.

Slider: A link which moves in a straight path along a fixed line (e.g., a piston in a cylinder), or a link which moves in a straight path relative to a moving link (e.g., in a slot in a rotating link).

Slider crank: A mechanism consisting of a crank, a connecting rod and a slider. A basic component of a reciprocating engine.

Sliding contact: Relative movement along the common tangent at the point of contact.

Slope: Defined as the rise divided by the run of the tangent to a curve at a given point.

Speed: The scalar magnitude of a velocity vector. Also, the magnitude of angular velocity.

Spiral bevel gears: Bevel gears with a spiral rather than a straight tooth design. Used for high-speed, high-load applications.

Spur gear: Gear with teeth cut parallel to the gear axis. Spur gears are used to transmit power between parallel shafts. The pitch surfaces are rolling cylinders.

Standard gears: Interchangeable gears with a prescribed pitch and pressure angle, cut to conform to one of several standard gear profiles.

Statics: A study of forces in bodies without regard to motion.

Stepless, variable-speed drive: Drive with a constant input speed in which output speed may be continuously varied through a given range without disengaging the drive.

Stroke *(S):* The motion of the slider from one extreme to the other. Also, the distance between the extreme positions.

Structure: Linkage designed and constructed in such a manner that relative motion between members is impossible.

Synchromesh clutch: A friction clutch contacts a mating friction surface to bring two colinear shafts to approximately the same speed. When both shafts are rotating at approximately the same speed, the toothed elements for each shaft are then brought into mesh.

Synthesis: Determination of linkage dimensions to satisfy particular input-output requirements. Design. The opposite of analysis.

Tangential (superscript *t.*): In the direction of the path. (the velocity direction)

Three link theorem: Kennedy's theorem.

Thrust: The force directed along the shaft of a helical or bevel gear.

Toggle linkage: Clamp-like mechanism made up of a four bar linkage combined with a slider crank linkage.

Torque *(T):* The moment of a force about a point or shaft; the force times its (perpendicular) distance to the point or shaft centerline expressed in inch pounds.

Trace point: In cam studies, the reference point for follower displacement. For cams with knife-edge followers the trace point corresponds to the initial position of the knife edge; with roller followers, the trace point corresponds to the roller center.

Traction drive: See FRICTION DRIVE.

Translation: Motion of a body such that all points have the same vector displacement. General motion is made up of rotation and translation.

Transmission: A gear drive or traction drive, ordinarily used to reduce rotational speed. Variable speed transmissions provide for changes in the ratio of output to input speed.

Transverse circular pitch *(p):* Distance between corresponding points on adjacent gear teeth, measured along the pitch circle of a helical gear.

Tredgold's approximation: The determination of an equivalent spur gear, with properties which approximate those of the gear being studied. The number of teeth for the equivalent spur gear are referred to as the equivalent, virtual, or formative number of teeth for the gear being studied.

Trial vector: A vector of unknown magnitude used to form a velocity polygon.

Undercutting: Cutting away that part of the gear tooth profile which will cause interference.

Uniform: Constant.

Universal joint: Device used to transmit power between two shafts under conditions of large misalignment and high torque.

Vector: A physical quantity possessing magnitude and direction (e.g., velocity or acceleration).

Velocity *(v)*: Absolute velocity. *Average velocity* refers to a change in displacement during a finite time interval divided by that time interval. Velocities are given in inches/second.

Velocity image: A set of points on a velocity polygon which correspond to points on a rigid link.

Velocity polygon: A graphical representation of velocities on a polar diagram. The absolute velocity of a point is represented by a vector drawn from a pole point *o*.

Whole depth: In gear studies, the radial distance between the addendum and dedendum circles.

Worm drive: A pair of helical gears with shafts at right angles. The *worm* usually has one or two teeth (threads) and drives the *worm wheel*.

Working depth: In gear studies, the radial distance between the addendum and clearance circles. Also, the sum of the addenda of two meshing gears.

Wrist pin: The joint between a slider and connecting rod.

Zerol bevel gears: Spiral bevel gears designed with a zero spiral angle to eliminate thrust.

Problems

Many of the following problems are based on illustrations which appear in the text proper. Where this is the case, the figure number and page number of the illustration are given. Illustrations which *accompany* the problems in this section are indicated with the prefix *P*.

Chapter 1 — Linkages and Motion

1.1 Change the structure shown in Fig. 1E, p. 3 into a mechanism by removing one link. (There are several solutions to this problem.)

1.2 List 3 to 5 machine components in each of the following categories: Motion described by (A) pure translation, (B) pure rotation, (C) combined rotation and translation.

In problems 1.3 through 1.6, vector angles are measured as in Fig. 7, p. 11 (counterclockwise from the horizontal axis). For the following problems: $A = 1$ at $30°$; $B = 2$ at $60°$; $C = 1.5$ at $180°$; and $D = 3$ at $225°$.

1.3 Find $A + B$. (A) Add the vectors using trigonometric functions. (B) Solve graphically.

1.4 Find $A + B + D$. Solve graphically.

1.5 Find $A + B + C + D$. Solve graphically.

1.6 Find $A + B + C - D$, i.e., $A + B + C + (-D)$. Solve graphically.

1.7 Find the velocity of a point on the circumference of a 30 in. diameter flywheel rotating at 800 RPM.

1.8 Low-carbon steel is turned on a lathe at typical surface speeds of 100-400 ft/min. Find the corresponding lathe spindle speeds in rev/min for (A) a 2 in. diameter bar, and (B) a 3 in. diameter bar.

1.9 Write an equation to determine lathe spindle speed n (in rev/min) when bar diameter d (in in.) and surface speed s (in ft/min) are given. Is the same equation valid if n represents the speed of a milling cutter of diameter d?

1.10 Find the average acceleration as a piston increases speed from 120 in/sec to 140 in/sec during a 0.01 second interval.

1.11 A body moving at 1000 mi/hr is brought to a stop in 0.05 sec. Find average acceleration in in/sec^2.

1.12 Find average angular acceleration (in rad/sec^2) as a flywheel goes (A) from zero to 1000 RPM in 20 sec, and (B) from 1000 RPM to 990 RPM in 0.5 sec.

1.13 In Fig. 9, p. 14, let $R = 2$ and $L = 4$. (A) Plot displacement x vs. crank angle θ for $\theta = 30°$, $60°$, and $90°$. If the crank rotates counterclockwise at 100 rev/min, find (B) the average piston velocity for θ between $30°$ and $60°$, and (C) the average piston velocity for θ between $60°$ and $90°$.

1.14 Design and dimension a pantograph, like that shown in Fig. 16A, p. 37, which may be used to double the size of the pattern.

1.15 Design and dimension a pantograph which may be used to increase pattern dimensions by 10%. Let the fixed pivot lie between the tracing point and the marking point or tool holder, like the pantograph shown in Fig. 16B, p. 38.

1.16 Referring to the swash plate pump shown in Fig. 23, p. 46, determine the dimensions of a pump with a capacity of 120 ft^3/hr at 600 RPM. (Assume 100% volumetric efficiency.) (B) Find average plunger velocity. (There are many possible solutions to this problem.)

1.17 Find the average piston velocity (between limiting positions) for an in-line slider crank mechanism (Fig. 28A, p. 52). Crank length is 2 in, and the crank rotates at 3000 RPM.

1.18 Find the average piston velocity (between limiting positions) for an offset slider crank mechanism ($E = 1$ in). See Fig. 28B, p. 52. Dimensions are those of Problem 1.17. The connecting rod length is 4 in. (There is one average speed when the piston moves to the left and another when it moves to the right.)

1.19 Repeat Problem 1.18 for $E = 1.5$ in.

Problems 1.20 through 1.28 refer to Fig. 29A, p. 55. For each of the following problems: (A) Determine whether the links can actually form a mechanism with the dimensions given. (B) If a mechanism exists, identify the motion relationship (crank rocker, drag link, double rocker, or indefinite). (C) Show the limiting positions if the mechanism is a crank rocker or double rocker mechanism.

1.20 $L_0 = 5$, $L_1 = 2$, $L_2 = 1.5$, $L_3 = 2$.
1.21 $L_0 = 1$, $L_1 = 2$, $L_2 = 1.5$, $L_3 = 3.5$.
1.22 $L_0 = 1$, $L_1 = 3.25$, $L_2 = 1.5$, $L_3 = 3.5$.
1.23 $L_0 = 1.5$, $L_1 = 4$, $L_2 = 2$, $L_3 = 3.5$.

1.24 $L_0 = 1, L_1 = 4, L_2 = 1.5, L_3 = 4.5.$
1.25 $L_0 = 2, L_1 = 1.25, L_2 = 2, L_3 = 3.$
1.26 $L_0 = 4, L_1 = 1, L_2 = 2, L_3 = 1.5.$
1.27 $L_0 = 3, L_1 = 2, L_2 = 3, L_3 = 2.$
1.28 $L_0 = 2.5, L_1 = 1, L_2 = 2.5, L_3 = 2.$

Problems 1.29 through 1.32 are based on a constant crank speed.

1.29 Design a mechanism with a 10 in. stroke and a forward to-return stroke time ratio of 2 to 1. Use a linkage similar to that shown in Fig. 34 on p. 63.
1.30 Repeat Prob. 1.29 for a time ratio of 2.5 to 1.
1.31 Design a mechanism with a stroke length which may be varied between 5 and 10 in. Forward-to-return stroke time ratio will be 1.5 to 1 at maximum stroke. Use a linkage similar to that shown in Fig. 35, p. 68.
1.32 Repeat Problem 1.31 for a time ratio of 2.5 to 1.

Problems 1.33 through 1.35 refer to Figs. 28B & C, p. 52.

1.33. $R = 2, L = 5,$ and $E = 0.4.$ (A) Find the forward-to-return stroke ratio,   . (B) Find the stroke length, S.
1.34 Repeat Problem 1.33 for an offset $E = 0.8$.
1.35 $R = 1, L = 3,$ and $E = 1.$ Plot the path of the midpoint of the connecting rod.
1.36 Design a linkage to generate the function $y = x^{1.5}$ for $1 < x < 5$. Let $\theta_1 = 60°$, $\phi_1 = 30°$; the range of θ and ϕ is 90°. See Figs. 38 and 39, pp. 76-77.

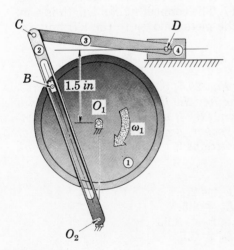

$O_1O_2 = 2\ in$
$O_1B = 1.25\ in$
$O_2C = 4\ in$
$CD = 3\ in$
Pin B is part of link 1

FIG. P1A

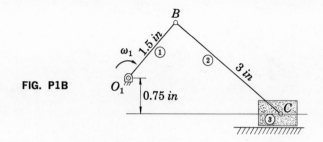

FIG. P1B

1.37 Describe the motion of each link in Fig. P1A. Show the linkage in its limiting positions (corresponding to extreme positions of the slider). Measure the angle through which link 1 turns as the slider moves from extreme left to extreme right. Compare this with the corresponding angle as the slider moves to the left. Find the stroke of the slider (distance between limiting positions).

1.38 Repeat the above assignment for Fig. P1B.

1.39 Link 1 in Fig. P1B rotates at a constant speed of 300 RPM counterclockwise. Find velocity and acceleration of point B at the instant shown. (B) Find the velocity and acceleration of point B when link 1 is undergoing an angular acceleration of 400 rad/sec².

Chapter 2 — Velocity Analyses

For each of the problems in this section: (A) Write the appropriate vector equation. (B) Solve graphically unless directed otherwise, using velocity polygon notation. (C) Dimension all vectors of the velocity polygon in in/sec. (D) Express angular velocities in rad/sec. and indicate direction. In problems 2.1 through 2.3, angles are measured counterclockwise from the first quadrant. Solve using a scale of 1 in. = 10 in/sec.

2.1 Velocity $v_B = 15$ in/sec at 45°. Velocity $v_{CB} = 20$ in/sec at 0°. Find v_C. (Use $v_C = v_B + v_{CB}$.)

2.2 Velocity $v_C = 30$ in/sec at 0°. Relative velocity $v_{CB} = 10$ in/sec at 135°. Find v_B. Use $v_B = v_C + (-v_{CB})$.

2.3 Velocity $v_B = 20$ in/sec at 45°. Relative velocity v_{CB} is an unknown vector at 315°. Velocity v_C is an unknown vector at 0°. Find v_{CB} and v_C. (Use $v_C = v_B + v_{CB}$.)

2.4 In Fig. P2, $\theta = 45°$ and $\omega_1 = 10$ rad/sec. Draw and dimension the velocity polygon. Find ω_2.

2.5 Repeat Problem 2.4 for $\theta = 120°$.

2.6 Repeat Problem 2.4 for the mechanism in the limiting position (with C to the extreme right).

2.7 In Fig. P3, $\omega_1 = 100$ rad/sec. Draw and dimension the velocity polygon. Find v_D and ω_2. Use the scale 1 in = 100 in/sec.

Mechanism

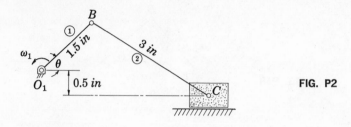

FIG. P2

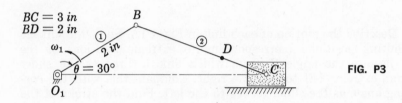

$BC = 3\ in$
$BD = 2\ in$

FIG. P3

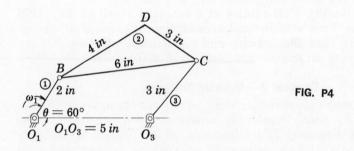

FIG. P4

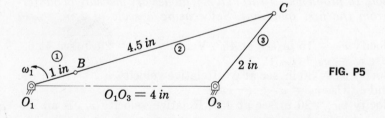

FIG. P5

2.8 In Fig. P4, $\omega_1 = 50$ rad/sec. Draw and dimension the velocity polygon. Find v_D, ω_2 and ω_3. Use the scale 1 in = 50 in/sec.

2.9 In Fig. P5, $\omega_1 = 20$ rad/sec. (A) Draw and dimension the velocity polygon for the limiting position shown. Find relative velocity v_{CB}. Use the scale 1 in = 10 in/sec. (B) Repeat the problem for the other limiting position.

514

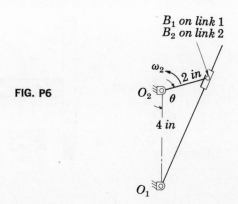

FIG. P6

2.10 In Fig. P6, $\theta = 105°$ and $\omega_2 = 20$ rad/sec. Draw and dimension the velocity polygon. Identify the sliding velocity. Find ω_1. Use the scale 1 in $= 20$ in/sec.

2.11 Repeat Problem 2.10 for $\theta = 30°$.

2.12 In Fig. P3, $\omega_1 = 100$ rad/sec. (A) Find v_C *analytically* for the position shown. (B) Find v_C analytically at both limiting positions.

FIG. P7

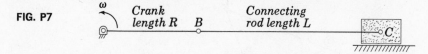

2.13 In Fig. P7, let the angular velocity of the crank be ω. (A) Draw the velocity polygon for the position shown. Identify relative velocity v_{CB}. (B) Repeat for the other limiting position.

FIG. P8

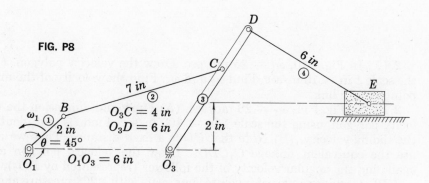

2:14 In Fig. P8, $\omega_1 = 100$ rad/sec. Draw and dimension the velocity polygon. Use the scale 1 in $= 100$ in/sec.

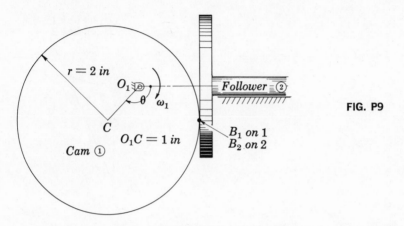

FIG. P9

2.15 In Fig. P9, $\theta = 135°$ and $\omega_1 = 10$ rad/sec. Draw and dimension the velocity polygon. Identify the follower velocity and sliding velocity. Use the scale 1 in = 5 in/sec.

2.16 Repeat Problem 2.15 for $\theta = 30°$.

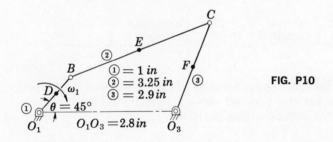

FIG. P10

2.17 In Fig. P10, $\omega_1 = 35$ rad/sec. Draw the velocity polygon. Use the scale 1 in = 10 in/sec. Find ω_2 and ω_3. Find the velocity of the midpoint of each link.

2.18 In Fig. P11, $\omega_1 = 20$ rad/sec. (A) Draw and dimension the velocity polygon, using the scale 1 in = 100 in/sec. Find ω_2 and identify the sliding velocity. (B) Note that CD is a fixed distance. Thus we can use the equivalent linkage O_1CDO_2. Draw the velocity polygon and again find the angular velocity of the follower (represented by DO_2).

2.19 Consider a pair of involute spur gears with a 20° pressure angle. Let the driver speed be 300 RPM clockwise and the follower speed be 1000 RPM counterclockwise. Find sliding velocity when contact occurs 1.2 in. from the pitch point.

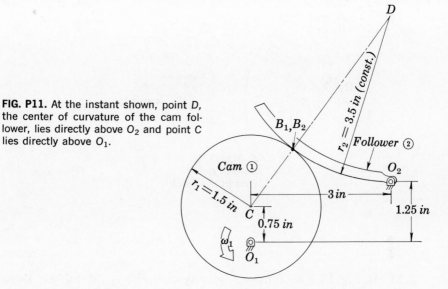

FIG. P11. At the instant shown, point *D*, the center of curvature of the cam follower, lies directly above O_2 and point C lies directly above O_1.

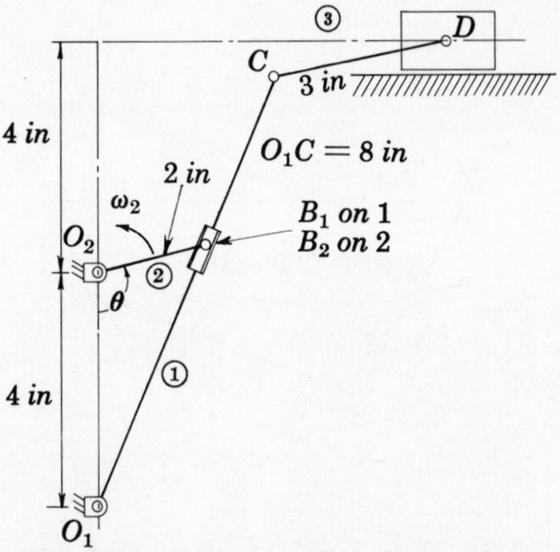

FIG. P12

2.20 In Fig. P12, $\theta = 105°$ and $\omega_2 = 20$ rad/sec. Draw and dimension the velocity polygon, using the scale 1 in $= 20$ in/sec.

2.21 Repeat Problem 2.20 for $\theta = 30°$.

2.22 In Fig. P9, $\omega_1 = 10$ rad/sec. Find the follower velocity analytically when (A) $\theta = 135°$. (B) $\theta = 30°$.

Mechanism

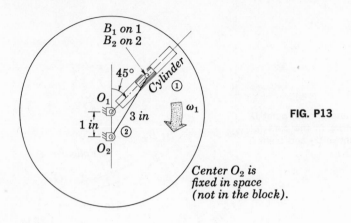

FIG. P13

Center O_2 is
fixed in space
(not in the block).

2.23 In Fig. P13, ω_1 (angular velocity of O_1B_1) = 30 rad/sec. Draw and dimension the velocity polygon, using the scale 1 in = 20 in/sec. Identify the sliding velocity and find ω_2, the angular velocity of O_2B_2.

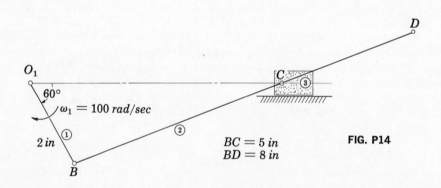

FIG. P14

$BC = 5\ in$
$BD = 8\ in$

2.24 For Fig. P14, draw and dimension the velocity polygon, using the scale 1 in = 100 in/sec. Find ω_2 and v_D.

2.25 Locate all of the centros in Fig. P14. Using centro 13, write an expression for slider velocity in terms of ω_1. Calculate v_C.

2.26 In Fig. P14, use centro 02 in order to write an expression for (A) ω_2 in terms of v_B. (B) ω_2/ω_1. (C) v_C in terms of ω_2. (D) v_D in terms of ω_2. (E) Calculate ω_2, v_C, and v_D.

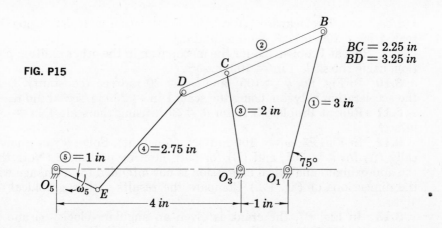

FIG. P15

$BC = 2.25\ in$
$BD = 3.25\ in$

②

C

D

③ $= 2\ in$

① $= 3\ in$

④ $=2.75\ in$

⑤ $=1\ in$

75°

O_5 — ω_5 E

O_3

O_1

4 in

1 in

2.27 In Fig. P15, $\omega_5 = 15$ rad/sec. Use a vector 3 in. long to represent the velocity of *B*. Complete the velocity polygon and determine the velocity scale. Dimension the polygon and find the angular velocity of each link.

Chapter 3 — Acceleration Analyses

Solve the problems which follow graphically unless otherwise instructed. Observe the following procedures (A) Draw and dimension the velocity polygon if this has not already been done. (B) Write the appropriate acceleration equation. (C) Compute and tabulate accelerations below the terms of the equation. (D) Solve the vector equation, using acceleration polygon notation. Dimension in in/sec². (E) Express angular accelerations in rad/sec² and indicate their directions.

3.1 In Fig. P2, $\theta = 45°$ and $\omega_1 = 10$ rad/sec (constant). Draw the acceleration polygon, using the scale 1 in $= 100$ in/sec². Find α_2.

3.2 Repeat Problem 3.1 for $\theta = 120°$.

3.3 Repeat Problem 3.1, for the mechanism in the limiting position (point *C* to the extreme right).

3.4 In Fig. P3, $\theta = 30°$ and $\omega_1 = 100$ rad/sec (constant). Draw the acceleration polygon, using the scale 1 in $= 10,000$ in/sec². Find a_D and α_2.

3.5 Repeat Problem 3.4 for $\alpha_1 = 2000$ rad/sec².

3.6 In Fig. P4, $\theta = 60°$, $\omega_1 = 50$ rad/sec clockwise, and $\alpha_1 = 500$ rad/sec² counterclockwise. Draw the acceleration polygon, using the scale 1 in $= 2000$ in/sec². Find a_D, α_2, and α_3.

3.7 Repeat Problem 3.6 for $\alpha_1 = 0$.

3.8 In Fig. P5, $\omega_1 = 20$ rad/sec counterclockwise and $\alpha_1 = 100$

rad/sec² counterclockwise. Draw the acceleration polygon, using the scale 1 in = 200 in/sec². Find α_2 and α_3.

3.9 Repeat Problem 3.8 for the mechanism in the other limiting position, using the scale 1 in = 100 in/sec².

3.10 In Fig. P6, $\theta = 105°$ and $\omega_2 = 20$ rad/sec (constant). Draw the acceleration polygon, using the scale 1 in = 200 in/sec². Find α_1.

3.11 Repeat Problem 3.10 for $\theta = 30°$, using the scale 1 in = 500 in/sec².

3.12 In Fig. P3, $\omega_1 = 100$ rad/sec (constant). Solve for a_C analytically (A) for $\theta = 30°$, and (B) for both limiting positions. (Note that the approximate analytical expression is not intended for a linkage with the dimensions of Fig. P3.) Compare the results with a graphical analysis.

3.13 In Fig. P7, the crank is given an angular velocity ω and an angular acceleration α (both counterclockwise). (A) Draw the acceleration polygon for the position shown. Write an expression for a_C in terms of ω, R, and L. (B) Draw the acceleration polygon for the other limiting position. (C) Examine the effect of α on the value of a_C when this mechnism is in a limiting position.

3.14 In Fig. P8, $\omega_1 = 100$ rad/sec (constant). Draw the acceleration polygon, using the scale 1 in = 10,000 in/sec².

3.15 Repeat Problem 3.14 for $\alpha_1 = 2000$ rad/sec².

3.16 In Fig. P9, $\theta = 135°$ and $\omega_1 = 10$ rad/sec (constant). Note that distance B_1C on the cam is constant. Thus, we may take C as a double point—C_1 on the cam and C_2 on the follower. Using point C, draw the acceleration polygon, using the scale 1 in = 50 in/sec².

3.17 Repeat Problem 3.16 for $\theta = 30°$.

3.18 In Fig. P10, $\omega_1 = 35$ rad/sec (constant). Draw the acceleration polygon, using the scale 1 in = 200 in/sec². Find the acceleration of the midpoint of each link (D, E, and F).

3.19 In Fig. P11, $\omega_1 = 20$ rad/sec counterclockwise (constant). Note that CD is a fixed distance. Thus, the cam and follower can be replaced by an equivalent four bar linkage, O_1CDO_2. Draw the velocity and acceleration polygons for the equivalent linkage. Find α_2, the angular acceleration of the follower (represented by O_2D).

3.20 In Fig. P12, $\theta = 105°$ and $\omega_2 = 20$ rad/sec (constant). Draw the acceleration polygon, using the scale 1 in = 200 in/sec². Find α_3.

3.21 Repeat Problem 3.20 for $\theta = 30°$. Use the scale 1 in = 500 in/sec².

3.22 In Fig. P13, $\omega_1 = 30$ rad/sec (constant). Draw the velocity and acceleration polygons, using the scales 1 in = 20 in/sec and 1 in = 1000 in/sec². Find α_2.

3.23 In Fig. P14, $\omega_1 = 100$ rad/sec and $\alpha_1 = 2000$ rad/sec² (both clockwise). Draw the velocity and acceleration polygons, using the scales 1 in = 100 in/sec and 1 in = 10,000 in/sec². Identify a_D and find α_2.

3.24 An in-line slider crank linkage has a crank length of 4 in. and connecting rod length of 10 in. Maximum slider acceleration occurs at the limiting position with the slider farthest from the crankshaft. At what crank velocity will slider acceleration reach 50,000 in/sec²?

3.25 In Fig. P15, $\omega_5 = 15$ rad/sec and $\alpha_1 = 0$. Draw the acceleration polygon using the scale 1 in = 50 in/sec². Explain the difficulty encountered in solving this problem were α_5 specified instead of α_1.

FIG. P16

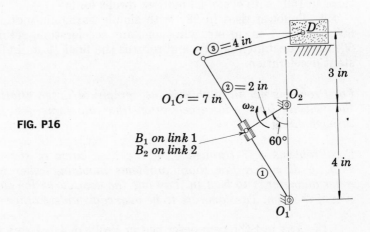

3.26 In Fig. P16, draw the acceleration polygon for the limiting position shown. Let $\omega_2 = 100$ rad/sec (constant). Use the scales 1 in = 100 in/sec and 1 in = 10,000 in/sec². Find α_1 and α_3.

Chapter 4 — Cam Analysis and Design

For Problems 4.1 through 4.8, draw the displacement-time diagrams. The follower rise for each problem is to be 2 in.

4.1 Follower rises 2 in. in 150° with constant velocity, dwells for 30°, returns in 150° with constant velocity, and dwells 30°.

4.2 Follower rises 1 in. in 75° with constant acceleration, rises 1 in. in 75° with constant deceleration, dwells 30°, returns 1 in. in 75° with constant acceleration, continues to return with 75° of constant deceleration, then dwells 30°.

4.3 Follower rises 1 in. in 60° with simple harmonic motion, dwells 30°, rises another 1 in. in 60° with simple harmonic motion, dwells 30°, then returns in 150° with simple harmonic motion and dwells for the remaining 30°.

4.4 Follower rises in 210°, returns in 150°, both with cycloidal motion.

521

4.5 Follower rises ½ in. in 30° with constant acceleration, rises 1 in. in 30° with constant velocity, rises ½ in. in 30° with constant deceleration, dwells 30°, returns 1 in. in 90° with constant acceleration, returns 1 in. in 90° with constant deceleration, dwells 60°.

4.6 Follower rises in 90° with simple harmonic motion, dwells for 45°, returns in 180° with constant acceleration and constant deceleration, dwells 45°.

4.7 Follower rises in 150° with constant velocity, dwells for 30°, returns in 150° with cycloidal motion, dwells for 30°.

4.8 Follower rises in 90° with simple harmonic motion, dwells for 60°, returns 1 in. in 90° with constant acceleration, returns ½ in. in 60° with constant velocity, and returns the final ½ in. in 60° with constant deceleration.

For Problems 4.9 through 4.16 use graphical differentiation to obtain the velocity-time and acceleration-time diagrams for Problems 4.1 through 4.8.

For Problems 4.17 through 4.24, the base circle of the cam is to be 4 in. in diameter. For those problems involving roller followers, the roller diameter is to be 1 in. Lay out the cam curve for clockwise rotation of the cam. The cams are to be disk cams unless otherwise specified.

4.17 Lay out the cam described in Problem 4.1. Use a reciprocating knife-edge follower.

4.18 Lay out the cam described in Problem 4.2. Use a reciprocatng roller follower.

4.19 Lay out the cam described in Problem 4.3. Use a reciprocating, offset, roller follower. The follower is to be offset 1 in. to the right of the center of the camshaft. What is the maximum pressure angle?

4.20 Lay out the cam described in Problem 4.4. Use a reciprocating flat-faced follower.

4.21 Lay out the cam described in Problem 4.5. Use a reciprocating, offset, flat-faced follower. The follower is to be offset 1 in. to the right of the center of the camshaft.

4.22 Layout the cam described in Problem 4.6. Use a reciprocating, oblique, flat-faced follower. The follower face makes a 70° angle with the follower line of travel.

4.23 Design a cam for an oscillating, pivoted, flat-faced follower (like that shown in Fig. P17) to provide the following motion sequence: the follower rotates clockwise for 15° with constant velocity in 150° of cam rotation, dwells for 30°, returns with cycloidal motion in 150° of cam rotation, dwells for 30°.

4.24 Design a cam for a pivoted, roller follower (like that shown in Fig. P18) to provide the following motion sequence: Follower rotates

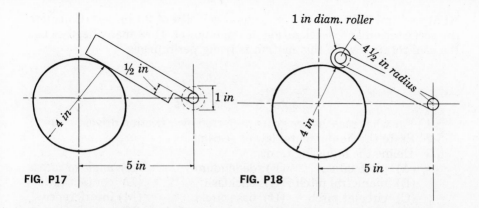

FIG. P17   FIG. P18

clockwise 20° with simple harmonic motion in 90° of cam rotation, dwells for 60°, returns 10° with constant acceleration in 90° of cam rotation, returns 5° with constant velocity in 60° of cam rotation, and returns 5° with constant deceleration in 60° of cam rotation.

4.25 A follower rises 4 in. with constant velocity in 180° of cam rotation. It then returns with constant velocity during the next 180° of cam rotation. If the cam rotates at 50 RPM, calculate the velocity and acceleration of the follower.

4.26 Repeat Problem 4.25 for follower rise with constant acceleration. Calculate (A) the acceleration of the follower, (B) maximum velocity of the follower, and (C) the jerk when cam angle is 60°.

4.27 Repeat Problem 4.25 for constant acceleration and deceleration of the follower. Calculate (A) maximum acceleration of the follower, (B) maximum velocity of the follower, (C) the velocity of the follower when follower displacement is 3 in., and (D) the follower displacement and jerk when the cam angle is 120°.

4.28 Repeat Problem 4.27 for simple harmonic motion of the follower.

4.29 Repeat Problem 4.27 for cycloidal motion of the follower.

4.30 Repeat Problem 4.27 for parabolic motion of the follower.

4.31 A cam follower rises 2 in. in 180° of cam rotation. The constant acceleration for the first part of the rise is three times as great as the constant deceleration for the second part of the lift period. If the cam is rotating at 300 RPM, determine the value of the acceleration.

4.32 A disc cam rotates at 375 RPM. The follower rises ¾ in. with constant acceleration in 80° of cam rotation, then rises an additional ¾ in. with constant deceleration in the next 80° of cam rotation. Find the acceleration and maximum velocity of the follower.

4.33 The follower of a disc cam rises ½ in. with constant acceleration, rises an additional ¾ in. with constant velocity, and then rises an additional ½ in. with constant deceleration. The cam rotates at 200

523

RPM and the follower has a maximum velocity of 35 in./sec. Calculate the acceleration and deceleration of the follower. How many degrees has the cam rotated while this motion is being performed?

Chapter 5 — Spur Gears

5.1 For what reasons are gears preferred over friction drives?

5.2 State the fundamental law of gearing.

5.3 Define the following terms:

(A) pitch circle	(F) dedendum	(K) angle of recess
(B) diametral pitch	(G) backlash	(L) contact ratio
(C) circular pitch	(H) base circle	(M) interference
(D) pitch point	(I) pressure angle	(N) speed ratio
(E) addendum	(J) angle of approach	

5.4 What are the methods used to eliminate interference?

5.5 What is the pitch diameter of a 40 tooth spur gear having a circular pitch of 1.5708 in?

5.6 How many RPM is a spur gear turning at, if it has 28 teeth, a circular pitch of .7854 in. and a pitch line velocity of 12 ft/sec?

5.7 A spur gear having 35 teeth is rotating at 350 RPM and is to drive another spur gear at 520 RPM. (A) What is the value of the velocity ratio, and (B) how many teeth must the second gear have?

5.8 An external, 20°, full-depth spur gear has a diametral pitch of 3. The spur gear drives an internal gear with 75 teeth to produce a velocity ratio of 1/3. Determine the center distance.

5.9 A 20° full-depth spur gear has 24 teeth and a circular pitch of .7854 in. Determine (A) the working depth, (B) the base circle diameter, and (C) the outside diameter.

5.10 A spur gear is rotating at 300 RPM, and is in mesh with a second spur gear having 60 teeth and a diametral pitch of 4. The velocity ratio of the pair of meshing gears is 1/3. What is the magnitude of the pitch line velocity?

5.11 Two meshing spur gears have a diametral pitch of 4, a velocity ratio of 1/5, and a center distance of 15 in. How many teeth do the gears have?

5.12 A pinion has 32 teeth, a diametral pitch of 4, and a 20° pressure angle. The driven gear is such that the velocity ratio is 1/3. (A) What is the center distance? (B) What is the base circle radius of the driven gear?

5.13 Two meshing 20° spur gears have a diametral pitch of 5. The pinion has 35 teeth, and the center distance is 15 in. (A) How many teeth does the driven gear have? (B) To what value should the center distance be increased in order for the actual pressure angle to become 24°?

5.14 Two meshing full-depth spur gears have 20° pressure angles, addendums of 1/3 in., and a velocity ratio of 1/2. The pinion has 24 teeth. Calculate the contact ratio.

5.15 Two meshing full-depth spur gears have 25° pressure angles. The pinion has 32 teeth and a base pitch of 0.712, while the gear has 48 teeth. How many teeth are in contact?

5.16 Two meshing 20° full-depth gears have a diametral pitch of 3, the pinion has 12 teeth and the velocity ratio is to be 1/2. How much of the addenda must be removed in order to prevent interference?

5.17 The same data as for previous problem. What value must the pressure angle be made in order to prevent interference?

5.18 A 25° full-depth spur gear with 45 teeth has an addendum of 1/3 in. What is the minimum number of teeth the pinion may have without interference occurring?

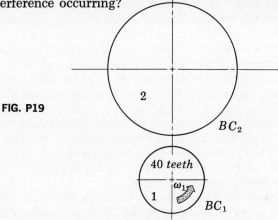

FIG. P19

5.19 In Fig. P19, two base circles are shown. Gear 1 drives. (A) Show line of action, (B) Label interference points I, I_2, and pitch point P, (C) Show maximum permissible addenda on gears 1 and 2 without interference, (D) Find contact ratio with maximum addenda.

5.20 A spur gear with 32 teeth and a diametral pitch of 4 is meshed with a second gear having a pitch diameter of 16 in. Both gears are external, standard, full depth 14½° involute gears. Determine (A) the number of teeth on the second gear, (B) the standard addendum, (C) the maximum addendum for gear number one for which no interference will occur.

5.21 A shaft rotating at 2000 RPM has a 20 tooth, 5 diametral pitch pinion gear keyed to it. The pinion meshes with another spur gear whose center is 6 in. from the centerline of the first shaft. Compounded with the gear is a double-threaded, left hand worm which drives a 56 tooth wormwheel keyed to the shaft of an 8 in. diameter hoisting drum. Calculate the distance a load, attached to a cable wrapped around the drum, moves through in one minute.

Mechanism

5.22 Find the maximum addendum of a $14\frac{1}{2}°$ pressure angle rack which is to mesh with a 6 in. diameter pinion. Label rack addendum A.

5.23 In Prob. 5-22, assume that the pinion has 15 full-depth teeth. (Note that addendum $= 1/P_d$ *for pinion only*.) (A) Label the beginning and end of contact with the pinion driving clockwise. (B) Determine the contact ratio. (C) Is the contact ratio adequate?

5.24 Find the minimum pressure angle required for a rack to mesh with a 6 in. diameter pinion if both the rack and pinion are to have full-depth teeth. (Addendum $= 1/P_d$.)

Chapter 6 — Helical, Worm, and Bevel Gears

6.1 Two helical gears, mounted on parallel shafts, are in mesh. They have a diametral pitch of 5, a 40° helix angle, and 20 and 30 teeth respectively. Calculate the normal circular pitch and the virtual number of teeth.

6.2 Two meshing helical gears have a 25° transverse pressure angle and a 20° normal pressure angle. They have a diametral pitch of 10, with 15 and 45 teeth respectively. Determine the center distance of the equivalent spur gears (spur gears having same properties as the helical gears).

6.3 Two parallel shafts are spaced 5 in. apart. A pair of helical gears are to be selected to provide a velocity ratio of about $\frac{1}{2}$. The normal diametral pitch is to be 6, the normal pressure angle is to be 20°, and the gears are to have at least 20 teeth. Determine the number of teeth for the gears and the transverse pressure angle.

6.4 A helical pinion has a normal pressure angle of 20°, a transverse pressure angle of 25°, and rotates at 2000 RPM. It is to drive a meshing helical gear so that the speed ratio is $\frac{1}{4}$. The centers of the shafts are 10 inches apart. Determine the normal diametral pitch and the pitch diameters if the pinion has 20 teeth.

6.5 For the gears shown in Fig. 5A on p. 333, label the rotations of each gear and also indicate the direction of the thrust load for each gear.

6.6 Two meshing helical gears on parallel shafts have a normal pressure angle of 20° and a transverse pressure angle of 23°. The normal circular pitch is 0.6 inches. If the speed ratio is to be 0.4, determine the number of teeth for each gear.

6.7 Two helical gears of the same hand are used to connect two shafts that are 90° apart. The smaller gear has 24 teeth, and a helix angle of 35°. Determine the center distance between the shafts if the speed ratio is $\frac{1}{2}$. The normal circular pitch is 0.7854 in.

6.8 Repeat Problem 6.7, but assume that the gears are of opposite hand and that the shaft angle is 10°.

6.9 Two left-handed helical gears having the same helix angle are used to connect two shafts 60° apart. The velocity ratio is to be 0.4 and

526

the gears have a normal diametral pitch of 4. If the center distance is to be about 12 inches, determine the numbers of teeth for each gear.

6.10 Two bevel gears are to be used to connect two shafts that are 90° apart. The pinion has 18 teeth and a diametal pitch of 6. If the velocity ratio is to be .4, determine (A) the pitch angles, (B) the back cone radii, and (C) the virtual number of teeth for the gear.

6.11 Repeat Problem 6.10 for two shafts that are 60° apart.

6.12 Repeat Problem 6.10 for two shafts that are 110° apart.

6.13 Determine the pitch diameters of a worm gear set having a velocity ratio of .1 and a center distance of $2\frac{1}{2}$ in., if the worm has 3 teeth and a lead of 1 in.

6.14 A worm gear set has a velocity ratio of 0.05. The worm has 2 teeth, a lead of 3 in. and a pitch diameter of $1\frac{1}{2}$ in. Determine the helix angle and pitch diameter of the worm gear.

6.15 A worm gear set is to have a velocity ratio of 0.05. The worm has 3 teeth, a lead angle of 20° and a circular pitch of 1.5 in. Determine the center distance.

6.16 A worm gear set has a velocity ratio of 0.04. Find the center distance if the worm has 3 teeth, a pitch diameter of 2.5 in. and an axial pitch of .5 in.

6.17 A worm gear set has a speed ratio of 0.05, a lead angle of 20° and a center distance of 10 in. Determine the pitch diameters.

Chapter 7 — Drive Trains

7.1 In Fig. 3, p. 378 (reverted gear train), input shaft 1 rotates at 2000 RPM. $N_1 = 20$ and $N_4 = 40$. Find the highest and lowest output speeds obtainable if the tooth numbers for gears 2 and 3 are to be no less than 20 and no more than 60. (Note that shafts 1 and 4 lie on the same centerline.)

7.2 In Fig. P20, find the speed and direction of rotation of gear 4. Gear 1 rotates at 1000 RPM as shown.

7.3 Specify the gears for a speed changer similar to that shown in Fig. 5, p. 380 (speed changer employing idler), having available output to input speed ratios of 0.8, 0.75, 0.6, 0.5, and 0.4. The smallest gear cannot have less than 20 teeth.

7.4 Sketch a transmission similar to that shown in Fig. 6A, p. 382 (three speed transmission). A synchromesh clutch is to be used in all gears. (B) For the transmission above, specify tooth numbers to produce (approximately) the following output to input speed ratios: $n_o/n_i = +1$, $+0.5$, $+0.25$, -0.25. No gear may have less than 18 teeth.

7.5 Specify the gears required to obtain an output to input speed ratio of exactly 1131/2000 with a gear train similar to that shown in Fig. 3, p. 378 (reverted gear train). Use gears of not less than 20 nor more than 50 teeth.

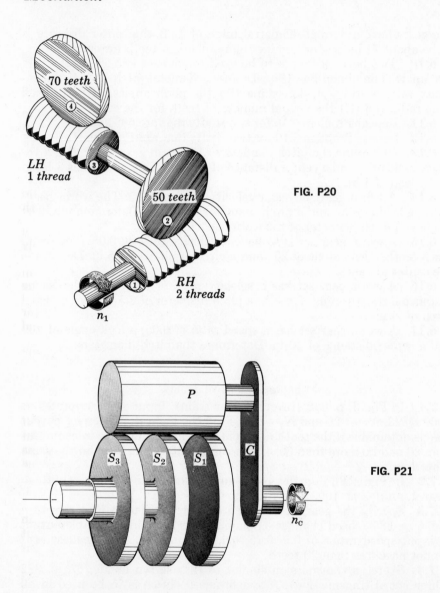

70 *teeth*

④

LH
1 thread

③

50 *teeth*

②

FIG. P20

RH
2 threads

①

n_1

P

S_3 S_2 S_1 C

FIG. P21

n_c

7.6 In Fig. P21, tooth numbers are $N_P = 30$, $N_{S1} = 50$, $N_{S2} = 49$, and $N_{S3} = 51$. Gear S_1 is fixed, and the carrier speed is 100 RPM clockwise. Find the rotation speed and the direction of S_2 and S_3, which are mounted on separate shafts. Use the tabular method. (Note: if the three sun gears have the same diameter, their pitches will be slightly different and the drive will not, theoretically, be precise.)

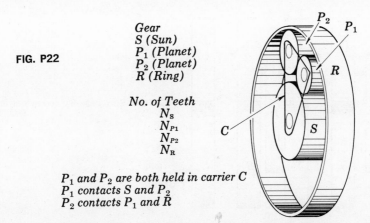

FIG. P22

Gear
S (Sun)
P_1 (Planet)
P_2 (Planet)
R (Ring)

No. of Teeth
N_S
N_{P1}
N_{P2}
N_R

P_1 and P_2 are both held in carrier C
P_1 contacts S and P_2
P_2 contacts P_1 and R

7.7 In Fig. P22, assume that the sun gear is fixed. Find the speed of each gear by the tabular method if the planet carrier speed, n_C, is 200 RPM clockwise. Answer in terms of tooth numbers: N_S, etc.

7.8 Repeat Problem 7.7 for the case where the ring gear is fixed.

7.9 In Fig. 9, p. 392 (planetary speed reducer), ring gear R_1 is fixed. The sun gear rotates at 100 RPM clockwise. (A) Find the output speed if tooth numbers are $N_{R1} = 95$, $N_{P2} = 21$, $N_{P1} = 20$, $N_{R2} = 100$, and $N_s = 55$. (B) Consider the same problem, but let R_2 serve as the input gear rotating at 100 RPM, and let S serve as the output gear. Will a gear train actually operate in this manner?

7.10 Using a speed reducer similar to Fig. 10, p. 393 (planetary train with four planets), and with the ring gear fixed, obtain an output speed of approximately 1000 RPM with input speed 3500 RPM. (A) Specify the tooth numbers, letting the smallest gear have 20 teeth. (B) Determine the exact output speed for the gears you selected. (C) If the planets are to be equally spaced, how many will the design call for?

7.11 In Fig. P23, carrier C rotates at 1000 RPM clockwise and sun

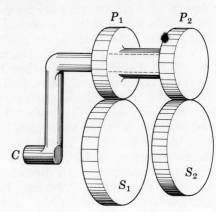

FIG. P23. Carrier C and sun gears S_1 and S_2 rotate independently about the same axis. Planets P_1 and P_2 are on the same shaft, which is free to rotate with respect to the carrier.

Mechanisms

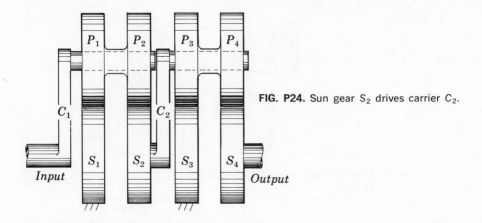

FIG. P24. Sun gear S_2 drives carrier C_2.

gear S_1 is fixed. Tooth numbers are $N_{S1} = 51$, $N_{P1} = 20$, $N_{P2} = 19$, and $N_{S2} = 50$. Find the speed and direction of rotation for each gear using the tabular method.

7.12 Repeat Problem 7.11 for the case where sun gear S_2 is fixed.

7.13. In Fig. P24, tooth numbers are: $N_{S1} = N_{S3} = 101$, $N_{S2} = N_{S4} = 100$, $N_{P1} = N_{P3} = 100$, and $N_{P2} = N_{P4} = 99$. Sun gears S_1 and S_3 are fixed. If the input shaft turns at 60 RPM, how long will it take for one revolution of the output shaft?

7.14 In Fig. P22, $n_s = 400$ RPM clockwise, and $n_R = 300$ RPM clockwise. Let $N_S = 40$ teeth and $N_R = 100$ teeth. Find the carrier speed.

7.15 In Fig. P23, let speeds n_C and n_{S1} be given. Find n_{S2} in terms of speeds n_C and n_{S1} and tooth numbers N_{S1}, N_{P1}, N_{P2}, and N_{S2}.

7.16 In Fig. 17, p. 408 (bevel gear differential), let the planet P have 20 teeth and both sun gears 30 teeth. Gear S_1 drives the left rear axle and S_2 the right rear axle of a vehicle making a right turn at 20 MPH. The 26 in. diameter tires are 56 in. apart (center to center). The right wheel rolls in a 30 ft. radius path. Find the speed of the carrier and each sun gear, and the speed of the planet with respect to the carrier.

7.17 In Fig. P25, tooth numbers are: $N_{S1} = 35$, $N_P = 22$, and $N_{S2} = 25$. (A) If gear S_1 makes 40 rotations clockwise and S_2 makes 15 rotations counterclockwise, find the angular displacement of the carrier by the tabular method. How many rotations does the planet make about its own axis? (B) Represent the motion of S_1 and S_2 by x and y respectively. Write an expression for carrier motion in terms of x and y.

7.18 In Fig. 27A, p. 421 (variable-speed belt drive), pulley pitch diameters are $d_1 = 4$ in. and $d_4 = 10$ in. Both countershaft pulleys are to have a minimum pitch diameter of 5 in. Determine the range of d_2 and d_3 so that output speed may be varied from 400 to 1400 RPM with a motor speed of 1800 RPM.

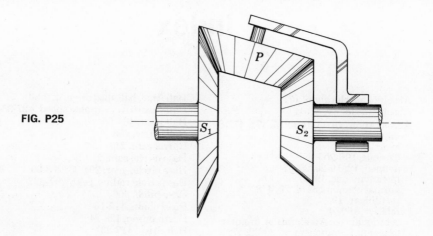

FIG. P25

7.19 In Fig. 32, p. 426 (disc drive with idler wheel), the input shaft rotates at 90 RPM counterclockwise. Input and output shaft centerlines are 2 in. apart. Find idler positions for output speeds of 16, 33⅓, 45, and 78 RPM counterclockwise.

7.20 Sketch a variable speed drive similar to Fig. 31, p. 425 (wheel-disc drive) to produce output speeds from 2000 RPM through zero to 2000 RPM reverse with constant input speed of 1000 RPM. Hint: disc 2 may be used as input and disc 1 as output.

7.21 In Fig. 42B, p. 441 (planetary cone transmission), let the ring gear have 45 teeth and the planets 15 teeth. If the reaction ring has an inside diameter of 5 in., what would the required cone diameters be for output speeds ranging from 450 RPM clockwise to 180 RPM counterclockwise, with 1800 RPM input clockwise. Give cone diameters at points of contact for extreme positions of the reaction ring. (Note: the data for this problem does not represent actual dimensions of any commercially available transmission.)

7.22 Design a mechanism similar to Fig. 52, p. 460 (ratchet-pawl mechanism) to provide feed rates of .005 to .012 in./cycle, in increments of .001 in.

7.23 (A) A Hooke-type universal joint has 20° misalignment. Find output shaft speed range if the input shaft rotates at a constant 1000 RPM. (B) Find the permissible misalignment with this type of joint if the speed variation is limited to ±2%.

Index